New Connections 2009

PLAYS FOR YOUNG PEOPLE

*For a complete list of volumes and individual titles
available in the* Connections *series, see page 611*

New Connections 2009

PLAYS FOR YOUNG PEOPLE

Blackout
Dirty Dirty Princess
The Dummy Tree
A Handbag
Heartbreak Beautiful
The Heights
The Séance
Six Parties
Success
The Things She Sees
Trammel
The Vikings and Darwin

faber and faber

First published in 2009
by Faber and Faber Limited
74–77 Great Russell Street, London WC1B 3DA

Typeset by Country Setting, Kingsdown, Kent CT14 8ES
Printed in England by CPI Bookmarque, Croydon, Surrey

Introduction © Anthony Banks 2009
Blackout © Davey Anderson 2009
Dirty Dirty Princess © Georgia Fitch 2009
The Dummy Tree: a Musical Fairy Tale © Conor Mitchell 2009
A Handbag © Anthony Horowitz 2009
Heartbreak Beautiful © Christopher William Hill 2009
The Heights © Lisa McGee 2009
The Séance © Anthony Neilson 2009
Six Parties © William Boyd 2009
Success © Nick Drake 2009
The Things She Sees © Ben Power, Charles Boyle 2009
Trammel © Michael Lesslie 2009
The Vikings and Darwin © David Mamet 2009

The rights of Davey Anderson, William Boyd, Charles Boyle,
Nick Drake, Georgia Fitch, Christopher William Hill,
Anthony Horowitz, Michael Lesslie, Lisa McGee, David Mamet,
Conor Mitchell, Anthony Neilson and Ben Power to be identified
as the authors of these works have been asserted in accordance
with Section 77 of the Copyright, Designs and Patents Act 1988

Information regarding applications for performance
will be found preceding the individual plays

A CIP record for this book is available from the British Library

978-0-571-25135-3

2 4 6 8 10 9 7 5 3 1

Contents

Introduction

The National Theatre's 'New Connections' programme
was recently described by the *Guardian* as one of the
most productive generators of new writing in the country.
The way these new scripts come into being is as simple as
the formula which has made 'Connections' a success
story for over a decade. The National approaches a
dozen established writers who they believe have a voice
which will create an exciting piece of original drama for
young actors to perform. The writers then workshop
their ideas with young actors, a process which ensures the
completed script encompasses a truly teenage vantage
point. The aspiration is to ensure that the range of plays
in the portfolio mirrors the diverse programming of the
National Theatre as a whole, and that its appeal and
reach is to anyone and everyone.

Anthony Horowitz is a prolific writer of children's books,
television drama and journalism. A few years ago, he
wrote a play called *Mindgame*. A psychological thriller for
three actors, it is set in a room in some kind of institution
for the mentally unstable. It's a conjuring-trick of a play
in which self-important, middle-aged professionals bluff
and baffle each other about their true identities. Recently,
Anthony met and interviewed several young offenders held
in maximum-security units in various parts of the country,
and from that realised he wanted to write a companion
piece to *Mindgame*, for six young people trapped in a
similar institutional space. *A Handbag* portrays a group of
young people rehearsing Oscar Wilde's *The Importance of
Being Earnest*. But the choice of play seems strange and

inappropriate, the cast has almost no understanding of what they are doing, and the place where they will be performing is certainly not a theatre. As they struggle to make sense of the text, we see that they are actually fighting for their own survival. This is a dark and disturbing comedy that explores crime and punishment in an increasingly vengeful world and questions whether there is a group in society that is actually beyond redemption.

In early 2008, Glaswegian playwright, director and composer Davey Anderson was introduced by the children's charity Barnardo's to a seventeen-year-old Glaswegian lad with an urgent story to tell. During several frank conversations between the young man and the playwright, the extraordinary tale of the protagonist's one-way ticket to nowhere and his unexpected redemptive U-turn from despair emerged. *Blackout* is a dazzling piece of theatre with a driving narrative. The length, twenty minutes, was prescribed. The aspiration was to create a play which could be performed by a company of any size and with very mixed abilities with limited rehearsal time. Although shorter than most plays, it is still a complete story which conveys an entire world with an acute sense of urgency. The central character explains: 'All I can remember is: I could hear screaming. It was like being in a dream but still being awake at the same time. And all I can hear is – please, don't, stop it! And then . . . I don't know. Next morning, I was in a jail cell. I didnae know how I got there. And I was like that – aw naw, what did I do?' It's a play about getting bullied, fighting back, trying to make a name for yourself, turning vicious, doing something stupid, losing everything, then finding your way again.

Georgia Fitch was born in the East End of London, and was an actor before becoming a writer. She writes very naturalistic dialogue and her plays are populated with

characters who have the potent stench of real life about
them. When creating the story for *Dirty Dirty Princess*
Georgia found she went on an imaginative journey that
was very dark and upsetting. The tale of Stacey is one
which she thinks crucial for teenagers to know, and she
hopes it will be an alarm siren, informing all who read it
or see it about the precariousness of growing up too fast.
The 'princess' of the title is thirteen and all her mates think
she's well sexy. Her mum keeps her in the latest fashion,
so she always looks like a proper princess. At her cousin's
party, she ventures upstairs with seventeen-year-old Daniel
Johnson, an athlete tipped to run in the Olympics. That
night's encounter leads to a spiral of events which test her
trust in boys, her relationship with her mum, and lead
her to seek advice from a Christian support group. It's a
play about the consequences of silence, jealousy and
trying to find a way of simply being thirteen.

When London was announced as the host city for the
2012 Olympics, Christopher William Hill decided he
wanted to write a romantic comedy which takes place
during a sequence of PE lessons. The play he has written
is inspired by personal memories of his own family: his
brother, a keen athlete, and his mother, who died shortly
before he wrote the play. It's for a large ensemble cast
with lots of energy, who have what it takes to sprint
through the multitude of scenes and dialogue without
breaking into a sweat. AJ is the best athlete St Bart's
Comprehensive has ever seen; his brother, Dan, wants to
push him to the limit. Amber has other ideas: she's
desperate to settle down with AJ, have kids, get fat and
watch daytime TV. AJ, however, only has eyes for Ellie, a
geek with a heart of gold and a lethal set of dental braces.
But the course of true love never did run smooth, and
Oscar is determined to pair up with Ellie himself, no
matter what the cost – even if it means breeding an army

of killer bird-bees. *Heartbreak Beautiful* is a fast-paced comedy about life, love and sport.

'New Connections' is a nationwide programme, which spans the length and breadth of these islands, and also around the globe, embracing characters and stories from a multitude of cultural and ethnic backgrounds. Novelist William Boyd expressed a desire to write a play based on his own childhood experience in Africa, which explores various harmonies and tensions found when two sets of people from very different backgrounds live in the same place. Although *Six Parties* is loosely set in Africa, this play could easily be relocated to a setting which would be pertinent and have resonance for audiences in a similarly divided community. As the title suggests, the action of the play takes place around six parties over a period of a few months. A group of young people, all in their late teens – two girls, four boys, white and black – encounter each other at these gatherings. The dynamics vary as the months roll on: power, sex, fun, patronage, friendship, inebriation, betrayal. But by the end of the sixth party all the fun and friendship have gone, lines have been drawn in the sand, we discover who wields the real power in this group and we know who has genuine strength of character, and who hasn't.

As these plays are being rehearsed and performed, the country is in the grip of the 'credit crunch', an economic downturn which is having unexpected effects in all areas of living. Nick Drake has created a highly poetic play which takes inspiration from a series of eight paintings by the eighteenth-century artist William Hogarth, *The Rake's Progress*; and the central figure in these paintings is transported into *Success*. Tom Rakewell is a lucky man. In one midsummer night he makes a fortune and meets Lucy, the love of his life. He is immediately engulfed by well-wishers, led by the all-powerful Nick Shadow.

Everyone who is anyone is keen to be his friend, and to help him spend his new cash on clothes, parties and the high life. It seems he has the world at his feet, and all his dreams of success have come true. But what is the cost of success? And what does success really mean if you lose the thing of greatest value in your life? Just when Tom thinks he has it all, he finds himself falling into the dark heart of the city where everyone is struggling to survive. The play is a collision of the eighteenth and twenty-first centuries, and a story of luck, success, money, false friends and true love.

Schools and youth theatres always enjoy producing musicals which classically enable massive numbers of young actors to take part by singing, dancing, and playing musical instruments. Conor Mitchell's new musical *The Dummy Tree* differs in requiring seven talented actor-singers and an accomplished accompanist on piano. The single setting is an outdoor landscape in which grows a solo tree, upon whose branches hang hundreds of children's dummies. Legend has it that mothers take their young ones to the tree to persuade them to give up their dummy and begin the journey towards adulthood. In this story a young man of seventeen goes to a dummy tree on the morning of his wedding to meet his birth mother. She wrote him a letter when he was two saying that if he ever got married she would meet him on that morning for the first time. In a different time-zone, under the same tree, sits a seventeen-year-old girl with a pram. She is trying to persuade her little boy to let go of his dummy.

Lisa McGee grew up in 1980s Derry, Northern Ireland, during the troubles. Her two previous plays, *Jump* and *Girls and Dolls*, are both celebrations of her fascination with what is real and what is imagined, and *The Heights* follows the same fantastical trajectory. Lisa's acute sense of fun is paramount when exploring dark dispositions such as aloneness, which the central character seeks to overcome by telling stories. Technically the play is a fizzing firework display of theatrical reveals: the audience become detectives and should take great delight in the fathoming out of what is fact and what is fiction. At the centre of the story is the reclusive Lillie Lee, who lives on the Heights estate. Confined to her bedroom by sickness, Lillie feels isolated and abnormal. Her bedroom window is her only connection to the outside world, and from this she obsessively watches her neighbours and keeps herself occupied by making up stories about them. An unusual encounter with Dara, another girl from the estate, leads the two teenagers to strike up a firm friendship that is potentially dangerous. *The Heights* conveys what it's like to be different from others, examines the idea of storytelling and the power of the imagination and looks at how the lines between fact and fiction can easily become blurred, with hilarious and disastrous results.

When Scottish writer Anthony Neilson began work on his play *The Séance* he had a fairly clear idea of the dark area of magic he wanted to explore. The process began with a rowdy bunch of young teens and a magician experimenting with illusions in the NT Studio. Anthony usually directs his plays as he writes them, involving the actors in the creative process which, he says, should always be 'fun, silly and imaginative'. His plays characteristically entice the audience to experience an intense emotional response, with thought as an adjunct. In this play, a group of teenage friends attempt to contact a dead school friend by means of a séance, but the tensions released thereby are more frightening than any supernatural phenomenon they could have envisaged. It's a frank and sometimes funny drama about a group of friends on the cusp of adulthood, who are just dimly beginning to perceive that life and love are finite.

Over the last few years, the National's stages have hosted increasingly ambitious productions which utilise rich media in a variety of ways, using photography, film and animation. *The Things She Sees* offers youth theatre companies an opportunity to join in with this exciting new way of making theatre. Charles Boyle's original story tells a very timely tale of a young girl in a big city grappling with her family heritage, which is a melting pot of cultures and nationalities. Ben Power has adapted the novel in a way which will empower companies staging the piece to experiment in hugely ambitious visual styles, embracing techniques and technology both primitive and sophisticated. The play is an adventure story set in West London, an area densely packed with dwellers of not only widely differing ethnic backgrounds, but also wildly differing social class. The thirteen-year-old girl's name is Dizzy and she spends the play searching across the city for her missing father. We discover that she has inherited a magic power from her ancestors in Morocco, in which she can see fragments of the future which become invaluable in her quest to reunite her present-day family.

There is always at least one international playwright included in each portfolio of 'Connections' scripts, and this year it's America's most famous living playwright, David Mamet. His plays often compress and explode the acute tensions found between disempowered individuals, and are well known for language which is ripe and cynically vicious. *The Vikings and Darwin* differs somewhat in tone, its temperament being contemplative and philosophical, whilst the rhythm is vintage Mamet. A dialogue between A and B, it can be performed by two actors, or two groups of actors. What emerges for the audience, upon hearing the conversation, is a deeply philosophical argument about whether aggression is an acceptable solution to seemingly irreconcilable conflicts.

Michael Lesslie is the youngest of this year's writers. Not long since a scholarship pupil of one of Britain's most exclusive public schools, Michael has written *Trammel* from characters and events he witnessed whilst a student himself. To ensure the texture of his play was exact, he returned to his school, and several others, and conducted interviews with boys in Years Twelve and Thirteen while under immense pressures to attain excellent examination results and gain places at the leading universities. The play is therefore set in the academies of English power, in the present day. Aron, a popular, brilliant kid from a local comprehensive, reluctantly takes on a scholarship to the single-sex public school that looms over his town. When dire home responsibilities force him to adapt to its conservative doctrines, he quickly becomes seduced by the power they can offer and is compelled to choose between his two ways of life. Soon, however, Aron's fellow pupils see his conversion as a threat, and put to work the manipulative skills in which they have been trained in order to preserve their old system of government. A chilling insight into the institutions that shape the British elite, and the all-too-human ambition behind them, this is a tale of duty, friendship and rivalry that has resonance for all ages and backgrounds.

These plays have been produced by two hundred youth theatre companies nationwide this year, all of whom have transferred their productions to festivals which have been hosted by our partner theatres: Bath Theatre Royal, Brewery Arts Kendal, Chichester Festival Theatre, Edinburgh Lyceum Theatre, Hampstead Theatre London, The Lowry Salford, Norwich Playhouse and The Garage, Plymouth Theatre Royal, Rose Theatre Kingston, Royal and Derngate Northampton, Stephen Joseph Theatre Scarborough, Wales Millennium Centre, Watford Palace Theatre and West Yorkshire Playhouse.

INTRODUCTION

The 'Connections' formula continues to grow and thrive overseas with established programmes now running in Italy, Norway, Portugal and Brazil, and evolving in France, Georgia, Netherlands and the United States.

One production of each of these plays will be presented at the National Theatre from 1 to 7 July 2009.

ANTHONY BANKS
Associate Director,
National Theatre Discover Programme

BLACKOUT

Davey Anderson

Davey Anderson is a writer, director and musician. His plays include *Snuff* (Arches Theatre, winner of the Arches Award for Stage Directors, 2005), *Wired* (Oran Mor), Rupture (Traverse/ NTS Workshop), *Liar* (TAG/Citizens Theatre/ Sounds of Progress) and *Outspoken* (TAG/ Citizens Theatre). He was also Musical Director on *Be Near Me* (NTS/Donmar), Associate Director on *Architecting* (The TEAM/NTS Workshop) and Associate Director (Music) on *Black Watch*, as Director in Residence with the National Theatre of Scotland, 2006–07.

Author's Note

This play does not come with a blueprint or a set of
instructions for staging. As you will see, there are no
distinct stage directions and no markings in the margin to
indicate who says what. Neither does it present a verbatim
transcript of my interviews with the young person whose
story it tells, although most of the words are his rather
than mine. The text printed here is rather intended to be
a piece of verbal storytelling, left bare to invite different
visual and theatrical interpretations. The words can be
spoken by any number of actors, from one to one hundred.
The lines may be altered, where appropriate, to suit the
dialect of the performers. And the staging can be as
simple or elaborate as you like. My only request is that
some things are left to the audience's imagination.

*Inspired by the stories of a
young offender from Glasgow*

ONE

Imagine
You wake up
You open your eyes
And you're like that
Where am I?
A small room
Bright lights
White walls
A metal door
Oh my God!
Imagine you wake up and you're in a jail cell.
You go up to the door.
You bang your fists.
Screaming
Shouting
What am I doing in here?
And imagine the polis guy comes up to the door.
And he's like that
Keep it doon.
And you're like
Whit did I dae?
Aw, do you not know?
You shake your head.
Whit?
And the polis guy just looks at you like you're a pure
    thug or something.
Imagine he just looks at you and he goes
You're getting charged with attempted murder, wee man.
You'd be like that
Aw naw

What did I do?
And you'd start remembering
Everything
Right from the beginning
You would try to remember
How did I get here?

TWO

So you'd start remembering your dad.
He was a woman-beater.
He beat up your mum every day
From the day they got married right up to the day they
    got divorced.
He used to beat her to a pulp.
So she stopped working.
She wouldn't go out the house.
Cos she was embarrassed.
She didn't want to walk down the street with her face all
    black and blue.
And you'd remember that your ma didnae want you to
    grow up to be like him.
She wanted you to be a famous lawyer
Or a famous doctor
Or a famous whatever.
And you'd remember that you were poor.
But you weren't poor poor.
Cos your mum still made sure there was a dinner on the
    table every night.
She'd give you her last penny
She didn't care about herself.
But you'd remember that you never really spoke to her.
Cos you'd come home from school and go straight up the
    stairs.
James?

6

BLACKOUT

Aye.
Your dinner's out.
You'd come down.
Grab the plate.
Thanks, Ma.
Back up the stairs.
So you never really spoke to her.

THREE

But you'd remember your granddad.
He was the closest thing you had to a proper father.
He put you under his wing.
He did everything a dad would do.
He'd hold your hand
He'd walk you down to the shops
He'd play daft wee games with you
But best of all, he'd take you to the Rangers game every
    Saturday.
He'd take you to see the Orange Walks.
You'd remember how he taught you to play the flute.
But you'd not to play 'The Sash'
Or hang the Ulster flag out the window.
He taught you to keep that kind of thing to yourself.
But then he got his cancer.
You'd remember that.
So every night you'd go and sit with him.
Play a game of cards
Help him do a jigsaw
Have a cup of tea and look out the back window.
You'd remember that that was where the boys fae your
    scheme used to fight with the boys fae the scheme
    doon the road.
They'd run at each other with bottles and bricks.
Then it would be poles and baseball bats.

7

And then it would be knives.
You'd be looking out the window going
Is that a wee boy with a sword?
Am I really seeing this?
And you and your granddad
You would just sit there and go
What are they fighting for?
Cos your grandda never went out and started hitting
    people.
He got his point across with his mouth, not with his hands.
He would just have to talk to you and people would
    listen to him.
And you'd remember you always wanted to grow up to
    be just like him.

FOUR

But when you were growing up, you didnae have that
    many pals.
Cos you were too quiet.
You were shy.
You were the wee, shy, nerdy boy.
You didnae fit in with anybody.
And the pals you did have, they just used you, if you know
    what I mean.
Cos, know if it was a pure brilliant sunny day, they
    would all go away and leave you in the house.
But know if it was raining outside, they would come roon
    tae your bit and go
Hi James
I've no seen you in ages.
How have you been?
Can we come in and sit for a while?
They didnae care about you
They just wanted somewhere tae sit.

FIVE

And say it was at school
You would get beaten up for being a goth
Just cos you had long hair and wore black combats.
They used to call you
The gimp!
Haw, look at him.
Ya dirty goth!
Dae you shag deid people?
Whit?
You go up the graveyards and hing aboot there, din't ye?
Naw.
Aye ye dae. I've seen ye.
Pure digging up the coffins and raping the corpses.
Ya dirty beast!
And you'd remember the beatings.
One of the bullies would take off his belt
He'd wrap it round his knuckles
And whack you with it.
Ahh!
Then they'd throw you down the stairs
Don't!
Kick you in the ribs
Stop it!
Death to the gimp!
And they would swagger off
And leave you there, lying on the ground
Curled up into a wee ball.
You'd remember that.
You'd remember every punch.

SIX

And you'd remember you had nobody to turn to.
Cos your grandda was in the hospital.
So you'd just sit in your room and watch horror films
Night after night.
Or read books about serial killers.
Or just look at all the pictures.
You had a bloodlust for it.
It gave you a thrill
Reading about killers.
Cos they're normal people.
But they're mysterious.
What makes them tick?
What makes them go insane?
What can make somebody dae it tae somebody?
It fascinated you.

SEVEN

Imagine
You're in a jail cell
And you start remembering all this.
But you can't remember what you've done.
And then they take you to a Secure Care Unit.
And they take away your belt.
And they take away your laces.
And they take away anything you could use to try and
    kill yourself.
Then this key worker guy comes in to speak to you.
And you ask him
What did I do?
Son, I can't tell you.
How can you no tell me?

You need to ask for a file.
So you ask for the file.
And he goes away to get it.
Imagine waiting for him to come back.
Your mind would be racing.
Remembering . . .

EIGHT

Wan night
You got beaten up, just for having long hair.
These boys chased you home with meat cleavers and
  machetes
Shouting
Death to the gimp!
Trying to chop you up
All the way to your front door.
Hi James.
How was school?
Straight up the stairs.
Into your bedroom.
Slam!
You look in the mirror.
I'm not a gimp.
You get a pair of scissors.
You cut your hair pure short.
Shave it right to the skin.
James?
Then you look at yourself.
Your dinner's out.
I'm coming.
I'll show them no tae mess about wae me.
Grab the plate.
Thanks, Ma.
Wait a wee minute.

What?
What happened to your hair?
You shrug.
I got rid of it.
She looks at you funny.
You look like a skinhead.

NINE

That's when you started watching films like *Romper
    Stomper*
And *American History* X
And you thought to yourself
That's whit I'll dae.
So you started wearing the big Doc Martens boots
The bomber jacket
The braces
Everything.

TEN

And then you went into school.
And people would just look at you like
Ooff
He's a pure psycho.
But it felt good.
Cos you were getting tae them.
And then you'd dae the Nazi salute.
And the teachers were like
Stand outside this room.
What have you got this on for?
Cos I like it.
Go home and change into your uniform.

You're not allowed back into the school until you change
your clothes.
So you went
Fine. It's my life. I'll wear what I want. I'll say what I
want. I'll dae what I want.
And you sparked up a fag
And started walking about the school
Smoking
Acting like a hard man.
Haw, look
Check the state of him.
And when the bullies saw you, instead of running away,
you went
Right, who's first?
Whit you gonnae dae, ya daftie?
Two seconds.
Whit?
And you went
Fssssssssssssss.
You put the fag out on your bare skin.
Who's first then?
Are you aw right?
C'mon, who's gieing me the first punch?
James . . .
Go. I'll put my hands behind my back.
You need tae get your heid sorted oot, mate. You're no
right.
Then you pick up a chair
And throw it at the fucker.
So he starts punching you
Fists flying
They all start battering you.
James!
What are you doing?
That's not like you.

But you're standing there
With your face red raw.
Aw, it feels great, but din't it?

ELEVEN

And you'd remember that that's when you started loving
    the pain.
The punches didnae hurt any more.
You just got used to having that energy flow
That feeling of blood pumping through your veins.
And you'd sit there in your room
With the big Nazi posters up on the wall
And you'd listen to music
With that guitar
And that beat that gets you intae it
And you'd wonder what it was like to burst somebody's lip
Or to slice them open
To butcher them.
It made you feel high and mighty just thinking about it.

TWELVE

And you'd remember the night that it finally happened . . .
It was raining.
James?
That's your mum.
Shouting up the stairs.
You turn off the music.
I'm just away up the hospital to see your granddad.
You don't respond.
D'you want to come with me?
No the night, Ma.
Are ye sure?

Nah, I want to stay in and watch this film.
Well, d'you want to go up and see him the morra night?
Aye, Ma. Fine.
Right.
I'll tell him you were asking after him.
See you later.
She goes out into the rain.
You put on a slasher film.
Slash
Chop
Rip
Stab
Blood and guts.
You look at it blankly.
It's not enough for you any more.
Then there's a knock at the door
You press pause.
Open the door.
Awright, James.
Awright.
Whit ye daeing?
Nothing. Just sitting in my room.
Is yer maw in?
Naw.
Are you on your own?
Aye.
Yas, man, big Jim's got an empty!
Yas!
They all crowd in.
C'mon.
D'ye want a joint?
Emmm, no the noo.
Whit ye watching?
Nothing.
What's this?
That's a swastika.

Whit ye daeing with a swastika on your wall?
Are you a Nazi or something?
Snigger.
Aye.
They all look at you.
Whit ye intae all that for?
Cos I'm an Aryan. I need tae protect my white blood.
Oh aye. And how are ye gonnae dae that?
Wait till you see this.
You slip your hand under the bed
And you pull out a sword.
Fuck's sake.
What is that?
A Black Mamba.
Where d'ye get it?
I found it.
Did ye fuck?
How much did that set ye back?
You shrug.
I'll buy it aff ye for a fiver.
Nut.
A tenner then.
Fuck off.
Twenty quid.
Check the damage ye could dae wae that.
Have ye chopped somebody yet?
You smile.
So proud.
Look at him
The psycho.
Then . . .
Keys in the door.
Quick
Hide the blade.
Footsteps on the stairs.

What's going on here?
Nothing, Mum.
Suspicious.
You only call her 'Mum' when you've done something
    wrong.
We're just watching a film.
I think it's time your friends went home.
See ye after.
Bye, James.
Catch ye.
They disappear.
And your mum just looks at you.
James, sit down, I've got something to tell you.
Don't, Ma.
I'm sorry, James.
Ma, don't!
James, calm down.
Don't.
I'm sorry. It happened.

THIRTEEN

That's what you'd remember.
You'd remember the night that your grandda died.
That's when you died inside.
You'd remember how you wanted to hold somebody
    down to the ground
And stab their eyes out.
Or get a baseball bat
And skelp it aff somebody's heid.
Just to get the anger out of you.
Cos it was building up
All this anger.
And you didnae have a way to let it out.

FOURTEEN

Imagine that all this is going through your head as you're
    waiting in a wee room with no belt and no laces.
And then the key worker guy comes back with your file.
He hands it to you and you start to read.
But you can't concentrate on the words
So you ask him to read it for you.
What does it say?
Gonnae just tell me!
Do you really not remember?
You shake your head.
Assault.
Arson.
Attempted murder.
Do you remember now?
Some of it.
Why don't you tell me what happened?
I'll try.
So you start to tell the story . . .

FIFTEEN

Where were you?
You were in the town.
Who were you with?
You were with your pals.
Your pals' pals.
People they knew.
But you didn't know them?
Naw.
Where were your friends?
They all went away and left you with these folk you
    didnae know.

Why?
You don't know.
But it starts coming back to you.
One of them hands you a bottle of vodka.
Here, d'you want a stank?
And you're like
Aye.
Drink it straight.
How?
Just drink it straight.
So you went
You took a wee bit of it.
It tasted weird.
Naw, here
Something's wrang wae this.
And they went
Just down it.
And you went
Fine.
Cos you didnae want tae look like the wee nerdy
    boy.
And you took a big stank of it.
And there was ecstasy
And there was Valium
And you didnae know what was in it.
And by the time your pals came back, you were in some
    state.
James?
You were like Dr Jekyll and Mr Hyde.
Awright, mate?
Cos wan minute you'd be fine.
Where have ye been? I've been pure missing ye.
And then the next minute
Aye, where have ye been, aye, where have ye been, aye,
    where have ye been?
Like that.

Leaving me here, aye? D'ye want me to come over there
    and smash ye aboot?
Calm doon.
And you were looking at people.
But you were nae just looking at them.
You were looking at them like you were picking a victim.
James, come on
We need to get you hame.
And you remember them taking you hame.
But then . . .

SIXTEEN

All you can remember is
Screaming
You could hear screaming.
It was like being in a dream
But still being awake at the same time.
And all you can hear is
James?
Are you alright?
And you can feel your blood boiling over.
What's happened to you?
What have you took?
James?
And you start punching
James, don't!
And kicking
James, stop it!
And you feel your hands around somebody's throat.
What are you doing?
Squeezing.
Don't!
Stop it!
Please!

BLACKOUT

James!
Don't!
And then screaming
And then
Everything went black.

SEVENTEEN

Imagine you did that to somebody.
And you don't know why you did it.
You just
You wanted payback.
You were hurting so much
You wanted to hurt somebody else.
But the payback you done, you didnae mean.
You just needed a friend.
You just needed someone to talk to.
But instead you nearly killed somebody that night.
Aye
You remember
You remember it all.

EIGHTEEN

Now imagine this
They take you to a courtroom
And they put you in front of a judge
And the judge says
Son, I see thousands of boys like you
Every year
Getting charged with these exact same crimes.
And most of them end up in jail for anything up to ten
    years.
And you're standing there

Shaking like a leaf
Thinking
God.
Ten years.
Please don't.
That's me finished.
Then she says
But some of them
I look at some of them standing there
And I know they don't belong in jail.
I know they just made a stupid mistake
And what they really need is somebody to give them a
    chance.
And she looks you right in the eye.
You're one of the lucky ones.
I'm going to give you a probation sentence.
Three years.
And you're like
Thank you.
But if you mess up during that time, you'll do ten years in
    jail.
Do you understand?
Yes.
You may leave my courtroom.
That's you free to go.

NINETEEN

You step outside
Into the sunshine
You take a deep breath
And there's your mum
Waiting.
She looks at you.
You look at her.

How is she ever gonnae trust you again?
But she walks towards you.
Mum, I'm sorry.
And she bursts out greeting.
Then she goes
What are you going to do with yourself?

TWENTY

Imagine.
Imagine if all that happened to you.
What would you do?
You know what I would do?
I would start to talk.
I would tell people my story.
Cos when I got angry
I nearly lost everything.
And all I really wanted was somebody to sit up and take
    notice.
And then you would go home.
You would take down all your Nazi posters.
You'd get rid of all your knives.
You would look in the mirror and try to imagine
What comes next?
And then you'd get into bed.
You'd pull up the covers.
And you'd turn off the light.
Blackout.

Production Notes

Blackout was originally commissioned by the National
Theatre as part of their 'Theatre of Debate' season, which
ran alongside the 'New Connections' festival in 2008.
The idea behind the project was to create a series of
short plays with young people on the front line of issues
making headlines in the newspapers at the time – things
like teenage pregnacy, homelessness, exclusion from
school, and, in the case of *Blackout*, violent crime. So the
NT got in touch with various young people's charities in
different parts of the UK and teamed up local playwrights
with teenagers who had a compelling story to tell.

In Glasgow, Davey Anderson was put in touch with a
teenage boy who was being mentored by Barnado's
Youth Involvement Project. He had been charged with
assault, arson and attempted murder, but was lucky to be
serving only a probation sentence rather than spending
a long period in jail. Davey interviewed this young man
a number of times over the course of a few weeks,
accumulating several hours of recorded material, and was
struck by how eloquently he spoke about his experiences
and how much he wanted to take control of his life by
making sense of his own personal history.

Davey then went away and selected segments from these
interviews, piecing together various anecdotes into a
single short narrative. The resulting play is a fictionalised
account of the events surrounding the violent crime that
this young man committed. It deliberately tells the story
from the point of view of the perpetrator rather than the
victim. However, it also attempts to question this simple

binary, and get the audience thinking about what leads young people to commit violent acts, how they should be punished (or rehabilitated) and, crucially, how these kinds of crimes can be prevented.

TOWARDS DISCOVERING THE PLAY

WHAT IS THE PLAY ABOUT?

Exercise: write down the story in one sentence. What is the central conflict?

Is it about a young man's struggle to be noticed, whatever the cost? Is it a story of revenge, forgiveness and redemption? Or is it about a family's failure to break the cycle of violence within a divided community?

Davey suggested that the central conflict might be James's struggle to take control of his life. This encompasses all the mini-struggles that make up the overall story – for example, James's search for a father figure, his attempts to win the respect of his peers, his search for information about his crime and his punishment. Viewed in this way, every encounter presents an obstacle or an opportunity in achieving this goal, and each character either helps or hinders him, or both.

When writing the piece, Davey thought about the plot as being like a detective story, where we begin with the investigator who is confronted with a mystery, then flash back to the events leading up to the crime. Finally, once the mystery is 'solved' – by James, if not the audience – we discover what happens to him as a result of the crime.

HOW DO WE TELL THE STORY?

Exercise: write down the key moments in the narrative.

Write each one on a separate sheet of paper. Lay them out side by side so that you can visually chart James's journey throughout the play. Try to make the moments very specific. Think about how they change James. Why is it significant? What is the chain of cause and effect?

If you decide, for example, that the focus of the story should be on James's transformation from vulnerable outsider into potential killer, think about the key stages in that journey: the moment he is nearly stabbed because of his long hair, the moment he shaves his head, the moment his classmates first see him dressed as a skinhead, the moment he puts out the cigarette on his bare skin, the moment he downs the vodka spiked with drugs, etc.

How can these key moments be told in pictures? Imagine them in as much detail as possible. Where and when do they happen? How will they look and sound and feel as part of your production?

HOW DO I BRING THE CHARACTERS TO LIFE?

Exercise: give each character a name and a backstory.

Ask the actors to write down: their character's gender, their age, what sort of accommodation they live in, where they get their money from, something they lack in life, a secret, a memory, something they wish for, something they fear, etc. Then 'hot seat' each actor in character to discover more about them.

There is a danger in this play that the characters could become two-dimensional archetypes. A way to avoid this is to make sure that they each have their own wants, their own needs and their own internal conflict. This is especially important when there are groups of characters. So rather than having a monolithic swarm of bullies, work out the group dynamics.

WHAT IS HAPPENING IN EACH SCENE?

Exercise: improvise the scene thinking about the competing wants of the characters.

Read the scene. Discuss what happens. Start by stating the obvious – literally, what happens? For example, in the first scene James tries to get information out of the police officer and the police officer tries to shut him up. Then dig deeper to unearth the dramatic action. Ask the actors lots of questions about their character, the relationships, the situation.

What happened just before the scene started? Was the police officer there when James was brought into the cell? Where is he and what is he doing when James tries to get his attention? Does he believe James doesn't remember committing the crime? Why does he want him to be quiet?

Create a still image of the opening moment of the scene. Ask the rest of the cast to interpret the image. What is the power dynamic between the characters? What do each of the characters want? Who are we rooting for? Ask the actors to improvise the scene.

Try improvising the scene with very different objectives. What if the police officer really wants to comfort and reassure James, but is prevented from doing so by his official role? This will play very differently to a scene in which the police officer just wants to put James in his place in order to make himself feel important.

HOW DO I ASSIGN THE LINES?

Exercise: experiment with different narrators.

The first step is to distinguish between the lines of dialogue and the narration. Read the scene with just the lines of dialogue. Then read the scene again with one actor speaking the narration. Ask the cast: who is this person? Who are they addressing? Why? What are they trying to do to the other characters, or the audience, by saying these lines?

Try having characters within the scene narrating their own action, or narrating each other's action. Try dividing the lines between several narrators. Investigate how this changes the dynamics of the moment. How does it change the sense of a line if the actor playing Mum says it to James rather than the actor playing Dad?

WHAT DO I PUT ON STAGE?

Exercise: try staging the scenes with the bare minimum of stuff on stage.

Davey described his vision of the play working like a pop-up book, with each location appearing instantly from nowhere and disappearing again, to be replaced by the next scene, just as quickly.

There is only one rule that he wanted to impose on the directors: no blackouts!

From a workshop by Davey Anderson,
with notes by Tim Stark

DIRTY DIRTY PRINCESS

Georgia Fitch

Georgia Fitch co-wrote *The Footballer's Wife* and *Come Dancing* (with Tracy O'Flaherty). Other plays include *Arrivals*, *Alone* and *Adrenalin Heart* (also on radio) and *I Like Mine with a Kiss*. For radio, she has written *Fortune's Always Hiding*, *The Mother of . . .*, *Untitled Lover*, *I Met a Boy* and *Romeo and Juliet in Southwark*. She also collaborated on *Dis-Assembly* for the Serpentine Gallery and co-created *Darke Town* for TV. Following her Writer's Attachment to the Royal Court last year, she is currently developing her play *Ten Cigarettes* and is also under commission to the Royal Shakespeare Company.

Characters

Stacey, thirteen
Luke, thirteen
Miesha, thirteen
Sue, Stacey's mum, early thirties
Mark, Stacey's cousin, seventeen
Jessica, Christian Support Group leader, eighteen
Lois, fourteen
Katy, fourteen
Jade, thirteen
Chloe, fifteen
Lisa, fifteen
Fiona, fourteen
Billie, sixteen
Billie's Gang
Nell, eighteen

Time
The present

Setting
A community on the edge of a big city

Notes
Capitals denote emotional intensity rather than volume

A dash (–) indicates coming in quickly with the next line

Three dots show a thinking space

Stacey is standing in front of her street front door that leads to her modest terraced house. A telly can be heard and Stacey continually looks around to make sure nobody is listening to her conversation with Luke. She keeps pulling her pink hoodie down, stretching it over her body, in the direction and safety of her knees. Luke leans forward into her. He is bigger than her, and uses this to his advantage.

Stacey What, Luke?

Luke I wasn't invited to the party –

Stacey I don't think my cousin knows you –

Luke They say he will be a big big star at the Olympics –

Stacey My cousin?

Luke Daniel Johnson, innit!

Stacey . . .

Luke Speaking to Daniel last night . . . talking about things . . . talking about you, Stacey . . . Princess!

Stacey I have to go in now . . . my mum is cooking my tea and my dad wants me to help him with –

Luke So you let Daniel Johnson *sex* you at your cousin's party . . . in the bedroom . . .

Stacey . . .

Luke Naked on top of the duvet with him –

Stacey . . .

Luke He gave you nine out of ten!

Stacey . . .

Luke You went upstairs with a seventeen-year-old . . . Everybody saw you leave the room together . . .

Stacey I didn't have sex.

Luke Come on, Stacey . . . Daniel is fit, yeah . . . sex you up good?

Stacey I speak to you again . . . like for the first time in . . . what, two years? And it's all immediately horrible!

Luke So sorry for stealing your silver and gold pens at primary school, Stacey . . . So sorry for tripping you up, pushing you sometimes –

Stacey Pulling my hair and punching me and –

Luke Daniel Johnson!

Stacey Why Luke, why?

Luke Don't blame me for all the other boys at primary . . . Sexy . . . sexy girl!

Stacey Just let me go, Luke . . . Look . . . just let me fade away . . . please?

Luke You and your friends . . . dropping crisps on the classroom floor . . . saying, 'Eat it Luke Palmer, eat it, we know you are starving . . . We know he is really really really poor.' Laughing and laughing . . .

Stacey THE LIAR LUKE PALMER –

Luke Stacey the sket! Stacey the nine-out-of-ten sket!

He laughs. She starts to move away. He stops laughing.

Stacey Look, we are having spaghetti bolognese . . .

Luke (*indicating to her house, genuine*) Buckingham Palace!

Stacey And it's horrible if the pasta gets cold and my dad shouts and then my mum –

Luke Nah, your mummy's alright you know . . . when we all went on that school trip –

Stacey And your nan hadn't made you any sandwiches, you didn't have a packed lunch –

Luke So the Princess's mum gave me her cheese and onion roll and some crisps . . . The Princess's mum is alright, man –

Stacey I am not a princess . . . we don't have loads of
money, Luke . . . duh . . . duh –

Luke Where did you go on holiday this year, Princess?
Somewhere very hot again? Because you still got your
nice little tan . . . Is it all over?

Stacey . . .

Luke Daniel says it was . . .

Stacey Hurting me that day . . . the last day of primary
school, ripping my clothes and now these lies . . . Why
are you doing this to me, Luke? Why do you hate me
so much?

Luke All your family together on holiday, eh? Drinking
lots of beer, watching football with your daddy –

Stacey Look, I am sorry that you haven't got a proper . . .
mum and dad and all that . . . living together like . . .
but your nan loves you . . . I met her and I know . . .
I know she loves you!

Luke . . .

Stacey I am going in now, alright? . . . I am going in!

She attempts to go.

Luke You have a plasma telly in your bedroom . . .

Stacey It doesn't mean we are millionaires . . . Alright,
my life isn't perfect . . . my life isn't some fairy tale –

Luke Daniel Johnson . . . Dan the Man . . . running for
his gold . . .

Stacey . . .

Luke Maybe no longer a princess . . .

Stacey FOR THE LAST TIME – DIDN'T HAVE SEX WITH
HIM, ALRIGHT –

Luke Stacey do not lie to me . . . Don't fib . . . Princess?

Stacey I AM NOT LYING . . . I AM NOT LYING, LUKE . . .
LEAVE ME ALONE PLEASE, I –

Luke Going to cry?

Stacey Is it money you want?

Luke Think I am another thing that can be bought?

Stacey I CAN GET YOU SOME MONEY IF YOU WANT ME
TO . . . I have some money in my piggy bank . . . Let
me get it for you . . . Let me get it for you, alright!

Luke Your hair looks nice today . . . real nice –

Stacey I cut it – it's a bit short for me . . .

Luke Like it when you straighten it!

Stacey Thanks . . . thank you . . .

Luke Growing up fine, Stacey . . . so ripe –

Stacey . . .

Luke I want to say something . . .

Stacey . . .

Luke I want to say –

Stacey – all those words you boyz love to use . . .

Luke I love you, Princess . . . I love you . . .

Stacey Look, my tea is ready . . .

Luke I love you . . . I love you so so much . . . I love you
bad *sket*!

Stacey Don't spread rumours about me . . . please?

Luke Daniel said . . . 'Yeah, Stacey . . . now she is hot!'

Stacey Look, me and you were years ago . . .

Daniel And Daniel and you were only last week!

Stacey quickly exits.

*She sits alone during lunchtime at school. Pupils pass
and there is a lot of noise. Miesha comes and sits next
to her. She stares at Stacey, who is lost in a world of
her own.*

Miesha If you want to talk, Stacey . . .

Stacey What do you think is a really not-good thing to do?

Miesha Kill someone, be a paedophile . . . turn from God –

Stacey (*to herself*) Kissing, nearly having . . . doing
things with older boys and . . .

Miesha Well, if he is not your boyfriend, and there isn't
mutual trust and respect, and well, sex before marriage
isn't right really, well, that's what we try to advocate in
my Christian group, see . . .

Stacey Please don't tell anyone . . .

Miesha How long have we been in the same class? . . .
Do I gossip . . . chat . . .? (*Beat.*) You told me the other
day that I had a kind face!

Stacey This boy . . . Luke Palmer, right . . . Luke –

Miesha Luke . . . Luke Palmer . . . Should I know him?

Stacey Massive mouth and well he wants to ruin my life
and he knows this older boy called Daniel who I met
at . . . at a party and Daniel said I was hot and I didn't
know what was happening and I didn't let him have
sex with me, I pushed him off, just like I pushed Luke
off at primary school and I had all my clothes on with
Daniel and if my parents found out and everyone now
thinks I am a –

Miesha Take a breath!

Silence.

Stacey Know you are into your Goddy stuff like and all
that . . . seen all those books in your bag but –

Miesha It all gives me focus –

Stacey Does it help . . . having your God to talk to . . .?
You know, at night and when you . . . just before you
fall to . . . when your head hits the pillow . . . before
you start to dream and . . .

Miesha I know that whatever happens or whatever I have
done, and if I am truly sorry for what I have done . . .
He won't stop loving me . . . He is in my heart and I
am in His . . . so there!

Stacey Does he always answer your prayers?

Miesha (*knowingly*) Well, my dad hasn't come back to
us all yet . . . and everyone is still upset . . . but look.
(*She goes to her bag.*) My oldest brother Lewis got me
a new phone . . . so most of the time I get what I ask
for, innit! (*She winks and laughs at Stacey.*)

Stacey looks at Miesha's phone.

Stacey Is your brother always nice to you?

Miesha He is the best, man . . . always there for me . . . he believes in God big-time too . . . always supporting my choices . . . talking to me about important –

Stacey We don't believe in anything in our house . . . we don't seem to believe in anything whatsoever . . . I need something to . . . to hold on to . . . to hold on to . . . to –

Miesha Your parents love you . . . cos all parents love their children deep down –

Stacey I feel I am just my mum's doll sometimes, Miesha, the thing she buys clothes for and makes me wear, to show off in front of her new friends . . .

Miesha Stacey, you should come to my study group . . . I keep telling you . . . Come and learn and share, man! Come and learn and share about sexuality and purity –

Stacey But I am not a new kind of Christian . . . happy-clappy isn't me . . . it's just not me!

Miesha But it's just what you need . . . it saved me, believe!

Stacey Wouldn't know what to wear . . . wouldn't know –

Miesha Don't dress like you want to attract boys, okay? Of course you can look fashionable, look sharp as a Christian . . . and maybe even some Christian boys might think you look sexy . . . And let's face it . . . with you, Stacey, boys will always think you look sexy . . .

Stacey . . .

Miesha But when you are a Christian . . . you are not dressing because you want to be kissed or touched by boys, or you even want their attention . . . You are dressing purely for –

Stacey Jesus . . . you get me?

Miesha You get me!

They smile at each other.

On a scale of one to ten, how lost and empty do you think you really are?

Stacey Lost and empty?

Miesha Needing something to hold on to . . .

Stacey I don't understand . . . I don't understand anything . . .

Miesha To know God is to know everything . . . and that is all you need to know . . .

Stacey . . .

Miesha (*taking back her phone*) Do you like my crucifixion screensaver?

Stacey He looks like he is in a lot of pain . . .

Miesha It was all for us . . . He died for us y'know . . . to save us from our sins . . .

Stacey I am just so scared . . . panicked all the time . . .

Miesha moves towards Stacey.

Miesha Let me give you a hug . . . come here . . . come here . . .

Stacey . . .

Miesha (*getting hold of Stacey's hand*) It's alright . . . everything will be alright . . . believe . . . *believe*!

Stacey lets go of Miesha's hand and exits. Stacey goes into her house and starts looking for food in the kitchen. Sue, her mother, gives her a cup of tea.

Sue Saw that Luke Palmer just walk by the house again. He's a strange one . . . What did he want the other night?

Stacey Nothing . . . What's it to you?

She takes a big gulp.

Sue Remember him from your primary school . . . such a funny thing. (*Thinking back.*) So naughty but always wanted to come and stand by me, when he saw me . . .

Stacey He just wants to be liked, and he still likes you, Mum –

Sue Everyone likes me, don't they?

Stacey (*imitating in her mum's voice*) 'Because I am so young and trendy and have all the latest things and I don't judge the other types . . . even when I have been crying –'

Sue I won't give you that dress I bought for you today . . .

Stacey You can't buy love, Mum . . . you can't keep trying to buy love!

Big, big beat.

Sue Your cousin called –

Stacey What did get-a-life . . . Mark want?

Sue He didn't get that job he went after . . .

Stacey Well, he should have concentrated at school more, instead of dreaming about football . . . which he was –

Sue So where is Luke Palmer living now?

Stacey He's not a celebrity, Mummy . . . you won't see him in *Hello!* magazine –

Sue Was he in care or something . . . poor little boy really –

Stacey He lived with his nan . . . Don't you remember anything at all?

Sue Just watch it, okay?

Stacey His nan who had a beard and grey hair to her toes and who smoked and peeled potatoes in her stained nightdress? Still probably does live with her, I think . . . WHO CARES ABOUT LUKE PALMER ANYHOW! CAN WE CHANGE THE SUBJECT PLEASE?!

Stacey gets some chocolate from her bag and starts to eat it.

Sue You have just had your dinner, young lady . . . you will get fat . . .

Stacey Want to be porky . . .

Sue Princess, you will get very very fat and then you really won't be a princess any more and –

Stacey Don't call me that, alright . . . DON'T CALL ME THAT, OKAY . . . It makes me sick!

Sue What's wrong . . . what's the matter. Stacey? So
bloody moody these days . . . and I am starting not to
like you, not to like you any . . . Look!

Sue moves towards her daughter.

Stacey NO!

Moving away from her mother.

Don't touch me, Mum . . . don't touch me okay . . .?
Nobody is allowed to touch me any more, alright?

She draws a circle around herself with her hand.

This is sacred space, okay? Do you understand, Mummy?
Do you understand? Nobody is allowed to touch me . . .
any more!

Sue I don't need this kind behaviour in my life, Stacey . . .
I don't need it . . . do you understand?

Stacey . . .

Exit Sue. Time passes.

*Mark and Stacey at Stacey's house, sitting on a sofa,
some distance apart.*

Stacey . . .

Mark I just want to look out for you . . . you are my
little cousin . . . Little –

Stacey If you call me a princess . . . I will hit you!

Mark Come on then . . . come on then . . .

*He gets up and starts to prepare to box like a man.
Stacey is not impressed with her cousin's boxing,
Mark sits back down.*

Mark . . .

Stacey Look, Mark . . . I did kind of kiss Daniel Johnson
. . . but he kissed . . . touched me first . . . He asked
for my number and then put my number in his phone

and said he would call me . . . I wouldn't go out with
him . . . I would be too scared . . . he's –

Mark Dan the Man has about four girls at once . . . he
lost his virginity at eight!

Stacey . . .

Mark You were on the bed with him though, Stace . . .
I went into my room and you were on my bed with
DAN THE MAN, and he had his arm around you, and
your dress was falling off your shoulder and . . . Mr
going-to-run-in-the-Olympics . . . YEAH RIGHT . . .
was about to –

Stacey We were just chatting . . . about music . . . about!

Mark 50 Cent, Kanye West?

Stacey Shakira!

Mark What's so special about him then? WHAT'S SO
SPECIAL ABOUT DANIEL JOHNSON, WHAT HAS HE
REALLY GOT THAT THE REST OF US HAVEN'T GOT?
WHY IS HE THE MAN?

Stacey . . .

Mark I am just interested, that's all, and I am trying to
look out for you!

Stacey How's your football going . . . Still –?

Mark My little cousin is getting a reputation and well,
I –

Stacey IT WON'T BE TRUE . . . IT'LL ALL BE LIES . . .
IT'S ALWAYS LIES, BOYZ TELL LIES AND ALL BOYZ
ARE THE SAME –

Mark Daniel Johnson –

Stacey I don't want to talk about the party any more . . .
How's the football . . . how is your football going,
Mark?

Mark Dan wearing the all latest gear, all the top tunes on
his iPhone . . . six foot two and his six-pack, innit!

Stacey Don't say anything to Mum and Dad.

Mark You don't know what you got, Stacey . . . you
don't know what you got . . . popping along to the
party –

Stacey Please, Mark . . . don't . . . Stop it, okay? No
more, please . . .

Mark And I saw your little light was shining from you as
always . . . looking like your true angel self . . . but
something was different and something is always
different with you now . . . SOMETHING IS ALWAYS
DIFFERENT WITH YOU THESE DAYS AND IT SORT OF
MAKES ME SAD, STACEY . . . (*Beat.*)

Stacey Mark, this is –

Mark But eh, you looked so good in that dress, man, and
you just stood there in the corner and you smiled at
everyone and your lonely eyes inviting boys in, inviting
him in and then he – Daniel Johnson walks over to
you, and you give him all your attention without a
second thought and his breath on you, heating you up,
and now you're getting hot, hot . . . but you don't
move away, and then you dance, cos Daniel says you
dance and we all watch you, the room stops to look
at you both, and you flick your hair and your hips
pretend?

Stacey . . .

Mark You moving and grooving together in some kind
of time and you smile for him and you don't notice me
or anyone else and then he gonna go for his gold . . .
takes your hand and leads you out . . . out and up . . .
up to the . . . my room and the . . . (*Changing quickly.*)
Yeah, you are gonna say I should get myself a
girlfriend –

Stacey And a job . . .

Mark Someone of me own age . . . I know that, I know
. . . What, you think I don't know that, Stacey?

Stacey I didn't do anything bad . . . I DIDN'T DO
ANYTHING REALLY WRONG –

Mark Would you –
Stacey Would I . . .

Mark moves towards Stacey.

Mark Would you kiss me please, Stacey?
Stacey . . .
Mark Like you kiss all the other boys . . . you do things
for all of them . . . so . . . for your cousin . . . a little
kiss . . . a little, little . . . you are so gorgeous . . . *so so* –
Stacey Mark . . .

Stacey gets up.

Mark Sorry, that was wrong . . . very wrong . . .
Stacey I thought I could trust you . . . I thought I could
bloody trust you . . .
Mark At my party . . . Dan the Man . . . running for his
gold . . .
Stacey I didn't have sex!
Mark Nobody believes you . . . Liar . . .

*Stacey goes and sits with Miesha in her study group
with her group of girlfriends. Jessica welcomes and
addresses the group. She has a manual and a notebook
and a long pencil which she fiddles with continually.
The girls have Bibles, various kinds of Christian
literature and workbooks.*

Jessica Thank you all for giving up your Saturday morning
yet again and coming to my house. We welcome Stacey
as our new member today and we thank Miesha for
bringing another friend to our special group. As
always, if there is anyone who you may feel just needs
some time to reflect and share, then my door is always
open. (*Big beat.*) I myself have had a challenging week,
my parents have been there for me, but I have been
very tired and I have been afraid . . . As always,
however, I have found comfort in talking to God, and

44

working through my issues with Him and what I want
to share with you all today is what I have been reading
again in this difficult week. I was, you see, myself
tempted to call my ex-boyfriend around Wednesday, so
this might give you an idea of why I am speaking from
my heart today. (*She reads from her manual.*) For
guarding your heart and your mind and –

Lois Your spirit!

Miesha And your body –

Jessica And of course most importantly your God-given
body . . . And therefore saving yourself for your
husband-to-be and Jesus the –

Lois Ultimate groom?

Jessica Is the best thing . . . and the most important thing
we can ever do, at this time in our lives . . . But we have
to remember . . . we always have to remember . . .

Katy That we are all sinners and we all were born with
original –

All Sin!

Jessica See you have all been doing your homework!
(*Reading from her notepad.*) So – (*In control.*) Because
all of us are deeply committed to helping and stopping
any member from indulging in self-destructive sexual
experiences – (*Off the notepad.*) – experiences that not
only hurt us . . . but deeply attack God . . . we should
start with sharing, and you could let me know how
your week has –

Miesha I watched three soaps this week, Jessica –

Jade I poked a lot of boys on Facebook, in fact I could
not stop poking . . .

Chloe I downloaded some images of . . . he used to be in –

Jade And I had some conversations online and they got a
bit . . . well . . . a bit . . . he . . . asked me if I was a
virgin and . . . Supposed to be meeting up with him in
Tooting.

45

Lisa *Now* magazine – dull . . . and there was something
else I read . . . not really an official sin, like . . . but it
said girls these days . . . girls like us – our demographic,
yeah? They just want to be sexy and not clever . . . what
does everyone think?

Jessica Well . . . well . . . well?

Jade He also, yeah . . . asked me what colour knickers
I was wearing. (*To the group.*) and lots of girls had
written gross things on his wall . . . Someone else . . .
probably has something more interesting and, er . . .
yeah . . . yeah!

Katy I started to read my mum's book, *Women Are from
Mars, Men Are from Venus* . . . not very fulfilling,
anyway . . . nothing as enriching as the New
Testament, Jessica!

Jessica Did anyone . . . fly solo?

All girls turn away.

Jessica Did anyone feel the need to fly solo?

All . . .

Jessica Nobody flew solo and therefore that is very –

Fiona Good?

They all look at Fiona. Big pause.

Jessica When you fill your mind with unclean stuff, you
stir dangerous desires . . . desires that should only be
allowed in at the very least marriage: between two
people who love each other . . . Yeah?

Fiona Yeah?

All Yeah!

Jessica (*back to notepad*) The media –

Katy (*to Fiona*) Television and internet –

Fiona (*standing up to her*) Don't patronise me, alright?
I do go to school. At least I don't agree and nod my
head at everything she (*pointing to Jessica*) says like
you do . . .

Jessica Suffocating us with ways to be, how to pump our lips, show off our curves . . . ways that rip apart our sexual integrity and as always . . . We have to keep walking away from this addictive stuff –

Miesha – for when you starve your fondness for sin . . . it stops having power over you . . . so . . .

All in the group look at her.

Fiona . . . if you stop thinking about boys, sex, if you go around with your eyes closed, it all just goes away . . . Is that right, Jessica?

Jessica tries to find the right words, the group starts to compete – again, much avoidance and high energy.

Lois We have to keep on trying to get our love from our family and friends . . .

Jessica Exactly, Lois . . .

Chloe We are not victims . . . we can control our emotions. We don't need to look to strangers . . . to score emotionally –

Katy Honour God and only God with your body, Jessica –

Lisa If we keep on hooking up with lots of different boys, over and over again . . . we won't ever be able to stay with anyone . . . Too much choice . . . is not a good thing . . .

They all look at Lisa, who hugs her huge frumpy home-knitted cardigan and finds a smile.

Jessica Passionate kissing leads to other stuff . . . so –

Jade Nobody must touch your . . . breasts –

Fiona Shame?

Lois Sitting on men's laps and –

Jade Does that mean my I can't sit on my dad's lap, Jessica?

Jessica Any kind of sex and flying . . .

Fiona Solo . . .

All Flying solo . . .

Lisa Because the Bible says that indulging in daydreams about people you are not married to . . . is a major sin and –

Jessica Brilliant. Lisa –

Lisa . . .

Jessica What do boys really want, girls? I mean, decent Christian boys and not boys like my ex . . . Jason my ex, who . . .

Fiona Man, you were in love with . . . but he didn't want to go to no church and he wanted some jiggy jiggy?

Miesha Boys want a girl who puts God first and loves him with all of her heart!

Katy A girl who has a decent self-image –

Lois Positive in her outlook and she does love her family –

Jade She doesn't buy rubbish –

Lois (*to Jade*) Or meet losers in Tooting!

Katy Motherhood will come naturally to her . . .

Fiona Educated?

Lisa She will be right behind her husband and into what he wants to do with his life.

Fiona Nah . . . sod that!

Jessica (*very confident*) Stacey, perhaps you could tell us what you think . . .

Stacey cannot speak.

Fiona I just say the first thing that comes into my head . . . always have and always . . .

Stacey Speaking up for yourself . . . standing your ground . . . Proving your innocence . . .

Fiona The Bible bits, all this . . . parrot-fashion and homework . . . I don't know . . . just some of it is a bit screwed up, weird . . .

Everyone looks at Fiona.

Why do people look at me funny? . . . (*To Stacey, looking
directly into her eyes.*) Stacey, did you go to bed with
Daniel Johnson? Luke Palmer said you did . . . I mean,
who wouldn't? Now Daniel Johnson . . . bring it on . . .
Hello . . . Hello, Big Gold-Medal Big Boy . . . Out of
ten, Stace? . . . I LIKE YOU, Y'KNOW, STACEY!

Jessica Tomorrow at my church, our church, if I could
just know who is coming to the service, if I could have
a show of hands . . . if I could just have a show of
hands please . . .

Fiona Why does everyone find it so hard to be honest?

Lisa This gives us all something, Stacey . . . something
absolute and constant to cling to . . . it works, if you
keep coming along . . . it does work.

*The group chat amongst themselves, a few hands go
up. Stacey leaves the group.*

*Billie, Daniel's long-term girlfriend, stands with her
gang. She has Stacey by the hair and Stacey is
surrounded.*

Billie He drinks too much drink, innit, and running and
drink don't mix . . . and if he wants to go for gold,
then he has to stop that . . . I know that, his coach
knows that and he knows that. He gets up early to
train and his body is then out of the flow like if he
smokes and drinks . . . and then he makes bad choices .
. . choices like you, Princess . . . choices like . . . Just like
Ashley did with Cheryl . . . just like Ashley Cole did to
his woman . . . remember? (*Billie tightens her grip.*)
Seeing you about for years, innit, little girl in ankle
socks, tap-dancing in the street, Mummy and Daddy's
pride and joy . . . living in a plasma Buckingham
Palace, clean windows, shiny front door with Daddy's

BMW parked outside! Walking your dog, head to toe in yer Primark Pink, laughing with your friend and I HATE YOU . . . I HATE ALL GIRLS LIKE YOU, BUT I ESPECIALLY HATE GIRLS REALLY LIKE YOU BECAUSE INSIDE YOU IS HEARTLESS, GAL, VERY VERY HEARTLESS, AND YOU CARE ABOUT NOBODY BUT YOURSELF . . . It's the – (*Acting and performing to her gang.*) I am oh so lucky girl, innit, the girl who has and takes everything she wants, never had anything bad happen to her in life, no tears or nightmares at bedtime for Princess . . . cos you know the world belongs to you, THE PERFECT WORLD IS YOUR DOLL'S HOUSE AND YOU ARRANGE THE FURNITURE JUST THE WAY YOU WANT and you can own any girl's Action Man, yeah . . . Well, little Barbie sket . . . dirty dirty Princess . . . Not so clean now innit?

Billie throws her to the ground and rubs Stacey's face in the mud. Stacey tries to wipe her face.

See, you think you are so, so special . . . but you are nothing, not worth a text, and just like us now . . . Some ho . . . some little thing that Daniel was tricked by because he had too too much drink . . . some pink bitch sket leading him on and . . . it meant nothing . . . and you meant nothing to him, see . . . *see?*

She is performing even more to her gang. They smile back sheepishly.

I don't want to seriously hurt you or kill you even . . . cos I have bigger fish to fry and Luke Palmer pleaded to go easy on you . . . but if you ever sex up my man again . . . I will put you in hospital for a long *long* time . . . you hear . . . YOU HEAR ME . . .? Now go back to Barbie, Mummy with all the shopping bags and Buckingham Palace and don't walk these streets no more . . . I don't want to see you about. You get me? You get me? (*Beat.*) You hear? (*Big, big beat.*) You hear . . . ?

Stacey Yes . . . I hear you . . .

Billie Give me that ring. I said give me that ring . . .

Stacey takes off her ring.

Thank you . . . Princess . . . thank you very very much.

Stacey walks into her house. Mark sits with Sue.

Stacey Was messing with Miesha . . . no questions, please –

She exits.

Mark She's been proper fighting –

Sue (*calling off*) Have you been fighting . . . Have you been fighting, Stacey?

Stacey enters.

Stacey I haven't been fighting, okay?

Sue What's been going on?

Stacey I don't have to answer to anyone . . .

Sue You are thirteen and you answer to me . . . I AM YOUR MOTHER IN CASE YOU JUST FORGOT . . . NOW HAVE SOME RESPECT, YOUNG LADY, FOR YOUR MOTHER AND YOUR FAMILY . . .

Stacey Why are you here again, Mark?

Sue He's been fixing up the new telly for the kitchen . . .

Mark That a problem for you, Stacey . . . Princess?

Stacey Been moaning about how you is so hard done by and there is nothing worth striving for? New people moving in and taking all our work . . . blah blah blah . . . What is the country coming to?!

Sue Don't be rude . . . don't be rude to your cousin . . .

Stacey I am going to my room . . . I am going to my room, alright?

Sue What is wrong with you . . . what is wrong with you, Stacey? How many times do I have to tell you, I don't need this awful behaviour, okay?

Stacey Where's my dad?

Sue He's doing a bit of overtime . . .

Stacey You haven't got a clue what you are doing with your life . . . have you, Mummy?

Sue I haven't hit you for years . . . but you are coming so close . . . COMING SO VERY VERY CLOSE . . .

Stacey I WANT TO LEAVE THE AREA –

Sue I thought you liked it here . . .

Stacey I HATE IT! IT'S MESSED UP AND IT'S DEAD –

Sue Well, more and more strange types are moving in but . . . I THOUGHT YOU LIKED IT HERE . . .

Stacey If we don't move . . . I will turn to Jesus big time . . . And I will be a new kind of Christian completely. Like Miesha . . . can totally switch off, see . . . have no responsibility to my real self . . . just smile all the time, convince tougher people that I am suddenly a nutter and no longer a threat to any of the girls and keep the boys away –

Sue Stacey, you are going mad . . .

Stacey I am trying to survive in this town . . . in this dead land . . . on these grubby streets. You get me?

Sue I thought that Miesha was a bad influence. What did I say, Mark . . . What did I say, eh?

Stacey What are you giving me to believe in, Mum? You haven't got any answers . . . you haven't got any answers . . . because you never asked yourself any questions, Mummy!

Mark Look, should I go?

Sue No, stay. You stay, Mark . . . stay or I just might hurt her . . .

Stacey He wanted me to . . .

Mark Stacey . . .

Stacey He wanted me to . . .

Mark Stace . . .

Sue looks at Stacey's hand. She takes hold of her arm, Stacey fights off her mother.

Sue Where is your ring, Stacey? Where is your ring? Nan bought you that . . . Don't tell me you lost it. You are so careless! Don't know what to do with you any more. I don't know what to do with you any more . . . So so ungrateful!

Doorbell rings. They all look at each other. Sue leaves.

Stacey Stop staring at me, Mark. Stop staring at . . . Look, if you really want to see my breasts, my bosoms . . . I'll show you them, alright? They are not bad, are they . . . they are not bad at all? Out of ten, Mark . . . what do you give 'em, eh?

Stacey pulls up her top. Mark looks away. Sue returns with Luke Palmer. They both look at Stacey, Stacey pulls down her top. Silence.

Luke We call her Princess . . . We call her . . . Princess, Princess!

Sue . . .

Stacey I DON'T WANT HIM IN THIS HOUSE, ALRIGHT? (*To Sue about Luke.*) GET HIM OUT – (*To Sue about Mark.*) AND GET HIM OUT OF MY HOUSE NOW. GET BOTH OF THEM OUT THIS VERY MINUTE –

Sue Er . . .

Luke I can see what you are, Stacey . . . I can see what and who you really are. See –

Stacey Luke said he loves me . . . first told me when we were ten that he wanted me to be his girl . . . Then he punctured my signed-by-the-stars football!

Mark Look, Luke, this isn't a good time . . . really not a good time . . .

Stacey Luke still knows jack about love . . . because if you love someone you don't filthy their name . . . spread violent lies . . . make them frightened of their own shadow and . . .

Sue What?

Luke Stacey . . .

Mark Stacey, just be quiet . . . Don't you think you have upset your mum enough already today?

Stacey I don't care . . . I am beyond caring. I will say what I like!

Sue I don't understand!

Stacey Love is about wanting the person you love to be the best they can be, allowing them to shine as bright as they can possibly shine . . . not totally letting them off the hook if they have done dodgy or mean stuff or if they are being a bit of a brat. But it's about caring and it's certainly not about –

Sue Where are all these words coming from, Stacey?

Stacey (*beat, change, and then to Luke*) Look, I wouldn't go near or touch you with a bargepole, alright? Pikey, freak . . . THICK AS PIG-SHIT OTHER BOY –

Luke My nan is in hospital . . . lung cancer, innit, she is just sleeping all the time now. I have to go into some kind of care thing tomorrow, Stacey . . . Came to say goodbye to you and goodbye to you, Mrs –

Sue Sue –

Luke Nan will die . . . she hasn't got any money for her funeral, y'know . . . So I have to get some money somehow . . . somewhere . . . whatever it takes. Y'know what I am saying, Stacey?

Mark Gonna get yourself a gun, big man?

Luke I know people . . . on the street . . . you hear me?

Stacey I don't believe a word you say . . . I don't believe in you . . .

Luke Me and you . . .

Sue I have to get Stacey's tea now, Luke . . . Sorry about
your nan . . . but I am sure . . .

Mark You said your bit, boy . . . You said your . . . acted
out your scene from a movie –

Luke Princess?

Stacey Luke, you don't have to behave like this!

Luke Daniel Johnson . . . going for the gold . . . first over
the finish line –

Stacey Get out of my house . . . I hate you!

*Time passes. A deserted school playground, after
school has finished for the day. Stacey is eating
chocolate, unaware that she is even eating. Nell, head
girl of the Sixth Form, comes over to Stacey.*

Nell Haven't you got a home to go to?

Stacey . . .

Nell Why you here so late on your own?

Stacey I had to stay behind and have a chat with my
form tutor . . . Miss Tilley . . .

Nell Her red-wine teeth . . .

Stacey From the night before . . .

Nell I kept looking at her bright red lipstick at lunchtime.
How comes a woman gets to forty and she still can't
put on lipstick? She should have mastered applying
make-up with a continual hangover by now . . .

Stacey Our lessons are so funny with her . . .

Nell One minute she is very serious talking about the
group –

Stacey Getting the best results ever –

Nell Then she goes a bit crazy and does her sad silly
voices. We always say . . . Miss and the Merlot again –
Red-wine Tilley . . . Game on, girls . . . game on!

Stacey She isn't married, is she . . . ?

Nell Who would marry her?

Stacey I do like her, though –

Nell I don't think she will be here next year . . .

Stacey But she told me that she thought this was a community and a school that is on the up. 'These are inspiring times to be living in and going to this school . . .'

Nell She's been asked to leave . . . Our secret, okay?

Stacey . . .

Nell Did she do the . . . (*Mocking liberal Miss Tilley.*) 'You have such potential and a huge future ahead, should you get back on course and decide to drive yourself to it . . .'

Stacey 'There are more opportunities than ever for you to be whatever you want to be, young woman –'

Nell 'You can create yourself anew each day and be the artist of your own life . . . but it takes courage and it takes graft and . . .'

Stacey Yeah, she said all that to me . . .

Nell If only she could apply it to her own life . . . Well, she can't and she can't control her demons, and that is why she is for the big push!

Stacey Why don't you like her?

Nell Because she is self-indulgent and refuses to grow up!

Stacey She was trying to be kind to me . . .

Nell Do you want to tell me what is wrong?

Stacey . . .

Nell In confidence, like . . . I mean, I am nearer your age than Miss Tilley . . . They did make me head girl . . .

Stacey . . .

Nell I am doing Psychology A level!

Silence. Nell makes Stacey lie down.

Stacey I have been self-sabotaging . . .

Nell Why?

Stacey Falling behind with my work . . .

Nell Why?

Stacey There's so much noise in my head . . .

Nell What kind off noise?

Stacey I keep having baths . . .

Nell Did someone hurt you?

Stacey Everybody is talking about me and the words make me feel . . . very very bad . . .

Nell Why is everyone talking about you?

Stacey Do you think I am a princess?

Nell No . . .

Stacey And Miss Tilley is no way a queen?

Nell A queen is the last thing Tilley is . . .

Stacey She will govern a kingdom one day . . .

Nell I don't think so . . .

Stacey She will articulate her noble purpose – it will just be in a different school, a different kind of setting . . .

Nell If she doesn't die soon . . .

Stacey Magical, Miss . . . you is magical . . . that is what I said to Miss Tilley!

Nell You are not making any sense . . .

Big silence.

Stacey Do you ever want to get someone or some event out of your head so much . . . but however much you try you just can't, like . . . they . . . it keeps on coming back . . . in your dreams even . . .

Nell Dreams are important, they guide us and tell us things . . . so tell me about your dreams.

Stacey I am going to be late . . . my mum will be angry!

She gets up to go.

Nell Look, why don't we arrange a time to meet tomorrow? What about lunchtime . . . any time . . . Come and find me . . . or I will come and find you . . .

Stacey When I was at primary school . . . this boy Luke . . . well, I had no choice back then . . . not like with Daniel . . .

Stacey exits, leaving Nell alone and intrigued.

Stacey and Miesha are at the Christian group. Lois joins them. Stacey is in a tracksuit and her hair is scraped back. The group slowly dribbles in.

Lois Loads of what Jessica says is veering to nonsense . . . She is a control freak really . . . and nowhere near as intelligent as she thinks she is. She uses the information and twists it to suit her . . . but that is religion for you.

Miesha Why are you here then, Lois?

Lois And I don't buy that she is speaking truly from her heart . . .

Miesha Jessica just tries to help those devoid of clarity. *How to Pursue Purity in a Sex-Saturated World* is something she has read and is working for her. (*Beat.*) She is so glad you came back to us, Stacey . . . very glad!

Fiona enters. Stacey is very pleased to see her, and gives her a big friendly smile.

Fiona I got to wear glasses . . . don't know why . . . Doctor sent me for eye test and . . .

Stacey My mum wants to take me to the doctor, Fiona – thinks I might have something wrong with me and I might loose my figure . . . y'know, because I can't stop eating these days like . . .

Miesha Jesus loves you whether you are a size zero or a twenty-two, you get me . . . well, that's what I tell myself!

The group are all now present. They pray. Stacey sits close to Fiona.

Jessica Lord Jesus, help us as we endeavour to build virtuous lives and become the strong women that you want us to be. Silence the thoughts that tell us we are alone. Ignite our personal power, and make us strong enough to approach you, so that you can help us, in these times of intense need. Support us to be there for one another, as we take off our masks and attempt to be real.

Fiona Yes!

Jessica Teach us to love one another unconditionally, as you have loved us. Amen.

All Amen.

Jessica Giving away our power and asking ourselves what is abuse . . .

Big, big silence.

Lois Why are we talking about this today, Jessica?

Jessica Because last week I sensed something in the room . . . that a someone or even a few perhaps needed to explore . . .

Lois But are you qualified?

Jessica (*reading from notes*) 'While any form of sexual abuse or rape is an absolute tragedy, the real unhappy ending is when the abused person remains silent. She or he buries it so deep within themselves that they no longer know who they are; they are only the keeper of the secret.'

Miesha 'In some cases the abused person is so hurt and damaged that they start to inflict pain on others and that is a tragedy too.'

Jessica 'We are delicate and delightful children of the king of the universe, and even if someone treats you less than they should or uses your body or your mind or your heart or your –'

Lois Has Jason been calling you again?

Jessica '– for a purpose other than what God intended, we must never forget who we . . . who you really are and –'

Lois Know thy worth . . . know thy worth . . . know thy worth!

Jessica We have the right to be treated with dignity and respect and we have to treat others in the same –

Lois Draw a line in time . . . say that is my past . . . Now is today and now is my future.

Jessica So if you have been abused . . . what might you have done . . . you may have –

Jade Put up with that person like . . . because you so wanted them to be part of your life . . . anyway to keep the contact alive . . . gone over to Tooting . . .

Katy Believe that you somehow invited the abuse . . . you deserved it possibly . . . Was reading some of my mother's stuff again during the week . . .

Chloe Hated that person and wanted them dead . . . chopped up into a thousand pieces . . . head on a spike like . . . saw it in a film!

Lisa Suffered alone and in silence . . . because nobody would understand . . . or hear you –

Lois Assume that you will never be pure again . . . you have no market value . . . I know it all, Jessica . . . I KNOW IT ALL!

Jessica Stacey?

Stacey . . .

Lisa Carry it around with you everywhere . . . making you heavy . . . your story showing in your face . . . clouding your beauty . . .

Fiona I read this thing in *Glamour* magazine, right . . . flying-solo stuff? (*Big beat.*) Why does everyone look at me funny again? Is it cos of the things I say? Come on, girls . . . come on? You just all skim the surface, don't you . . . nobody really goes deep . . .

Lois If you gave us a chance . . .

Jessica I found this passage in the Old Testament the other night which I would like to share with you all. If I could just have some silence in the room for a minute . . . just for a minute . . .

Stacey walks out of the group. She looks back at Jessica and bumps into Billie.

Billie Can't fight you . . . cos I am having a baby, yeah? Little thing growing inside of me – Daniel's . . . well, that's got him now . . . never going to leave . . . responsibility. Well, fingers crossed . . . fingers very crossed . . .

Stacey . . .

Billie Calling it Prince if it's a boy –

Stacey After the singer?

Billie No, the dog I had as a kid, like . . .

Stacey Right . . .

Billie Princess . . .

Stacey If it's a girl . . .

Billie I knew this beautician from Dominica . . . she was called Princess like, also . . . used to wax my mum's legs for a fiver and I thought back then it's a pretty name so –

Stacey Princess . . .

Billie If it's a girl . . . although . . . I don't really want one of those, though.

Stacey Girls are tricky when they get older . . . and I mean, how do you protect them . . . is spoiling them with things irresponsible?

Billie Are you alright?

Stacey . . .

Billie Look, sorry and all that . . . for y'know . . . beating you and er . . .

Stacey . . .

Billie (*embarrassed and returning to the previous subject*) Well, boys have life, don't they, man?

Stacey Girls have life and can have a life too . . .

Billie Yeah . . . but boys . . . got to get what they want . . . go after it . . . make you laugh . . . EXCITING, MAN!

Stacey So Daniel going to fix up a house for you . . . decorate it nice . . . ?

Billie Well, he's got his training and Olympics real soon, so he gotta practise, he gotta keep his running going like . . . so he can't help me that much . . . Going to get his brother on the case –

Stacey . . .

Billie You can touch my stomach if yer want, Stace . . . Always remember this picture I saw of Scary Spice when I was little, like . . . with her belly and her tattoos . . . thought that's gonna be me one day, man, that is . . . that's gonna be me . . . wicked. Go on, Stace, man . . . touch it now . . . come . . . touch it . . . TOUCH IT!

Stacey doesn't move.

Give me your number and I will call you when I have it and then you can see it, innit, and you might, I dunno, wanna babysit or something . . . cos I think I trust you . . . I trust you . . . You hear?

Stacey Okay.

Stacey doesn't do anything.

Billie You seeing anyone yourself . . . Got a man like?

Stacey No –

Billie Well . . . gonna do yoga for mums now . . . on our estate . . . all a bit older than me, some with fancy-fancy voices . . . Daniel going to meet me afterwards like . . . well, if his training finishes on time . . .

Stacey Good luck then, Billie . . . Good luck and love!

Stacey starts to move away.

Billie Do you want your ring back?

Stacey Gold makes people very angry around here . . . You can keep it . . . pawn it . . . buy something for

your baby . . . something you might . . . something you
are going to need . . .

Billie Luke Palmer was in love with you, y'know . . . big
time . . .

Stacey I wouldn't call it love . . .

*Stacey walks into her house, Sue gives her a cup of tea.
Mark is sitting on the sofa.*

Sue Guess what?

Stacey Daddy will be home for his tea.

Sue Mark got a job – he popped in to tell us . . .

Stacey For real . . .

Mark It's only in a warehouse, but the money's alright.
Cash-and-carry place . . . get staff discount after a
couple of months . . .

Sue It's a stepping stone.

Stacey That's cool, Mark.

Mark They employ lots of foreigners mainly . . .

Stacey (*sarcastically*) How will you cope?

Mark Might get to learn Polish or Swahili.

Stacey Join a Sunday league football team . . . and then
you might just have something that looks like a life,
Mark.

Sue Watch it, Stace . . .

Mark Get myself a bird . . . Nice decent girlfriend on me
arm . . . One who hasn't given herself away to the
entire world . . .

Stacey Well done, Mark . . . well done. Pleased for you.

Sue When your dad gets in, we will open some Cava and
I have got some very nice food in for tea!

Stacey Mum . . .

Sue What?

Stacey Nothing . . .

Sue What?

Stacey Just might go to my room for a little bit . . . run a
bath . . .

Stacey exits.

Sue She'll get over it . . .

Mark What . . . get over what?

Sue Being a girl . . . being thirteen . . . thinking the world revolves around her.

Mark She's not one of us, Sue . . . It's like she's not from this family . . .

Sue You are telling me . . . Sometimes I say to myself, did I really give birth to Stacey?

Mark I don't get girls . . .

Sue . . .

Mark Are you alright, Sue? Is everything okay with you?

Sue Everything is fine . . . I've got a not-bad house, a husband who works hard, okay, a bit of a moody daughter . . . my job's not too bad . . . pays the bills. We are financially keeping our heads above water . . . What makes you think I am sad, Mark?

Mark . . .

Sue . . .

Time passes, Stacey and Miesha sit in the park, eating chocolate and crisps. It is a bright sunny day and an ice-cream van is in the distance . . .

Stacey It's the idea that we are born bad, born with this original sin, and we have to ask for strength, hand over our power to something outside of ourselves and then Jessica reading her bits out of a book that was written so long ago, a book I just can't relate to, get into . . .

Miesha The Old Testament has stood the test of time . . .

Stacey I think a lot of the Christian values are good, and it's basic commonsense and respect, like . . . but sin . . . Well, isn't there enough sin and guilt in the world already, and isn't sin just a way of scaring the shit out of you, so you conform, do what people say? Oh, it's all just more words, Miesha, messing with your head!

Miesha God sacrificed the thing He loved most in order
for all of us to learn our lessons and be great . . .
gorgeous people . . .

Stacey It's a good story . . . and manipulative –

Miesha All the group were asking about you . . .

Silence.

Miss Tilley went . . .

Stacey School is different without her . . .

Enter Luke.

Luke Alright. Stacey?

Stacey . . .

Luke Is it alright if I sit here . . . ? Was in the park like . . .
saw you from over there and . . .

He points to the faraway distance.

Stacey . . .

Miesha . . .

Big, big, big silence.

Stacey How's your nan, Luke?

Luke She died . . .

Stacey I am sorry . . .

Luke . . .

Stacey So what is going to happen to you, like . . . ?

Luke shrugs his shoulders.

Luke Miss her . . . miss her bad . . .

Stacey . . .

Luke Missing you . . .

Silence.

Stacey . . .

Luke You look different . . .

Stacey Good –

Luke Can I talk to you . . . please?

Stacey . . .

Luke I AM ALWAYS THINKING ABOUT YOU . . . I HAD THIS DREAM . . . THIS NIGHTMARE –

Stacey Who wants an ice cream?

Miesha . . .

Stacey Mum gave me ten pounds and a kiss this morning so . . . (*She goes to her bag.*) Will you go for us all, Miesha?

Miesha What?

Stacey Vanilla for me . . . Chocolate for you and Luke?

Luke Anything will do for me . . . thanks. Thank you . . .

Miesha takes the money and exits. More silence.

Luke I knew I wasn't important to you any more and I just had this feeling in me, see . . . I wanted you that day –

Stacey Our last day at primary school . . .

Luke I wanted to touch your skin . . . feel your . . . feel your . . .

Stacey My breasts . . .

Luke Ripping your clothes . . . your pink top . . . that was . . . out of order . . . evil. I don't know what came over me, Stace –

Stacey The other boys laughing and suddenly you're popular and I was terrified –

Luke Then hearing about you and Daniel . . . I was mad alright!

Stacey . . .

Luke You see things, pictures . . . how I should be now I am getting older . . . magazines and telly. It's everywhere, sex and all that . . . it can do your head in, y'know. Look at my phone, Stace . . . see what I was sent today . . . babes who –

Stacey turns her head, as Luke gets out his phone, then puts it quickly back in his pocket.

Stacey Just because I was dancing in the playground at school and just cos I felt I had to dance with Daniel.

Luke You dance in a way that isn't you. You are someone different . . . like older women in films, on the internet, with all the moves and style. And you, Stacey . . . well, you were always up for showing off . . . always forward –

Stacey . . .

Luke You are still a virgin!

Stacey You started this terror in me, Luke, and this dirty energy that refuses to go away. I can't trust any men now, and it's all your fault – it all started with you, and Daniel picked up the baton, and so did my . . . my cousin . . .

Luke I just want to be close to you again . . . like when it was safe . . .

Stacey All the rumours and lies and . . .

Luke Thanks for keeping quiet, not going to a teacher . . . getting me into even more trouble . . .

Stacey Silence is the real gold . . .

Luke Princess?

Stacey Princess is dead, Luke . . .

Luke No, she is just sleeping. She will wake up soon . . . she is just –

Stacey – waiting for her prince –

Luke – to ride up to her palace, fight the weeds, climb the walls, battle through into her bedroom . . . to kiss her and . . .

Stacey . . .

Luke You're valuable, Stace . . .

Stacey . . .

Luke My nan –

Stacey I know . . . I am sorry . . .
Luke She liked you . . . she said you were –
Stacey . . .
Luke – polite . . .

Silence.

Stacey We might be moving . . . innit, Luke . . . out to somewhere a bit greener. Too many people in this city now . . . too frightening . . . nobody knowing who they are any more . . . too much pressure to be and have everything and Mum wants a bigger, better house.
Luke . . .

Silence.

Could we go out some time, like . . . just you and me . . . Could we?
Stacey . . .

Miesha returns.

Miesha We are all having chocolate . . .

They all take their ice creams.

Luke Stacey . . . going out, well . . . it just means we could try to learn to . . . in a different kind of way . . . to value each . . . start again and . . .

Stacey takes a good look at him.

Stacey What's that in your pocket . . . ?

He gets out a tabloid tucked in his back pocket in a very manly but awkward way.

Luke *The Sun* . . . found it on the bus . . . do you want to look at it?
Miesha Are you religious?

Luke No . . .

Stacey (*looking out*) I don't want to see the world like
this . . . I just don't . . . I JUST DON'T!

Miesha . . .

Stacey It doesn't have to be like this . . .

> *Luke and Miesha look at Stacey. They all continue to
> eat their ice creams. Stacey steps forward. Lights
> slowly fade.*
>
> *End.*

Production Notes

Dirty Dirty Princess is a play about creating your own path, following what feels okay for you; saying no to things that don't sit right in your own value system; and not allowing yourself to be defined by someone else. Importantly, if young audiences take away anything from the play, I would like them to leave feeling that it is crucial to know your own boundaries and indeed to honour them and to honour yourself . . .

I feel we are all a mixture of many things, some defined by society as good and some as bad. We are all a big melting pot of light and shade, kindness and cruelty, hope and despair (the polar opposites infinitely continue). As I have got older, I have tried to embrace this. My realisation has come about because as a young person I really liked to ask questions. Young people do have to keep on asking questions and their questions are, as always, essential for the development of our humanity. Sue (Stacey's mother) never asked any questions; Stacey is going to be different. Stacey will be the artist of her own life and she will make mistakes, but she will grow and allow herself to be challenged, which is the essential thing.

I do think the socio-economic setting is important in this play. Luke's options are limited, like those of all the young people in Stacey's community. They have been dealt a tough hand, they don't have much cultural capital to play with, but they are strong, stronger than they could ever imagine . . .

Georgia Fitch

70

SETTING

Dirty Dirty Princess is set in a specific, increasingly marginalised world that is rarely represented on stage. When we look at plays set in contemporary Britain we often feel we 'know' the world of the play because we are alive now, and that there is therefore no need for detailed research. However, just as if we were rehearsing a play set in 1950s South Africa, it is essential that work begins with an exploration of the play's background and context.

There are specific local, social, political and economic circumstances that make the action of the play and the behaviour of the characters possible. What are these?

- A world where there is social housing which is located near privately owned homes.

- In this community Stacey's house is considered to be one of the best.

- The school is a comprehensive with a Sixth Form, and you can study Psychology there at A level.

- The community is small enough for Daniel to be famous.

- It is near enough to an urban centre for the characters to have internalised values, aspirations, acquisition of material goods, but far away enough to have maintained the feeling of a smaller, more isolated world with limited opportunities, where everyone knows one another's business.

- There seems to be little recreation space in this community. The characters in the play spend their time in the park, outside shops.

- There is high unemployment. For the adults, getting a job at a cash-and-carry is considered an achievement.

- We never learn what the dad does for a living. Does he have a legitimate business? If so, why doesn't he give Mark a job? It is a question that the writer deliberately leaves unanswered.

What are the benefits of asking these questions?

If it is a world the company are not familiar with, it helps them get under the skin of the world and the characters. Also, establishing facts can be a really good way of being specific with actors. For example, instead of noting the actress playing Sue by saying, 'I want you to be more upset / angry / broken,' etc., you can say, 'How much debt is she in? How would she behave if that debt was doubled? Let's do the scene again and this time remember those facts of her situation.' It is much easier for an actor to play a fact than it is to play an emotional state.

If, on the other hand, it is a world that the company are very familiar with, doing this research into the world and characters of the play can be a useful way of having a release valve if the rehearsals become too issue-driven. Asking these questions will make the group be specific about the play world and avoid rehearsals moving into a more therapeutic territory, which might not be the most useful way of making the play work as a piece of theatre.

Is it possible to shift the location of the play away from the south of England? Yes, but you would need to be specific about the relocation. Ask: 'What does the location need to be, to be true to the play?' In finding the right location for it, it is essential that you bend to the play, rather than making the play bend to you.

When you have decided where to set the action of the play, ask the company to do some research on the area and to bring you two facts about it. Find a link between the fact and the play so that the research becomes about making the performances richer, rather than an academic exercise.

For instance, if 'the local school sends twenty per cent of its pupils to university', ask the actors to decide what sort of opportunities their character is likely to have, what grades they get and what their career plans are.

With the facts that you have decided on as a group you could then create a map of the local area, including places such as Stacey's house, the school, where the Christian study group meets, the cash-and-carry, the park, etc

THE QUEST NARRATIVE

Dirty Dirty Princess fits into a traditional 'quest' narrative stucture in sharing its three essential elements: the call, the journey, and the return.

- There is a call to adventure, and after some false starts, and meeting and recruiting companions, the hero departs on the journey.

- The hero of the tale is overwhelmed by life, and takes off on a journey where more overwhelming events unfold.

- This threshold of departure crossed, the journey begins with some act of initiation that involves a series of trials.

- Along the journey the hero can be tempted and even atone for transgressions.

- By the end of the journey, the hero is transformed, returning with values that have also been transformed.

- In the return, the hero has mastered the pain and suffering of chaos.

THE NOTATIONS

What do Georgia's rhythmical notations mean for actors?

SMALL CAPITALS like this indicate intensity of thought or emotion, *not* shouting.

Three dots (. . .) indicate a thought continuing into the next line, *not* a tailing off of thought. The energy is kept alive as the character thinks for a split second. Other writers tend to use the same punctuation to suggest that a thought is tailing off or running out of energy, but Georgia would like actors to treat the ellipsis as a sort of 'reset button' for their thoughts.

Three dots (. . .) where the character doesn't speak but is named, is like a 'cut to' in television: a moment with that character, where we focus on them.

A dash at the end of a line (–) indicates an interruption, as often happens in everyday conversation.

Exercise: send out a few of the actors with a dictaphone to record a conversation they overhear. This could be at a bus stop, in a coffee shop, etc. Ask them to transcribe the conversation faithfully, including pauses, beats for thought, interruptions, etc., following Georgia's rhythmical notation and use of punctuation. Let them perform the conversation, faithfully following the transcript. How similar are the rhythms of these conversations to the ones Georgia has written in *Dirty Dirty Princess*?

ACTING STYLE

What are the potential pitfalls for the actors in *Dirty Dirty Princess*? Here are some acting 'crimes' to watch for:

- Bad listening: only thinking about one's own lines and not listening to what the other actor is giving.

- Describing or judging characters rather than simply playing them; the danger is of simplifying characters, particularly those who don't have many lines.

- Making characters 'nice': looking for sympathy from an audience.

- Playing states rather than wants. Wants are active and therefore actable, states are not. For example, watch out for when the actress playing Stacey is simply playing the state 'sad' as opposed to the more active 'trying to be happy'.

Exercise: the Post-It Note Game

This can be a really effective way of combating those pitfalls. Choose a piece of dialogue from *Dirty Dirty Princess* (no more than a page or so). Allocate the two parts and also choose two 'feeders'.

Have the actors stand opposite each other, with their feeder behind them. The feeder holds the script and 'feeds' a line at a time to the actor in a neutral manner. This allows the actor to perform the scene without being tied down by the script.

Give the actors a pad of Post-It notes and ask them to 'land' a note each time they make a point. There could be more than one note landed per line.

Discuss who is landing Post-It notes and when in the text they are doing it. If they are landing the notes after the line, encourage them to land notes on the line.

Now ask the actors to be specific about which word they are landing the notes on. Ask them to think about and explore which word is the most effective word in sending that Post-It to another person. Which words stand out? Which are the most active? This can be an effective way of getting actors to connect with each other and the text, and finding the most active words in a line without being given a line reading. It is also very effective in achieving an intensity of thought and emotion in the acting that does not rely on volume.

Now ask the actors to repeat the dialogue, and this time to explore the manner and location of landing the notes. What physical part of the other person are you trying to effect and how are you doing it? Is it a stealthy drive-by Post-It as you walk past, a direct Post-It to the chest, a tender Post-It to the hand? And so on.

Depending on the scene or context, the notes can represent anything from wounds to love – whatever you want them to be. By this stage of the exercise it will be useful to acknowledge how much eye- and physical contact there is between the performers and how specific and active the text is.

Now ask the actors to go back to the scenes and to perform them without feeders or Post-Its. What have they retained from the exercise? Have they managed to keep the same level of eye-contact, specificity of language?

Exercise: Wants

Another great exercise to establish a character's 'wants' and so keep the scene active. This gives the actor something very clear and strong to play at any given moment.

Choose a scene from the play – for example the opening scene between Stacey and Luke. Ask the actress playing Stacey to read all her lines in the scene together, ignoring Luke's lines for the moment. What do you hear? What is the effect of hearing all one character's lines in one go?

What is the simplest 'want' that can be sustained for all those lines? Always look for the 'want' that will work for the entire scene. For example if you decided Stacey's 'want' or 'objective' in this scene was to get back into the house, you would have to check that it sustains for every line, throughout the scene. You will soon see that 'to get back into the house' is not specific or durable enough, as there are moments or lines in the scene that do not fit with this.

As you discuss what Stacey's 'want' might be, you will start to discover that as you find a 'want' which is durable for the entire scene, you will also discover a 'want' which is extremely strong and interesting to play. For example you might end up with a 'want' for the scene which is 'I want to get Luke to leave me alone for ever'. This would be a fantastic starting point for Stacey on a first rehearsal on that scene. If you cannot decide which 'want' is most accurate for her, try different 'wants' in rehearsal to see which one is most effective.

Repeat this process for the character of Luke, to find a 'want' for the scene.

You should always try to include the names of the other characters in the scene in an actor's 'want': for instance, by playing 'get Stacey to love me', rather than 'get some love', the actor will automatically deliver more lines to the actress playing Stacey, and the scene will become clearer and more active. The danger with playing a want with no 'target' (such as 'to feel better') is that the acting will tend to become more internalised and the relationship between the characters on stage will be lost.

Now get the actors to play the scene just focusing on achieving their 'want'. This will give them something to hang on to and focus on in a first rehearsal. Be careful for any moments when any of their 'wants' go out of focus on the line. Is the scene more dynamic and engaging with the 'wants'? How many different ways can you see the characters trying to achieve a single 'want'?

Once you've identified the want, it's really up to the actor to decide *how* that want is achieved. For instance, if Luke wants to get Stacey to love him, he has a huge variety of means available to him in order to achieve his objective. He could 'cajole', 'tempt', 'blackmail', 'guilt-trip', 'bully', 'intimidate' or 'seduce'. A nimble actor might want to try a different 'means' of achieving his or her want on every line, but by being clear about the overall want, you are giving an actor a piece of scaffolding which he or she can use to build a performance.

THREE-DIMENSIONAL CHARACTERS

Here are some useful questions for the actors to research and then report back on to the group, helping them to inhabit the world of the play and their characters:

- What percentage of sexual assaults on young women are reported to the police? (For the actress playing Stacey.)

- What happens when a fourteen-year-old is taken into care? (For the actor playing Luke.)

- Which credit card offers the maximum amount of credit? (For the actress playing Sue.)

- What is the weekly wage for a seventeen-year-old working in a warehouse? (For the actor playing Mark.)

- Who is Shannon Ethridge? (For the actress playing Jessica.)

- What are the Teen Mania Ministries? (For the actress playing Miesha.)

- What is a chav? (For the actress playing Billie.)
- What are the common duties of a head girl? (For the actress playing Nell.)
- What is a 'victim mentality'? (For the actress playing Chloe.)
- How does someone become eligible for social housing?
- What is the Alpha Course? (For the actress playing Katy.)
- How much debt is the average British person in?
- What sort of state benefits would Luke's nan be on?

Use facts to create three-dimensional characters. Facts can be a really good way of noting actors and avoiding the pitfall of an actor judging or describing their character. You can play facts in a way that you can't play descriptions of people. Established facts in the rehearsal room can therefore be a very useful tool.

There is a temptation with some of the 'Christian group girls' to make them 'types' or cartoons because they do not have as much stage time as Stacey or some of the other characters. How can this be avoided? A useful area of research for those actors in the Christian group is *Every Young Woman's Battle Workbook* by Shannon Ethridge, a handbook full of exercises for a Christian group which Georgia used to help write those scenes.

You could use an exercise from the book as a basis for an improvisation which will allow the actors playing Fiona, Katy, Lisa, Jessica, Lois, Chloe, Miesha and Jade to explore fully what happens at their meetings.

Another improvisation could explore how the group functions and the reality of their situation by looking at three moments in a typical meeting:

- How they arrive. Do they arrive all together? Who is first, last etc.? What are the rituals of the group? Where do people put their coats?
- How the group functions in mid-debate.
- How they end the meeting and leave.

You could also do an improvisation which looks at how the group worked before Stacey joins and another for after she has joined, to explore how her presence affects the group dynamic.

THE TIMELINE

One of the unusual things about the play is that there are two inciting incidents which occur before the play begins. The first was between Stacey and Luke, and happened two years ago when Stacey was eleven; the other was the incident between Stacey and Daniel Johnson which happened just before the play starts. Doing this timeline exercise will help to establish concrete facts about the characters' back stories and their journeys in the play.

Take a wall of the rehearsal room and, using the time scale below, make a detailed linear map of the time in the play by sticking Post-Its on the wall in a line to represent each moment of time in the play, with one end of the wall being the earliest moment in the play and the other after it has ended. Try and be as specific as you can with this, leaving gaps on the wall for days that are not in the play and having Post-Its for different times of day, etc. Note where the time in the play suddenly leaps ahead a day or week at a time. On another section of wall create a time-line of events that happened before the play begins.

Ask each actor to write a list of character *facts* – things they know from the play to be true about that character's journey – and a list of *questions* they have about that character. For example for the character of Stacey, facts would include: just before the play begins she was at her cousin's party; she went upstairs with Daniel Johnson and they kissed. But the actress playing Stacey might have a question as to what exactly happened in that room. Each actor should be encouraged to go through the entire play and mine it for any facts they can find.

Ask the actors to write each fact on an individual Post-It note and place it on the timeline where they think it should go. Some might be guesses and a lot will probably have happened before the play has even begun. Once they have done this for every fact they have found, you should as a group try to convert as many of the questions into facts by interrogating the play, and add them to the wall.

Useful tip: the simplest, most logical answer to each question is usually the best. For instance, if the actor playing Mark decides that he is a real ladies' man and has already lost his virginity, then many of his lines and 'wants' become unplayable. Remember that the audience will tend to interpret the play in the most logical way they can: although your actors might be tempted to answer their character questions in creative and surprising ways, the audience will receive little of this information during a performance.

It's often far more productive to look for the simplest impression that the text gives you about a particular question, and to answer the question accordingly. As a director, you'll need to guide your actors towards choices which are 'playable' on stage, rather than indulging complex and outlandish back stories which don't help the actors to play the action.

Once complete, each individual actor should take the rest of the company on a tour of their life, describing each 'fact' and when it happened. This will allow the entire company to get a thorough understanding of the world of their character, the play and, most importantly, the gaps in their knowledge which they will have to fill in during the rehearsal period.

Here is Georgia's timescale of the play, which will help you with the timeline exercise.

BACK STORY

Two years ago: incident with Luke.

A week ago: incident with Daniel.

THE ACTION OF THE PLAY

Tuesday (early evening), week one: pp. 33–6.

Thursday (afternoon), week one: pp. 36–9.

Thursday (evening), week one: pp. 39–41.

(*Time passes.*)

Thursday (evening), week three: pp. 41–4.

Saturday (morning), week three: pp. 44–9.

Saturday (afternoon), week three: pp. 49–51.

Saturday (early evening), week three: pp. 51–5.

(*Time passes.*)

Tuesday (late afternoon), week six: pp. 55–8.

Saturday (morning), week six: pp. 58–61.

Saturday (afternoon), week six: pp. 61–3.

Saturday (evening), week six: pp. 63–4.

(*Time passes.*)

Sunday (afternoon), week nine: pp. 64–69.

SCENE CHANGES

Scene changes are part of the action of the play, and
could be a useful way of showing the passing of time.
Also, because of the intensity of the scenes, they are
useful moments for the audience to take a breath.

The most interesting thing about the scene changes *isn't*
the shifting of furniture (and the scenes aren't long
enough to justify the constant building and striking of
realistic kitchens and exteriors). The quest narrative is
not dependent on location: it's a psychological story
structure. How might this affect the scene changes? Is
Stacey onstage for all the scene changes. If so, what is
she doing? Is she still or constantly moving?

Consider the number of bodies onstage at any given time,
and the relationship between them. Think of the scene
changes as a storytelling opportunity, not as a logistical
difficulty. Dance or movement could be used to move
from one location to another. If anything needs taking
off, could an actor to do it (in a manner consistent with
what they have just been playing)?

DEFINING LINES

'These are the lines which define each character best.'
                                        Georgia Fitch

Stacey I am just so scared . . . panicked all the time . . .

Luke I love you, Princess . . . I love you . . .

Miesha I know that whatever happens or whatever I have
    done, and if I am truly sorry for what I have done . . .
    He won't stop loving me . . . He is in my heart and
    I am in His . . . so there!

Sue What makes you think I am sad, Mark?

Mark I don't get girls.

Jessica If I could just have some silence in the room for a minute . . . just for a minute . . .

Lois Positive in her outlook and she does love her family.

Katy I started to read my mum's book, *Women Are from Mars, Men Are from Venus*.

Chloe We are not victims . . . we can control our emotions . . . we don't need to look to strangers . . . to score emotionally.

Jade I poked a lot of boys on Facebook, in fact I could not stop poking.

Lisa It works, if you keep coming along . . . it does work.

Fiona Why does everyone find it so hard to be honest?

Billie Well, that's got him now . . . never going to leave . . .

Nell I am doing Psychology A level!

From a workshop by Lyndsey Turner,
with notes by Richard Twyman

THE DUMMY TREE
A Musical Fairy Tale

Conor Mitchell

Conor Mitchell is a musical dramatist from Co. Armagh, Ireland. His musical plays include *The Young Pornographer's Wife*, *The Musician*, *Merry Christmas Betty Ford*, *Diary of a Madman*, *Todd*, *Letters to an Absent Other* and *Mathilde*. As composer/lyricist: *Have a Nice Life* (Best Score, New York Musical Theatre Festival, 2006), *Missing Mel*. As composer: *Goblin Market*, *Pesach*, the award-winning film opera *Pretty Face* and over forty other theatre scores. He has written for the Ulster Youth Orchestra, been writer on attachment to the National Theatre Studio, writer in residence at LAMDA, music advisor to Youth Music Theatre UK and winner of the Arts Foundation Fellowship for musical theatre composition. He is under commission from Ransom Theatre Company, Library Theatre Manchester, LAMDA, University of Gothenberg, Nice People Theatre Company, Philadelphia, and Cahoots. He is also writing a one-man show, *Cycle of Trifles*, for Nigel Richards.

Characters

in order of appearance

The Mother
a seventeen-year-old girl

Paul
a seventeen-year-old bridegroom

Nob
Paul's best mate and best man

Mingam
another mate of Paul's, a bridesmaid

Kubrick
a fifteen-year-old cameraman

Binge
Mingam's younger sister

Paul's Sister
Paul's younger sister

Time: now

Place: anywhere that ain't posh

For Joan McPherson

A tree is on the stage. There are leaves on the ground. There is a bench under the tree with graffiti on it and a plaque. The branches of the tree are bejewelled with trinkets – dummies, tied up with pieces of coloured ribbon. Some have photos and personal notes attached. Some have been there for years, some for a day. A girl, The Mother, enters. She is pushing a baby's pushchair. When she sees the tree she stops.

The Mother
The wind blows
The leaves dance
We're here
We're here, Jack
Underneath the tree

She wheels the pushchair over to the bench under the tree.

Right where Mummy said it was
Clever Mummy
What is Mummy, Jack?
Mummy clever?

Pause.

Mummy came here years ago
With Mummy's mummy
Years and years ago
Yes she did
Yes she did, Jack (*Tickling him.*)
And she remembered

Enter Paul. He is dressed in a rented bridegroom's outfit – not the expensive kind. He stands and looks up at the tree, not seeing The Mother. He has a letter in his hand. He reads it.

Both
The place the wind blows
The leaves dance
The Mother
We're here, Jack
Both
Underneath a tree
Paul
I'm here . . .
The Mother
. . . We're here
Both
The place the wind blows
The leaves . . .

The baby cries.

Paul (*calling off*) Found it! It's this one!
The Mother (*comforting the baby*) Shhh. Just the wind.
Paul Nob!
The Mother . . . Can't hurt anyone. Smile, Jack.
Paul Over here!
The Mother Smile for Mummy. Look at the colours, Jack.
Nob (*off*) You find it?
Paul (*to himself*)
Right where someone
Said it was
The Mother
Right where Mummy said it was
Paul
Right where someone said
That it would be . . .

The Mother
    And she remembered . . .
Paul
    Underneath . . .
Both
    The tree –

Enter Nob wearing a best man's outfit of similar price.
Paul puts the letter in his pocket.

Nob Is that it?
Paul Yeah, wotcha think?
Nob I think it's a tree with crap in it.
Paul That's cos you've got no imagination.
Nob *And* I think I'm the one who'll get in the shit if you
    don't get there on time. Come on.
Paul We just got here.
Nob Paul, there are days for being early and days for
    being late. Now, you said you wanted to see it and
    now you have. Come on.
Paul Well . . . you go. I'll stay for a bit by myself. Clear
    my head. I've got an hour, Nob. Just some quiet – you
    know, before . . . well . . . before. (*He sits on the
    bench.*) I'll meet you there.
Nob Do you know what Mingam would do if I arrived
    without you, Paul? She would cut my balls off with a
    Brillo pad. And I really *like* my balls, Paul. (*Beat.*)
    Paul?
The Mother
    Don't act surprised, Jack
    Don't pull that face
    Hardly a shock, Jack
    This is the place
    I told you about last week
You don't remember though, do you?
Nob Are you listening to me? (*Beat*). My dad says people
    act strangely on their wedding day. It's the stress.

(*Beat*.) Alright, we'll stay for a *bit*. A *bit*, Paul. And I'm staying with you. (*He sits*.) Didn't know you liked trees so much. (*Looking up*.) What is all that crap anyway?

Paul Dummies.

The Mother You see . . .
Mummy bought a book, Jack
Eleven ninety-nine
But the shop'd got a sale on
Got the lot for seven
Which is fine
For a book

She produces the book and shows it to Jack

Paul Kids come 'ere . . . thing they do. I didn't. Never had one. Some kids just can't give it up so they bring them here and tie it to the tree. They tell the kid the fairies'll come and give them a present. Just heard about this place one day and always wanted to see it.

Nob But today?

Paul It *is* kinda brilliant, though.

Nob Vandalising a tree? Yeah, terrific.

Paul No, for kids that can't give it up.

Nob Wot, like addicts? 'I am addicted, Mummy. Take me to the rehab tree before I suck myself to death!'
(*Quick*.) Here, remember when Kenny Dillon said he could –

Nob Shut up, Nob.

Nob Right.

The Mother
Mummy read the book, Jack
Mummy likes to read
Mummy had a . . . little look, Jack
To see if she agreed
With *Mother and Child: Beginner's Guide*
Okay, I lied

It was ten
Take him to a dummy tree
Like my mum did me

Nob Apparently he was born with two ribs missin'.
That's how he was able to do it. Course, he never told
me *that* bit so there was me in a neck brace for a
fortnight / and a . . .

Paul Christ! It's like sharing a cell with the speaking
clock! If you're gonna stay, then sit and be quiet. And
I mean quiet, Nob. Like I said, I need to think, alright?
Is that alright with you?

Pause.

Nob You've changed your mind, haven't ya?

The Mother (*reading*) Chapter twenty-two.

Nob Christ, Paul. Brilliant bloody . . .

Nob / The Mother Timing.

The Mother (*reading*) When should a little one begin the
process of growing up?

Nob begins pacing.

Paul Have I said that? Have I? (*Beat.*) I want to sit on
this bench under this tree and think about . . . things,
before I make the . . . (*Beat.*) Lots of . . . things.

Nob Wot things?

Paul My things. Now sit down and . . . just sit down.
You're making me stressed.

Nob *I'm* making *you* stressed?

Paul Sit.

Nob I'm not a dog, Paul!

Paul If you're stayin', sit!

Nob sits down beside Paul.

Nob And I *do* have an imagination. I'm actually very
creative. I wrote a short story once. (*Beat*) Spent ages
on that best man speech.

Paul punches him in the arm to shut him up.

The Mother
Take him to a dummy tree
Like my mum did me
Underneath a dummy tree
He'll soon give up
That piece of plastic
Yes!
You will, Jack

Paul
Underneath a dummy tree

The Mother
It's what my mum did, me

Paul / The Mother
Underneath a dummy tree

Paul
I guess I'm just a little . . .

Nob
Little nervous?

The Mother
Yes

Paul
No

Nob
You are, Paul

The Mother
Cos Mummy bought a book, Jack
And books'll never lie
Book says
'Big boys don't suck dummies'
You know that as well as
I do

Nob
Underneath a rehab tree . . .

Paul
  Underneath a tree . . .
The Mother
  That's what the book says, see?
All Three
  Underneath a dummy tree
The Mother
  Tie it to the tree, Jack
  Give it to the tree!

She tries to get the dummy out of his mouth. The baby cries.

The Mother
  People grow up, Jack
  It's what they do
  Time to grow up, Jack
  Sometimes we're made to

The baby continues crying.

I'm going too fast, aren't I? It says you shouldn't rush. I'll go slower, Jack. (*Beat.*) Smile, Jack.

She sings him a lullaby and rocks the pushchair.

The wind blows
The leaves fall
Underneath the dummy tree
Okay
We'll wait

The baby stops crying.

Nob My dad knows quite a lot, actually. You'd never know by looking at him. Doesn't have a beard. A beard means you know a lot of things. Look at people like . . .
Paul Albert Einstein? Charles Darwin? (*Beat.*) God?

Nob No, Paul. Santa. Think about it. Santa works one day a year and gets away with it. Now that is the definition of smart in my eyes. I'm tellin' ya – it's the beard. Anyway, my dad – who doesn't have a beard but should – says that people act funny when they're about to tie the old knot. He had ten boiled eggs on brown toast the morning he married my step-mum.

Paul Ten eggs is a little excessive.

Nob *Brown* toast, Paul? *Brown*?

Paul Yeah. Right.

Nob

Nerves is normal
Nerves is good
Nerves is prob'ly wot ya got
Nerves is healthy
Understood?
You think you're freakin' out now
But you're not
Ya just got . . . cold feet
Which is sweet

The Mother (*reading*) 'Imagine yourself as them, put yourself in their position being asked to give something up, something precious. But remember, it is not a "giving up". it is an exchange. By surrendering the dummy the child is taking their first step on the journey to adulthood. Remember, when we cannot see the end of a long road we question the journey.' (*Closing the book.*) You get any of that?

Nob

Nerves is nat'shrill
Nerves is fine
Nerves, assumin' that it's them
Nerves is nature's
Little sign
At least you know you're human . . .
Then again . . . look,

Ya just got . . . cold feet
Which is sweet
Ya just got . . . cold feet
And I know I'm not
The ultra, like, qualified one
On the subject of
'Bloody 'ell, what 'ave I done?'
But I know enough 'bout grown-up stuff
Cos I watch TV
And on Channel Three
There was this 'ere
Doc-u-men-ta-ry called:

Nob	**The Mother**
Nerves	Nerves is racking
On your wedding day	Enjoy
Is quite okay	It's sometimes
	How you learn
No point in panicking, Paul	Nerves is normal
It's very normal	
In a man	In a boy
You give things up	You give things up
Get something in return	Get something in return
Ya just got cold feet	Ya just got cold feet
Which is sweet	

The Mother
What are you givin' up, Jack?
Nob
What are you frightened of, Paul?
The Mother
Nothin'.
Both
What do ya think you'll lose?
Paul It must have taken years for all those to get up
there. Each one with its own little story. How many do

you think there are? I'd say two hundred. Two hundred
stories – more.

The Mother
Wot are ya givin' up, Jack?

Nob
Perfectly standard behaviour

The Mother
Nothin'
What are ya gonna lose?

The Mother	**Nob**
Jack?	Paul?

Nob and The Mother
So if I were you
Would I have a wobble?
I might

Nob
Imagine all those people
Knowin' your business that night!
But a wobble, Paul

The Mother
And I promise, Jack

Nob
Is a wobble, that's all

The Mother
You won't look back

Nob / The Mother
And I know you'll say
Wot does he/she know, eh?
When it's me who has
To do the deed today
But nerves are normal
Nerves are fine
Nerves is norm'ly wot ya get
When you got cold feet

Nob
Which is sweet

Ya just got
Cold feet
The Mother
Cold feet
Nob
Cold feet
Which is . . . sweet

Paul is staring up into the tree and not listening to Nob.

Paul Someone's tied a bottle of gin to the tree.
Nob You listen to anything I just said?
The Mother Smile, Jack.
Paul Don't you think that's weird?
Nob Wot, weirder than you saying you wanted to see a
tree on your way to the church? Why, Nob? I don't
know, Nob. He won't say. Maybe it's cos he's weird.
That's what I find weird!
Mingam (*off*)
Where are you?
Where are you, Paul?
Paul Nob!
Nob Wot? She forced me out of me. I had no choice.
She's organising the whole thing.
Mingam
Where are you?
Where are you, Paul?
Paul?
Paul Well, she's your problem. You can tell her to piss off.
Nob You ever met . . .

*Enter Mingam in a huge, colourful bridesmaid's dress.
She is carrying a walkie-talkie. Kubrick follows her
with his camera.*

Nob Mingam! You found it. We got a bit lost, didn't we,
Paul?
Mingam Nob, I said one o'clock on the dot.

Nob I know, but he's got this tree thing going on.

Mingam Trees ain't on the schedule, Nob. And why did you turn off your walkie-talkie when I asked you to keep it on?

Nob Battery died.

Mingam Battery die on your phone, too?

Kubrick That Paul?

Kubrick heads for Paul and starts filming him.

Mingam Yes. Now don't forget to smile, Paul – it won't kill ya. (*Into the walkie-talkie.*) Mingam to Binge. Over?

The Mother Smile, Jack.

Kubrick Can you look into the camera, Paul, and say something about how you're feeling? Anything at all. Remember, the camera never lies. Oh wait, the lens cap's on.

Paul Get that thing out of my face! Who's he?

Kubrick I'm filming the day for you. Kubrick – I'm a mate of Binge's.

Mingam (*into walkie-talkie*) Mingam to Binge. Mingam to Binge. Get a move on.

Nob Can I be in it? I've a *very creative imagination* and people say I can act a bit.

Kubrick It's a documentary actually.

Nob So I can't be in it?

Kubrick Not if you're acting.

Nob So I can only be in it if I can't act?

Kubrick *Don't* act.

Nob Right, I won't.

Mingam
  Why are you here, Paul?
  Why am I?
  Under a tree, Paul
  In the middle of nowhere

I have some things I have to do, Paul
I don't have time to sit underneath a . . .

She doesn't know what it is.

Mingam What is that supposed to be?
Nob / Paul
It's a dummy tree
Mingam Well, stop sitting underneath the thing and
come on. You'll get tree on your suits.
Kubrick Fantastic location. Colour, form, identity . . .
Mingam Kube, you follow me from the back. And make
sure you get my plaits in focus. I want to look back
and watch perfection unravel on the screen.
Paul You just might.
Mingam (*in a world of her own*) My big day.
Kubrick What did he say?
Nob (*changing the subject*) So what's this film about,
then?
Kubrick (*patronisingly*) The wedding?
Mingam
My big day
Kubrick He *is* getting married today, isn't he?
Mingam
Everything's ready, Paul
Everything's done
Flowers all arranged, Paul
Tell me nothin's changed, Paul
Everything's sorted . . .
Apart from you, Paul
For
My big day
My big day
Perfectly planned by moi
Binge (*off*) Mingam?!
Mingam Oh, and there's been a change of plan.
Binge (*off*) These shoes!

Paul Who's that?
Mingam The change of plan.

Enter Binge in a grotesque bridesmaid dress that is way too large for her.

Binge Birmingham, I can't stop it itching in this . . . thing.
Mingam It's called a dress, Binge.
Binge She's two sizes bigger than me.
Mingam It fits perfectly. Stop moaning.
Binge I think I know this place.
Paul What is *that* doing here?
Binge Oh, thank you, Binge, for stepping in. You're welcome, Paul. Anything to help. I'm sure I've been here.
Mingam Michelle had to drop out. The fungal infection's spread – I warned her. Didn't I say? Yogurt's not enough to sort that out – did she listen?

Binge and Mingam both bark.

Don't worry, Binge'll be . . . fine. Won't you, sis? We practised everything this morning. Read through the order of service . . .
Kubrick (*suddenly excited*) Oh my God, guess what Binge said.
Binge Shut up, Kube!
Kubrick Binge read it and said, 'Guess what happens at the / end of the . . .'
Mingam Kubrick, don't mock. Not all of us know that the Arrival of the Queen of Sheba is a piece of music.
Binge Yeah, we're not all swots. (*Beat.*) So, Paul, how's it feel . . . you know . . . just before you sign your life away? Feeling nervous? Second thoughts? Not too late, Paul . . .

Mingam furiously takes out two tickets and waves them in front of Binge.

Mingam Binge! Westlife?

Paul You're bribing her?

Binge I'm not a social worker, Paul. I need paid if I'm gonna help you commit sexual suicide.

Mingam Here! Now! (*Dragging her aside.*) You will not ruin *my* day.

Binge Mingam, I hate to remind you of this but you're only a bridesmaid. It's not *your* day. It's his.

Mingam It's all relative.

Binge I'm sure I've been here.

The Mother Smile, Jack.

Mingam
My big day
My big day
With me as the main attraction
Everyone'll smile
When they see me dress
Floatin' up the aisle
In me M 'n' S
Bet ya people cry
When I read me prayer
Bet ya people die
When they see me hair
And the church, Paul
Looks like a dream, Paul
I've seen, Paul
Cos I've been, Paul
It's one-fifteen, Paul . . .

Pause

Paul!
Everyone's ready, Paul
Even her mum
Talk about ungrateful!

Binge She *is* payin' for the whole thing, Mingam.

Mingam That doesn't mean she gets to choose her own hat! Oh, before I forget, the music's all sorted now –

we got another band in the end – you'll have to thank
La Binge.

Binge

The band'll be great
Cos I booked my mate
There's a strummer and a drummer
Then there's him
No, wait,
There's a bloke on bass
Who I hear is ace
So there's four instead of three
Which is more but he's
Fantastic . . .

Mingam

Vicar's on his way
Says he'll keep it short
Don't forget to pray, Paul
(You're not in court)
Shame about the hymns
But I had no choice
Hymns are done by him
Says he's got this 'voice'
But the choir, Paul
Will be on fire, Paul
I hired a choir
All for

Binge

Apparently –
And he fancies me . . .

Mingam

My big day
My big day
Perfectly planned . . .
Only cost seven grand
That's nothing
For my big –

Binge

His big day
Their big day

Binge takes out a packet of cigarettes from deep within her dress.

Binge Anyone got a light?
Mingam Binge!
Binge It's just the one. Not gonna kill me.
Mingam (*grabbing the fag out of her mouth*) That dress's going back Thursday and it can't stink of fags.
Binge Tell Kube not to invite his mates, then.
Kubrick Funny.
Mingam DAY! Right, Paul, move!

Applause.

Kubrick Wait! Can I get some footage of everyone under the tree? We've got a little bit of time yet.
Mingam Well, alright, but make sure you get the left side of my face. I *hate* the right!
Kubrick Could I get Paul at the front and everyone else behind him?

They all position around Paul under the tree. Mingam pouts outrageously. Kubrick is at the front with his camera.

The Mother Why don't I put this away, eh? (*She puts the book away.*)
Kubrick Binge, a bit more to the right. (*She moves.*)
Binge Here?
Kubrick That's it. Mingam, stop pouting. You look like a handicap herring. (*She does.*) Okay, so just pretend the camera isn't here and talk to me, yeah? Right.

They are all rigid like an old photograph. They stare dead ahead – unmoving, with big false smiles.

Kubrick So, Paul. How does it feel to be you on this, the happiest day of your life? The day you walk down the aisle and say 'till death us do part'?

Paul Death? (*Beat.*) It feels . . .

Kubrick Not the camera – me.

Paul It feels . . . I don't know. It feels . . .

Silence.

Kubrick Does it feel . . . like you're not sure?

Chord.

Mingam (*maintaining a false smile*) Don't be ridiculous, of course he's sure.

Chord.

Kubrick Is that why you're here? Are you hiding because you're not sure you want to go through with it? Camera never lies, Paul.

Chord.

Nob He just likes trees. He's allowed to like trees, ya know. It's 2009!

Mingam We should go.

Kubrick
Something's changed

Mingam
Change the subject

Kubrick / Binge
He's changed his mind

Mingam
What's the time, Binge?

The Mother
I won't change my mind, Jack
I've made up my mind

Mingam
Change the subject please

The Mother
I won't change my mind

Kubrick
  Look at him
  Underneath a tree, he has
The Mother
  I won't
Mingam
  He hasn't
The Mother
  I can't
Mingam
  He can't
Paul I can. (*Beat.*) I know that's a tough concept for you to understand, Birmingam, but I can change my own mind.
Mingam (*through her teeth*) Paul, everyone's on their way.
Kubrick Now *this* is a documentary! Diaries of a runaway teen-groom. I smell a BAFTA! Paul, Paul, say something into the camera.
Paul Alright. How about, 'If you don't turn that thing off I'll smash it in / your face!'

They break the pose and Paul goes for Kubrick.

Mingam Paul! Turn it off, Kube.
Kubrick But . . .
Mingam Off! Paul, you're not / thinking . . .
Nob Listen, that's nerves talking. He wouldn't do that kinda thing – that's not Paul. Letting everyone down – his mum . . .
Paul Which one?
The Mother Do you know what tomorrow is, Jack?
Mingam People are waiting. Everything's arranged, so let's just go to the church and get it / over with, eh?
Paul Cos that's what it's about, isn't it? Not letting people down. That's what matters. That's what's important, yeah?

The Mother
  Tomorrow you'll be six months old
Paul A party? You don't get it, do you?
The Mother
  One little day that's all
The Mother and Paul
  This time tomorrow
  This time tomorrow
Mingam Tomorrow what, Paul?
The Mother and Paul
  Everything changes
Mingam Nothing changes. You're still you.
The Mother and Paul
  Everything changes
  In a day
  One day, that's all
  Everything changes
Nob Take no notice, Ming. It's nerves.
The Mother and Paul
  Tomorrow things won't be the same
  Tomorrow I don't have a choice
Mingam (*to Nob*) How long's he been like this?
Nob I don't / know.
Mingam What, he just woke up this morning and changed his mind?
Paul I haven't / changed –
Mingam Days?
Paul I said / I don't know!
Mingam Weeks? Months?
Paul A while. Alright!
Mingam Jesus, Paul. Why / didn't you . . .
Paul I know. Trust me, I don't feel very good about myself right now. (*Beat.*) It was always so far away . . . you know? . . . Didn't seem like it would ever really . . . It was *there* and I was *here* and then this morning it's like, *here*, and now it's like . . . (*Beat.*) Fuck!

Binge If he bails do I still get the tickets?!
Mingam You're not helping!
The Mother
    Tomorrow you'll be six months old
    And I know that that's young
    Isn't everyone young, Jack?
    Even your mum, Jack
    I know what being young means
    I do it every day
    But everyone grows up, Jack
    Everybody knows
    People lose things
    Give them up, Jack
    Make a choice, Jack
    And it hurts, Jack
    And everything changes in a day
Paul
    Everything changes in a day
The Mother
    Everything changes in a day
The Mother / Paul
    One day that's all
    People make choices
Mingam
    A little bit of nerves
    That's all
    All it is, Paul
    What's the time?
    A little bit of nerves
    What's the time?
    Want a choice?
    Here's a choice
    Choice you made
    I'm afraid
    That you did, Paul
    You chose to propose

So I guess, I suppose
We should go
There
Decided
Come on
You're invited
Cos . . .

She starts busily trying to usher everyone off.

Everything's ready, Paul
Everything's done
Everything's arranged, Paul
Much too late to change, Paul
Everyone's sorted
Everyone, Paul
Everyone you love, Paul

Pause.

The one you love, Paul

Pause.

Nob You do love her, Paul. You know that much, don't
ya?
Paul We only met two years ago, Nob. I don't know
what I know, ya know?
The Mother
I was fifteen years old
He was sixteen
There's a lot that you know
And a lot that you don't
When you're somewhere in between
Youth and being young
And now I'm not fifteen
And still so in between
But the things I know now
Someone young shouldn't know
So young

Paul
    We were fifteen years old
    Me and her
The Mother / Paul
    We were just two kids
Mingam
    Doesn't matter 'bout your age, Paul
The Mother / Paul
    Two kids that's all
Mingam
    Just a number on a page, Paul
Paul
    And two years later here I am
Mingam
    Age don't mean a thing
Paul
    Two years later seventeen
Mingam
    Years later seventeen
    Won't mean a thing
The Mother
    We were fifteen did I . . .
Mingam
    You said you loved her, do you . . .
Paul
    I don't know if I –
Paul, The Mother *and* **Mingam**
    – Know what 'love' means

    Pause

The Mother
    I was sixteen years old
    He was angry
    There's a lot you can say
    When they don't want to hear

The Mother / Paul
> When you're somewhere in between
> Youth and being young

The Mother retreats into herself and starts rambling into the distance.

The Mother
> So it's my fault?
> So it's me?
> So it's my fault
> Nothing to do with you?
> Nothing at all?
> I was fifteen
> Didn't know
> Yes I am
> Listen, I'm sixteen years old
> I can do what I like
> Okay, go!
> Go!
> Run away!
> Hide!
> I don't need you
> I don't need anyone
> I'll get a job
> I'll find a way
> I'll make it work
> And I will cope
> It will be hard
> But we will cope
> And everything changes in a day

Paul
> Everything changes in a day

The Mother
> Everything changes in a day

The Mother / Paul
> One day that's all

People make choices
Did I . . .
Will I . . .
Am I . . .
Am I making a mistake?
Paul
I have to choose
The Mother
A single day
Paul
I want to stay
The Mother
To make a choice
Paul
Decide
The Mother
Six months
Paul
Today
The Mother
Tomorrow
Paul
Today
The Mother
Tomorrow
The Mother and Paul
A choice?
Paul / The Mother I want to know what to do. Tell me
what to do!

*The Mother violently throws the baby to the ground
revealing the doll. The doll begins wailing. Paul stands
frozen, takes out the letter and reads it.*

The Mother
Stop crying
Stop crying

You're not real
Stop crying
Stop crying
Stop crying
Stop crying
Stop it
Stop it
You're not him
Stop it
You're not real
Mummy's angry
Mummy's scarred
Mummy's frightened
Stop crying, Jack

She stops suddenly.

The Mother Jack!

*She rushes to the doll and bundles it into her arms.
The doll stops crying.*

Paul Well? (*Beat.*) If you were me.

Kubrick But we're not.

Mingam If you don't go through with it all the presents'll
have to go back – you do realise that.

The Mother She was angry, that's all. Smile.

Paul You should go back – see if she's alright.

Mingam Your sister's there. 'Sides, I'm *your* mate, not
hers. I'm staying here!

The Mother She'll never be angry again.

Mingam I spent ages on those thank-you cards.

*The Mother sings the baby a lullaby. Mingam sits on
the bench.*

Binge You know you got a present from that taxi driver,
crazy Terence.

Mingam Not now!

Binge Lavender candles. Why would he send those? I
mean, it's not like he knows Paul or her, is it?

Kubrick Sounds like a Buddhist. They give things to
strangers. Can I turn the camera back on?

Mingam No!

Binge This is a man who every morning drives his taxi
around every telephone box in town and without
shame – oh, people see him, he's famous for it –
without shame steals any change that's been left in
'em. He's not a Buddhist. He's a thief.

Kubrick You always see the best in people, don't you?

Mingam / Nob So are we staying or going?

*Mingam's walkie-talkie starts to flash. A voice comes
out of it.*

Walkie-Talkie Mingam? You there? (*Beat.*) Ming?

Nob Answer it.

Mingam What do I tell her?

Paul Use your imagination.

Nob Oh, *she* has an imagination and I / don't?

Mingam She's *your* sister, Paul. You talk to her.

Paul She's not my sister.

Awkward pause.

Kubrick Am I missing something?

Mingam quickly picks up the walkie-talkie and answers it.

Mingam Reading you loud and clear. Roger. Roger. She
almost ready?

Walkie-Talkie Yeah. Bloody nervous though. If she's like
this I'd love to see Paul – can you imagine?

Mingam Yeah, imagine. Look, I gotta go / but . . .

Walkie-Talkie Wait. Could you pick her up some breath
mints on your way back? She's terrified she's gonna
spoil the kiss.

Pause

Ming? Is everything okay?

Mingam Yeh, you know, last-minute rush. Look, I should –

Walkie-Talkie Alright. See you back here in a bit and stop worrying. Everything is going to be fine. Polos, if they have them. Over!

Mingam Yeah. (*Beat.*) Over.

She hangs up and puts the walkie-talkie down. Everyone is still. They sit underneath the tree in silence for a moment. Everyone's vocal lines overlap to form a sextet. All the lines are sung to themselves. For a moment each one is alone.

Mingam
    My big day
    My big day
    Over before it started

Nob
    Nerves is normal

Nob and Mingam	**Paul / The Mother**
Over before you know	It's just a day

Mingam

My big day, the shame	It's just a day

Kubrick and Binge
    Normal ain't normal
    Underneath a tree

Nob
    Nerves is what you feel
    When you're seventeen
    And 'bout to get married, mate!

Mingam
    This is Nob's fault!

Getting louder and louder:

Paul / The Mother
Underneath a . . .
Underneath a . . .
Underneath a . . .

Suddenly quieter.

All
Underneath a dummy tree
I guess we wait and see
Underneath a dummy tree
Binge
Wait!
I've been here before
Mingam Stop saying that. You can't have.
Binge I'm sure –
Mingam Well, so am I, so shut up. He needs to think.
The Mother They all think I'm crazy, having you. Even
that woman that comes round. She says she understands
but I know she doesn't.

Binge takes a bottle of vodka out of her dress.

Mingam Binge!
Binge Calm down. It's only vodka. Not like we're going
anywhere.
Nob Got anything else under that dress?
Kubrick Ask Danny Taylor. He should know. (*To Binge.*)
Don't look at me like that. It's true.
The Mother It's true. The way she looks at me – looks at
you. I don't like her looking at us and 'understanding'.
Nob It's gone half-past, Paul.
Kubrick Can I turn this back on?
Mingam (*to Binge*) If you get pissed I'm not covering for
you again, alright? I'm sick of pretending it's prawns.
(*Beat.*) Well? You gonna give me a swig or wot? And
yes, Kubrick. Do what you like. Might help him make
up his mind.

The Mother 'It helps.' That's all I could tell her. 'Having him – it – having it *helps* me.' Should have seen her face when I called you Jack – just like him.

Binge hands the bottle to Mingam who takes an enormous gulp. It's very strong.

Binge Got it specially.
Mingam Who from? NASA?
Binge Danny nicked it off his dad's grave.

She drinks it again. Kubrick turns his camera back on.

The Mother We sat there – no one saying anything – you were wearing a blue bib – made your eyes stand out. You have my eyes. So does he. She gave me this.

The Mother takes out a form. Kubrick is filming Nob and Paul. Binge is sitting with Mingam. Mingam drinks.

Binge Oi! Slow down! That's gotta last me all night, reception or not!
Mingam Oh, who cares any more? (*She drinks again.*)
Kubrick So here we are – patiently waiting as teen-groom ponders the big question. In the words of that classic 'Silent Night': all – is – calm.
The Mother It's the form.
Nob It's the tree. Trees are known for their powers of relaxation, my dad says.
Kubrick Nob continues.
Nob I mean, here we are – skipping the red lights of life – but a tree just stands there – observing. Be two o'clock soon, Paul.
Mingam
    I always thought it would be me
    I always thought I'd be the first
    First down the aisle
    Out of all my friends
    Oh well

    Not meant to be I suppose
    I always saw myself in white . . .
One word, Binge.
Binge I didn't say anything!
Mingam
    I always saw myself
    Bouquet in my hand
    Like I dreamed
    Like I planned
    But then Micky met Elaine
Nob I'd be a crap tree. Imagine spending all that time
    growing each little leaf – getting it green enough – then
    another and another and just when you're almost
    finished, bam! Autumn. Typical. (*Beat.*) Think I'd
    rather be a shrub.
Paul Do you think she would ever want to see me again
    if I . . . you know . . . don't go through with it?
Nob Well . . .
Paul I don't think I could ever not see her again, ya know?
Nob Yeah, I think I do. (*Looks over at Mingam.*) Tick
    tock. Tick tock.
Mingam
    Me and Micky
    Micky Fallon
    'Member him?
    The silver shirt?
    Me and Micky
Binge
    Micky *Allen*
Mingam
    Both in love so much it hurt
    'Member Micky?
    Sat beside me
    Ev'ry Friday double French
    We would oo la la et cet'ra
    He would *avoir*

I would *être*
Oo, *l'amour*
Me and Micky, we would marry
Both in Paree by the Seine
But then Micky met Elaine

Kubrick I think you can not want to get married and still . . . love a person – if it's love you're actually talking about? I mean, just because you sign a piece of paper doesn't mean . . . well, it doesn't mean anything. Does it?

Paul Yeh, Kube. It does. It means . . .

The Mother I have to sign the form then, that's it . . .

Paul / The Mother No going back.

Mingam
'Member Freddy
Spotty face
Studied physics, ultra-smart
Kinda geeky
Wore a brace
Kinda kid that broke your heart
Me and Freddy
This was it
Time to end my little search
But then Freddy found the church
I always thought it would be me
Out of all my friends, but no
That was Paul who wants to throw
It all away
But what do I know, eh?

Paul I don't want to . . . you know . . .

Nob Hurt her? Look, my dad says no one ever died of a broken heart.

Paul He got proof of that?

Binge Maybe he's just coming to his senses. You should do the same. You've been acting like a right maniac ever since this wedding thing started. Don't look at me like that. You hijacked it and you know you did.

Mingam Well, that's because . . . Did I?

Binge Everyone? Did Ming hijack Paul's wedding or not? Ducks for yes – dogs for no. One – two – three.

Nob, Paul, Binge and Kubrick quack.
Mingam barks – in defence.
Everyone else quacks louder.
Mingam barks twice.
Everyone else quacks very loudly, three times.

Mingam I just wanted . . . I just wanted what Paul has. Had. Has.

Nob You do scare people off, Ming. I mean, you're only going out with someone for five minutes and you start talking about primary schools in the local area.

Mingam Is that what I'm like?

Everyone, including Mingam, quacks gently.

Nob You're going too fast, mate. You need to slow down – wait a bit.

Mingam I'm seventeen, Nob –

Mingam / Paul / The Mother I'm running out of time!

Nob
There's a someone for everyone
Somewhere
Just have to wait until
You find each other
Sometimes you have to stop looking
To find things
Like my dad says
And he should know
Ten years married
Goes to show

Paul Yeah. To his second wife.

Kubrick That's a point. You could get married today and tomorrow there's always divorce . . . if it don't work out, I mean. (*Beat.*) We were all thinking it.

Nob, Binge and Kubrick quack.

Paul Oh, thanks very much!
Nob It's getting close to / two, Paul.
Paul I know!
Mingam
    'Member Kevin?
    With the thighs
    Did karate, used to swim
    Beat up bouncers
    Twice his size
    That was Kevin, that was him
    Me and Kevin
    What a pair
    He'd protect me, keep me safe
    He had hands could crush a walnut
    Something else was pretty small but
    That don't count

(Well, I say that now.)

    Me and Kevin
    I was sure
    Sure that neither one would lose
    But then Kevin found musical theatre!
    It's like I've got a friggin' sign
    On my head that says:
    'Bonjour! Stay a month
    But please no more'
    And that's unfair
    Paul, what you've got is rare

Nob	**Mingam**
There's a someone	You've got what I want
For everyone	Want for me
Somewhere	Someone ready for 'I do'
Just have to wait	Where's the someone?

Until you find   Where's the 'he'?
Each other   Someone's out there
Sometimes you have   Yeah, but who?
To stop looking
To find things

Mingam
Wasn't Micky
Wasn't Freddy
Wasn't Kevin

Nob
Yeah, that's true

Mingam and Nob fall a little bit in love.

Mingam / Nob
But sometimes when
You least expect it
Love'll find
You

Kubrick I think I'm gonna puke.

Binge I remember! Kubrick – camera – now! I remember!

The Mother I remember I was so sure I wouldn't keep
him. She asked me all these questions, see? To make
sure I was sure and I *was* sure even when she said
they'd found him a family I was *still sure* but she came
back . . . weeks later with the adoption form and . . .
I'm not sure I'm sure any more.

Binge is holding court.

Binge So I'm thinking, 'Fairy present – what's that?' So I
say, 'Alright. Have it,' and give 'er the thing and she
ties it to the tree all neat like. I never really wanted it.
Just kept it cos I knew it pissed her off. Can't stand
things in my mouth.

They butt in.

Danny Taylor is a liar! God, I can't believe I forgot this.
    Where was I?
Kubrick She ties it to the tree.
Binge Right . . .
    So we go home.
Kubrick Into the camera.
Binge

    So we go home
    That's where the fairies
    Left the present, see?
    So we go home
    I'm so excited almost pee myself
    She comes out of the kitchen
    Hands behind her back
    Hold out your hand, she says
    Now close your eyes
    Now open wide, she says
    Ta da, surprise!

    Pause.

    A Twix
    A Twix?
    A stingy bloody Twix
    A Twix?
    That it?
    For my beloved tit?
    Wot kinda fairy's only got
    Twenty p
    That's when it suddenly
    Dawned on me
    It's her
    It's her!
    They've all been bloody her!
    Santa?
    Fairy?
    Please spare me

All her!
Lies, Mother, lies!
Lies, Mother, lies!

Kubrick It's like when you get your first Easter egg. The sheer disappointment you feel when you realise it's not actually solid chocolate.

Binge Exactly. These are life-defining moments.

Nob (*to Paul*) Quarter to two now.

Mingam I think Paul's situation here is a little / more . . .

Binge (*to the sky*) You stole my dummy!

Mingam There's no talking to her now. She's off on one.

Binge
Lies, Mother, lies!
Lies, Mother, lies!

(*Suddenly.*) I'm gonna get it back!

Mingam Wot?

Binge Must still be here.

Mingam You said you hated it.

Binge I lied! I want it back.

Mingam It's just an / old bit of . . .

Binge It was mine, Mingam. It was *mine* and it *meant* something. You never *had* something . . . apart from thrush? (*She searches the tree.*) Help me look.

Nob I'll help you look – both of you.

Mingam You don't / have to.

Nob No. (*Beat.*) I want to.

Mingam Do you? Do you really . . . *want* to?

Nob lovingly quacks. Mingam blushes.

Binge Oh, get a room! Kubrick, you stay with Paul and make sure he doesn't top himself.

Mingam, Nob and Binge search the tree. Kubrick is alone with Paul on the bench.

Kubrick You got a good day for it. Sorry.

Paul He's not a thief.

Kubrick Who?

Paul The taxi driver. Terry. He's not a thief.

Mingam What colour was it again?

Binge Blue. Had my name on it. My *real* name.

Paul He met this girl years ago. She was . . . she was not right he said – in the head. He married her. He said he didn't know why but he had to . . . had to look after her – save her. They were only married for a few years – real happy like.

The Mother Once I sign it that's it. Jack's theirs for good.

Nob finds a navy dummy.

Nob Is it this one? (*Shows Binge.*)

Binge Since when has navy been blue?

Paul She got sick. Real quick. He said that when they told her she was wasn't surprised. It was like she expected it, ya know? She just took it. She died a month later.

The Mother Time's up.

Nob Someone's tied a packet of fags over here.

The Mother Everyone has to give up something sometime.

Paul He goes round the phone boxes . . . every single one . . . every single morning in his cab and collects the leftover change – gives it to a charity. A heart charity. (*He suddenly stops.*)

Kubrick Wot?

Paul Something Nob said. It's nothing. (*Beat*) Twelve years he's driven that taxi around doing that. Let's everyone think what they want.

Kubrick How'd you know all that?

Paul I found . . . I went to where he lives. Had his address. He's not a thief. He just never stops trying to save her.

The Mother
What am I giving up, Jack?

Paul I got a letter.

The Mother
What do I know I'll lose?
Paul When I told Mum I wanted to get married she said
she had this letter and I needed to have it.
The Mother
People grow up, Jack
It's what they do

She takes the dummy tit from the doll's mouth.

Paul She was gonna wait until I was eighteen. That's
what they're told to do, see? But then . . . well . . .
The Mother
Sometimes we're made to

She ties it to the tree.

Kubrick Who was it from?
Paul My 'mum' . . . forget about it. I don't know you –
Why am I telling *you* this?
Kubrick Why are you *not* telling *them*?

Nob takes Jack's dummy off the tree.

Nob God, this one's ancient. Who did you belong to,
little dummy titty? Here. (*Gives it to Paul.*) You said
you never had one – well now you do. Paul, it's nearly
. . . forget it. Your decision, right?

Nob returns to searching the tree.

Kubrick
Everyone's a story
Everyone's a life
Everyone's a secret
That's what life's about
I guess
That's what being real is
Knowing something
Only you can know

Paul Secrets ain't so sweet.

Kubrick But that's what makes you 'you' – how you *know* who *you* are.

Paul Do you know who you are?

Kubrick Do you?

Pause

Paul I'm adopted – so no. (*Looking at the dummy.*) Two hundred and one little stories – underneath a tree. Anyone care, though?

Kubrick
Other people's stories
That what I'm about
Other people's truths
And lives and lies
Captured on a screen
Making life be heard
Be shown
Be seen
Be known
Be stories
Other people's dreams coming true
Maybe not – look at you
Other people's hopes and their fears
Made in minutes or years
Other people's stories
Showing people them
Mirrors getting turned
Again and again

Paul Thirteen weeks.

Kubrick Wot?

Paul They get you for thirteen weeks before they sign the adoption order – your family. They can give you back, see? Only mine didn't. But, and this is the thing I keep thinking about, your other . . . your 'real' mum has to sign it too or it don't count. Did you know that? Yeah, neither did I till recently. So she would have to be sure.

The Mother I don't know.

Paul It would have to be easy –

The Mother I want it to be easier.

Paul Because she already knew –

The Mother I don't know what I know.

Paul She didn't want you. Thirteen weeks is a long, long time to not change your mind. (*Beat.*) *That's* who I am. Someone someone else didn't want.

The Mother It's not about what you *want*. It's about *you*.

Kubrick
Other people's stories
Making people see
Everyone's a story like them
Everyone's a somewhere
And a when
Other people's you, Paul
Everyone's the same
Cos everyone must one day decide
To get out there or hide
I have a lens for me
You have your friends, a tree
And that's okay, cos see
Other people's stories
Are mine

The Mother I have their address. They wanted me to have it. That helps. Knowing that they wanted me to have it – that helps. (*Beat.*) Everyone has to give up something sometime. A doll is just a doll.

She takes the doll and tenderly places it under the tree.

Binge Oh my God! I found it! I actually found it! I can't believe it was here all those years. Look. Isn't it the most beautiful thing you've ever seen?

Nob and Mingam inspect it.

Nob Why does / it say . . .

Mingam Nob!

Nob That cannot be your real / name . . .

Mingam Nob!

Nob Alright. Just saying it's a bit unusual.

Binge puts the dummy in her mouth.

Mingam Binge, that's disgusting! (*Beat.*) Can I've a try?

Enter Paul's sister. She stands behind them and talks into the walkie-talkie. Mingam's walkie-talkie comes to life.

Paul's Sister Mingam? Over? Ming, where are you? I can't get through to Paul.

Mingam It's your sister. (*She answers.*) Hey! We're . . . I'm in the shop.

Paul's Sister Which shop?

Mingam The . . . the Polo shop.

Paul's Sister I'm standing right behind you, Ming.

They all turn round to see Paul's Sister there, walkie-talkie in hand.

Paul's Sister Having a picnic?

Mingam We were about to / go but . . .

Paul's Sister There is a girl sat waiting for her bridesmaids / to come . . .

Paul Mum and Dad send ya?

Paul's Sister They don't know you're here but they know something's up. They're not stupid. To*day*, Paul?!

Mingam How'd you know about here?

Paul's Sister You been drinking?

Binge Why don't we give them a little space, eh? Nob, Kube, come with me.

Nob Where to? We're in the middle of a field.

Binge I don't know. Other side of the tree?

Mingam (*a bit pissed*) We're on the walkie-talkie if / you
need . . .
Paul's Sister Go!

*Paul's Sister sits beside him on the bench. The others
exit. Paul's sister stares up at the tree.*

Paul's Sister They shouldn't have given you that letter.
They should have waited like they're supposed to.
(*Beat.*) You wouldn't have gone looking for her.
Paul Good thing I did or I wouldn't have found out.
Paul's Sister You would have. Just . . . not yet. I'll tell
you what, you wouldn't bloody be here now, would
ya? (*Beat.*) Since you were getting . . . they thought
you were 'ready'. What's that even mean? 'Ready'?
Paul Look, I'm not mad at them, right? I'm not – I know
the score – I always have, but getting that letter . . . It
made it all real. It was never *real*. You think it doesn't
matter, but then something changes and it does. It
becomes real. It matters. She matters.
Paul's Sister I know.
Paul But you don't. You don't . . . you can't know.
You're not adopted! You're not me! So don't try and
tell me you *know* when you don't. Alright?
Paul's Sister
I'm your sister
You're my brother
And I know you're two years older
But I've always thought you younger
My little brother
My little older brother Paul
Just me and him against the world
Me him and no one else
Remember, Paul, we used to say
It's only us, bruv
It's me and you, mate
You're my brother

    Always will be
    And nothing will change us
    You and me
    Not a wedding
    Not a letter
    Not a tree

Paul I was so sure I wanted to get hitched – made sense.
    Get married – get some sense of . . . I don't know,
    knowing who you are. I was offering myself to another
    person – a person I wanna love – I wanna love her –
    I really think I do – but I can't offer myself to someone
    if I don't know myself *myself*, because the letter and
    going looking – finding out – I feel like . . . I'll *never*
    know. I'll never know anything about *me*. About *Paul*.
    About . . .

    Pause.

What about Mum and Dad? What'll they think if I call it
    off?

Paul's Sister
    You're my brother
    And I only care about *you*
    What do *you* want?
    Yes, Paul, you
    Not me
    Not them
    Her
    You
    If you're doing the right thing
    Then do it
    If you're doing the wrong thing
    Then don't
    But make a decision
    Make a choice
    Time is up, Paul
    Growing up, Paul's

Gonna hurt
Cos growing up is choices, Paul
Life is making choices, Paul
Make a choice
But make the choice for you
Only you know you

The walkie-talkie comes to life.

Mingam (*on the walkie-talkie*) Are you there? Over.
Can we come back now? Only it's nearly two and the
Polos . . .

Paul's Sister Yeah. We're done. Over. (*She hangs up the
call.*) You can't sit under a tree for ever. She isn't
coming. Look, I better go back. I'll not say anything
but you need to decide now – for better or for worse,
as they say, eh?

*She gets up to go. Paul's Mother rips a blank page
from the back of the book, then finds a pen.*

Paul Thanks.

Paul's Sister For what? (*Beat.*) A letter's just a letter.
That's all it ever is, Paul.

The Mother Dear Jack. (*She writes.*)

Enter the others, gingerly.

Paul's Sister I'm going back – you lot are coming with me
and Nob you're going to the church to wait . . .

Nob But is he . . .

Paul's Sister Just go to the church. Take Spielberg with
you. Paul's gonna wait here by himself for five minutes.
He has something he needs to do.

The Mother I don't know if or when you'll read this.
Perhaps you won't ever.

Mingam hands Binge the tickets.

Mingam You should probably have these now. Who ya gonna take?

Binge Actually, I think you should keep them.

Mingam Why?

Binge Because . . . (*She subtly suggests something in Nob's direction.*)

Mingam Oh! (*Coyly.*) Nob?

Nob Yeh?

Mingam What's your opinion on Westlife?

Exit Mingam and Nob arm in arm. Binge and Kubrick go to leave.

The Mother Are you all grown-up? Are you happy? Are you even called Jack?

Binge Wait!

Binge runs to the tree and puts her dummy back on a branch.

Kubrick Don't you want it no more?

Binge There are other ways to grow up. Come on. I've got an idea for your new documentary.

Kubrick What is it?

Binge It's called making Danny Taylor jealous.

She kisses Kubrick. Nob enters.

Nob Well? Come on, *Aberdeen*. Your sister's waiting.

Kubrick Your name's Aberdeen?

Binge I'm gonna kill him!

Kubrick Wait! I'll film it! Evidence! See you there, Paul!

Binge runs after Nob and Kubrick follows offstage. Paul's Sister starts to leave but stops as she finds something on the ground.

The Mother I'm just a kid, Jack. I'm scared – scared of everything. Even loving you.

Paul's Sister Look. Someone's left a little doll here. (*To the doll.*) You've seen better days, haven't you? (*To Paul.*) Same eyes as you. (*She puts it down.*)

Paul's Sister
Remember, Paul, we used to say
It's me and you, bruv
Well, it still is, cos
You're my brother

Exit Paul's Sister. Paul takes out the letter and reads it, alone.

The Mother I know I'm not in your life, Jack, but I need you to know that if there ever comes a time – a single day when you're confused or lost or frightened or don't know what to do or who you are . .

There is a place
There is a tree
A place the wind blows
The leaves dance
A tree, Jack
I will be there, Jack
Underneath a tree
And I will tell you everything
Years and years from now
Every little thing
Yes I will
And you will, Jack
You'll want to know, Jack
Know that you're someone's son
Know that someone held you
For a moment as their own
And you were theirs
And theirs alone
But love is making choices, Jack
Choices that are yours

But not for you
Love is letting go, Jack
But always know, Jack
The place the wind blows
The leaves dance
Underneath a tree
I will always be
So if you need me
And I mean 'need' me
I will be here

Right where someone said it was
Right where someone said it was

Paul

Right where someone said it would be

The Mother

And she remembered

The Mother / Paul

The place the wind blows
The leaves dance
Underneath a tree
You / I will always be

The Mother

Waiting for my boy

The Mother / Paul

Waiting here for you

The Mother

Try to understand
Life is almost planned
To take us by surprise
Live a life, son

Though it kills her to say it.

Stay where you are
So I won't be around, Jack

But I'll always be there
And I'll never not love you

She turns to see him for the first time – touches his hand. He does not feel it or see her.

The Mother (*to Paul*) And don't go wasting any time worrying about me. I've met a man, see. He's kind. Says he wants to look after me . . . and . . . and I'm going to let him. He says he might even marry me one day if I . . . if that would make us happy. And it just might. It just might.

Paul has made his decision. He gets up and goes to leave the stage.

The Mother Maybe one day you'll meet him. His name is Terry. He drives a taxi. So I'm going to be okay. I am going to be okay, son.

He stops and looks up at the tree.

The Mother / Paul
Underneath a tree.

The Mother
And Paul?

He turns and looks at her.

The Mother
Smile.

He smiles. As the lights fade a small spotlight should catch the plaque on the bench so it almost glows and is the last thing to vanish.

The End

Production Notes

The Dummy Tree begins with two people, each at a moment of crisis, coming to a special place to seek clarity for the momentous decisions they have to make. It is not immediately apparent how they and their stories are related, and writer-composer Conor Mitchell likens the unfolding of the piece to the peeling of an orange: 'We don't know at first that these people sharing a bench are separated by many years, in different realities. The audience slowly gathers clues and new bits of information about what's happening and who they are until finally, at the end, the penny drops.'

It will be important for directors and actors to identify with absolute clarity as the action unfolds which of these bits of information are new to the characters and which are known or established before the play begins. Exploring and building the characters' *back stories* is vital. Each actor should know their basic biography; the history of her/his character's relationships with other characters; and the events and circumstances leading up to the 'today' of the play.

CHARACTER NOTES

THE MOTHER Her baby, Jack, has been placed with a foster/adoptive family for the past thirteen weeks, which is the period of time which the birth mother has to change her mind. Today is the final day she has to decide whether or not to sign over her child for permanent adoption.

Since her baby has been in care, she has bought a baby doll with blue eyes, like Jack's. She's found that the doll has helped her; and bringing the doll to the tree to take its dummy from it is a kind of transference or displacement activity with regard to signing the adoption form.

We deduce from things Paul says that The Mother ends up dying of a broken heart. There are two main clues to this in the text. First, when Nob says, 'My dad says no one ever died of a broken heart,' Paul responds with, 'He got proof of that?' Second, Paul tells Kubrick that Terry the taxi driver gives the money he collects to a heart charity because 'he just never stops trying to save her'.

PAUL Paul has always known he was adopted. He was, however, only recently given the letter written by his birth mother which he is holding when he first enters. He was given this about three months ago, when he asked his parents to sign the consent form for his wedding. This triggered Paul's adoptive mum to give him the letter that she had planned on saving until he turned eighteen.

After Paul received the letter, he went and sought out Terry – the taxi driver who ended up marrying Paul's birth mum. Terry knew that the dummy tree was special to Paul's mum, and he told Paul about the place.

MINGAM She is named after Birmingham, the place where she was conceived. A similar logic was used in naming her sister, whose real name is Aberdeen. But while Birmingham has embraced her name, her sister has tried to suppress hers and instead goes by the pseudonym Binge.

Mingam has hijacked Paul's wedding as her own 'big day'. It is important to interrogate the reasons behind this: does she want to be the centre of attention and, if so, why? Does she hope to meet someone at the wedding? Is she afraid that she herself may never get married so this is her opportunity to experience it vicariously? The director and actor should build a clear and logical psychological back story.

BINGE She has been recruited as a bridesmaid by her sister at the last minute, and her motivation for helping out is a pair of tickets for a Westlife concert. However, she ends up handing over the tickets to Mingam: perhaps this reveals that Binge has understood that her sister is lonely?

The level of Binge's anger at her mother and the dummy/Twix incident might seem disproportionately high. What are the other issues it is tied up with? The loss of childhood? Having to renegotiate your relationship with your parents as you grow up?

NOB It is important to decide if he has had his sights set on Mingham before today and, if so, how long for, and has there been any expression of his interest?

PAUL'S SISTER She is two years younger than Paul, but thinks of herself as his 'big sister'. You'll need to decide if she's in the same school or year as Binge and Kubrick.

KUBRICK He is in a sense an 'oracle' character, an outsider who comes into the situation and gets to the heart of the matter with blistering clarity: he sees Paul and says, 'Something's changed, he's changed his mind.'

Binge is the only person who knows Kubrick (with the possible exception of Paul's sister). To everyone else he is a stranger: yet this enables Paul to open up to him, to tell him things he can't say to his close friends.

Kubrick's objective when he first enters the world of the play is to make a great video, but there comes a point when he turns the camera off and realises that something more important is at stake.

CHARACTER RELATIONSHIPS

The relationships between the characters can be thought of in terms of pairs and sets, and some characters will be in more than one of these clusters.

So for example, one set might comprise Paul, Nob and Mingham – three mates, the same age, in the same year at school. Mingham would also be in another group – a pair with Binge, her sister. Binge, in turn, is part of another pair, with Kubrick.

Exercises

- Get the actors in the space to physicalise the different relationship clusters in the play as a set of separate tableaux. Then try to physicalise where the overlaps and links are.

- Choose a moment in the play, and get the actors to identify which relationship cluster is most important to them at that point. Repeat for other key moments. For characters in more than one cluster, their dominant relationship allegiances may change from moment to moment.

- Get the actors in the space to form a line according to their status, with the highest status person at one end, and the lowest status person at the other. Again, this exercise can be repeated for different key moments in the play, when shifts may occur along the line.

CHARACTER OBJECTIVES

It's very helpful with this piece to make clear and strong choices about what the characters *want* or *need* at any given moment – what we can call a character's 'intention', 'action' or 'objective'.

At the outset of the piece, each character will have one dominant thing they want or need: their 'super-objective'. For example, The Mother's super-objective might be expressed as: *to decide whether to give her baby up for adoption*. Everything The Mother does or says will in some way relate to this overall need.

The Mother's behaviour, however, can be broken down into smaller and more specific units of action. When she first enters, for example, her lyric, 'Right where Mummy said it was, Clever Mummy, what is Mummy, Jack?' could be played by the actor as *to reassure Jack*, or *to make Jack smile*. Deciding on character objectives will enable the director and actors to build specific, clear and detailed work, and will prove particularly useful when approaching acting through song.

Exercise: Character Focus

This exercise explores how the physical focus of a character relates to their objective.

- In the space, decide where the dummy tree is. Decide where the church and the route to the church are. Then bring in the actors one by one and get them to stand facing and with feet pointing in the direction of what their character wants at the moment when they first enter. Get them to stand near or far from the object of their want, depending on the strength of their intention. For example, you might decide that when Paul first enters the space, his objective is *to find guidance from the tree*. Therefore, the actor in this exercise would stand very close to the tree, facing it.

- Think about the context of the character's objective, or any obstacles there might be to achieving it. This might provide a second point of focus. So, in our example of Paul at the beginning of the play, the context of his objective is that he has just run in the opposite direction to the church where he is about to get married. Therefore, the church will be a second point of focus for him.

STAGING

A director of this piece (in collaboration with a designer if there is one) will want to explore the different options for where to place and how to realise the dummy tree. Some possibilities are:

- The tree has a trunk and branches, and is positioned centre stage.

- The tree has a trunk and branches, and is positioned to one side of the stage.

- The tree is suggested by branches or dummies hanging from directly above the playing space (e.g., the rig).

- The trunk of the tree is only suggested – by a low-level stump, or by roots – thus enabling characters to be seen when they are upstage of it, or when you are working in the round.

- The trunk of the tree is suggested by a circular bench, like the ones built round trees in some parks.

- The tree is imagined by the characters to be out front – that is, just off the front of the stage in the audience.

Wherever you decide to situate your tree, and however you decide to realise it, it may be helpful to consider whether to position it so that it should be a physical barrier, a literal obstacle between Paul and the wedding.

Positioning the tree centre stage provides possibilities for symmetry and mirroring on the stage space to the left and right of the tree. This may be interesting to explore with Paul and The Mother (see the third bullet point below).

Positioning the tree trunk in an onstage position, with room to move around, may create interesting possibilities for characters to circle, pursue, counter-circle, and so on.

Some other aspects of staging which you might want to consider include:

- Does The Mother's baby/doll need to be in a pushchair, or could she simply cradle him? When is the pushchair useful and when is it not?

- There are two different time frames/realities at play, and sometimes one 'world' falls out of focus for a while. What is the convention when the focus changes like this? Does the other world go into a frozen state, slow motion or other stylised mode? Or is the vocabulary of naturalism somehow kept alive?

- Are there any physical connections or echoes between Paul and The Mother in their two different realities? For example, performing similar simultaneous moves or crosses either side of the tree or stage; sitting or standing at the same time; sharing a particular gesture or way of standing, or other physical characteristic.

- How is the doll's crying realised? Generally in the theatre when we see a doll and hear a recording of a baby crying, we are conditioned to imagine that a 'real' baby is crying. You could explore the particular quality of the doll's crying (e.g., obviously artificial, or on a looped track which repeats and repeats). Or perhaps The Mother herself provides the crying sound, like a weird ventriloquist?

SOUND AND MUSIC

If you have resources for sound design, think about its potential role in the production, particularly with regard to the sound of the wind blowing.

What is the language of the opening of the piece? It is tempting to get drawn into the haunting and lyrical quality of the music, but be mindful of the characters' context and circumstances: Paul has fled his imminent wedding and Nob is under pressure to get him there on time; The Mother is out in public with a toy doll which she's pretending is a live baby (is she worried people might see her?), and is trying to make a momentous decision (is she anxious/upset/unhinged?)

When rehearsing *The Dummy Tree*, it's important to take seriously the idea of scheduling, and to draw on tried and tested musical theatre rehearsal structures to plan your time effectively. The learning of music should form a substantial part of the early stage of rehearsals, and should not be tacked on.

The music in this piece will be challenging for many performers; extensive and structured repetition is the key to success. Many performers, particularly younger ones, find structured repetition frustrating and tedious; but avoid the temptation to concede this and move on to the more 'interesting stuff' of acting and staging. Thorough note-bashing is an essential part of the first stages of rehearsal.

Recording devices are an invaluable aid in this process. Get the pianist to play the vocal line and left-hand accompaniment for an actor onto her/his mobile phone, iPod or dictaphone, so that the actor can listen to it and practise over and over again. Start by teaching solo music, then move on to the choral sections.

Once the music is secure there can be a temptation, particularly in ballads, for actors to stretch time – both musically and dramatically – to 'have their moment' or to 'really sing it'. Don't allow this. Never indulge a lovely voice at the expense of the dramatic pulse or objective. Don't allow the tempi in the piece to drag.

If your actors have regional accents or dialects, use them and channel the piece through them. If there are odd words or phrases which sound unnatural in the voices of your company, take the liberty of changing them.

Finally, don't get too hung up on singing the piece beautifully: clarity and specificity in the lyrics are more important.

From a workshop led by Phyllida Lloyd,
with notes by Mitchell Moreno

A HANDBAG

Anthony Horowitz

Anthony Horowitz has written over thirty books for teenagers: his Alex Rider series is a global phenomenon. He also writes for TV, including *Foyle's War*, *Midsomer Murders* and *Murder in Mind*. *Collision*, a new five-part series, will be shown in 2009. In addition, Anthony Horowitz has written for the cinema, the theatre and regularly contributes to the *Guardian* and *Sunday Telegraph*.

Characters

Rose
also Lady Bracknell

George
also Jack Worthing

Allan
also Algernon Moncrieff

Specs
also Algernon, Gwendolen, Jack, Cecily

Irene
also Gwendolen

Kinsey
also Lane

*The scene is Algernon Moncrieff's flat in Half-Moon
Street. The room is luxuriously and artistically furnished.
Except it isn't.*

This is a dress rehearsal of The Importance of Being
Earnest, *being performed in some sort of institution,
somewhere. The characters might appear in nineteenth-
century costume – or some sad stab at it.*

*And all but one of the characters have three names.
Their names in the play. The names that they call
themselves. And their real names, which we will never
discover.*

*Rose (as Lady Bracknell) and George (Jack Worthing)
are on stage, performing part of Act One. She is about
nineteen and trying hard to grasp the world in which she
finds herself. He is middle-class, articulate and seems to
be in charge.*

Rose (*Lady Bracknell*) Now to minor matters. Are your
parents living?

George (*Jack Worthing*) I am afraid I really don't know.
The fact is, Lady Bracknell, I said I had lost my
parents. It would be nearer the truth to say that my
parents have lost me . . . I don't actually know who
I am by birth. I was . . . well, I was found.

Rose (*Lady Bracknell*) Found?

George (*Jack Worthing*) The late Mr Thomas Cardew,
an old gentleman of a very charitable and kindly
disposition, found me, and gave me the name of
Worthing, because he happened to have a first-class

ticket for Worthing in his pocket at the time. Worthing is a place in Sussex: it is a seaside resort.

Rose (*Lady Bracknell*) Where did the charitable gentleman, who had a first-class ticket for this seaside resort, find you?

George (*Jack Worthing*) In a handbag.

Rose (*Lady Bracknell*) A handbag?

George (*Jack Worthing*) Yes, Lady Bracknell. I was in a handbag – a somewhat large, black-leather handbag with handles to it – an ordinary handbag, in fact.

Rose (*Lady Bracknell*) In what locality did this Mr James, or Thomas, Cardew, come across this ordinary handbag?

George (*Jack Worthing*) In the cloakroom at Victoria Station. It was given to him in mistake for his own.

Rose (*Lady Bracknell*) The cloakroom at Victoria Station?

George (*Jack Worthing*) Yes. The Brighton line.

Allan (Algernon Moncrieff) enters. Allan keeps his own council but he has a rough intelligence. He's largely self-taught . . . but it's left large gaps.

Allan (*Algernon Moncrieff*) Didn't it go off alright, old boy? You don't mean to say Gwendolen refused you? I know it is a way she has. She is always refusing people. I think it is most ill-natured of her.

A pause. Rose and George stare at Allan. He becomes aware that he's done something wrong.

Allan What's wrong?

George What do you think?

Allan Tell me.

George No, Allan. Why don't you try to work it out?

Allan I got the right line . . .

George Did you?

Allan Yeah. It's the right line. Definitely. (*As Algernon.*) Didn't it go off alright, old boy? You don't mean to say . . .

George (*interrupting*) It's the right line.

Rose The Brighton line.

Allan What then?

George Take a look at me. And just think for a minute. Am I alone?

Allan Alone in what sense?

George You're a twat, Allan.

Rose You shouldn't call him that.

George (*to Allan*) I'm with her. I'm in the middle of the scene. I'm still talking.

Rose You shouldn't use aggressive language. You know what it is? It's verbal bullying.

Allan So . . .?

George So, obviously, you've come on too soon.

Rose It's inappropriate behaviour.

George Rose. What are you going on about?

Rose You called him a twat.

George He is a twat. He came on a page too early.

Allan I come on at the end of the scene with Lady Bracknell.

George That's the point I'm trying to make. It's obvious I'm still talking to Lady Bracknell. I mean, there she is! Look at her! She's standing next to me. The scene hasn't ended.

Rose (*as Lady Bracknell*) The line is immaterial, Mr Worthing . . .

George Not now, Rose. (*To Allan.*) Weren't you listening?

Allan Do you want the honest truth here?

George You weren't listening.

Allan I was listening . . . after a fashion. But I wasn't really following. I was what you might call half listening.

George Am I half stupid or are you doing this on
purpose? You come on too early. You come on too
late. Sometimes you don't come on at all. It seems to
depend on the weather . . . or what mood you're in.
I don't know! I mean, you're new here, Allan. I'll grant
you that. Relatively new. Maybe I haven't quite worked
you out. But tell me. A simple yes or no. Are you
deliberately undermining me? Have you got something
against me?

Allan You're getting very worked up about this.

George Have you got something against me?

Allan No.

George Because if you have, you can tell me.

Allan I've got nothing against you, George.

George Would you have preferred someone else to be the
director?

Allan I can't think of a better director.

George Then, as director, can I remind you that we're
going to be performing this play in front of an
audience – a real audience, a live audience – one week
from now? We've got the stage. We've got the seats.
We've sold the tickets.

Rose We haven't sold any tickets.

George Alright. We've given the tickets away. But they've
still said they'll come – that's the same thing. They're
expecting a performance. (*To Allan.*) And you seem to
have set out to deliberately sabotage it.

Allan I came on a few lines early. My attention was
wandering, that's all. Specs should have told me. He
normally gives me my cue.

George Normally.

Allan In so far as anything about Specs is normal, yes.

George And where was Specs?

Allan He was there. (*Pointing.*) He was there . . .

George What was he doing?

Allan He was doing what he always does . . . at least, when the lights are on. He was reading. He had his head in a book.

George Which book? (*Pause.*) The book of the play?

Allan Obviously.

George He was reading the lines?

Allan Yes.

George Did he know what was going on?

Allan I suppose so. Why don't you ask him?

George I will ask him. I'll ask him now. (*Calling.*) Specs!

Specs doesn't come.

Rose He's not coming.

George Give him time.

Specs still doesn't come. Everyone is looking offstage.

Allan We could be here all week.

George You just have to be patient.

Allan He's not moving.

George He's got slow reactions.

Allan Well, it's your rehearsal. But I should just point out that, at this rate, we're not even going to get to the next scene.

George (*losing it*) Specs! Will you get out here!

At last Specs arrives. He is in charge of prompting and carries an ancient, hard-cover edition of the play with loose pages. He is not in costume. His glasses are hideously thick, distorting his eyes. Specs is a mess. He has a terrible stammer. But when he reads from books, he can speak normally.

Specs Yes, George?

Rose Look at him. You've frightened him. He's shaking like a leaf.

Allan None of the leaves in this place ever shake.

Rose That's because they're made out of plastic. It's a Health and Safety measure.

Allan I've never felt healthy here. Or particularly safe.

Rose Come here, Specs. I'll look after you.

Allan Physical contact isn't allowed.

Rose I'm offering him proximity. It's not the same.

George Specs. Listen to me. No one's going to hurt you. There's just one thing I want to know. Are you looking after Allan?

Specs Yes, George.

George But you didn't give him his cue.

Specs No.

George Why didn't you give him his cue?

Specs Because it wasn't the right time.

George That's a good answer. That's the right answer. (*To Allan.*) He couldn't give you the cue because it wasn't your cue. So why are you trying to blame him?

Allan I'm not trying to blame anyone.

George Specs has been here longer than any of us. Specs knows what he's doing. You just have to trust him.

Allan I do trust him.

George You think he's dysfunctional.

Allan I never said that.

George He is dysfunctional. He's got a certificate to prove it. But he knows what he's doing. And he's body and soul behind this play. Aren't you, Specs?

Specs tries to speak but can't articulate.

Allan Out of interest, and with all respect, why did you choose him to be the prompter?

George I didn't choose him. He volunteered.

Allan He could have played Algernon. He could still play Algernon. He knows all the lines. And – correct me if I've got this wrong but – he's got this stammer when he talks but he doesn't stammer when he reads, so wouldn't he be better out here performing?

George That's not possible.

Allan Why not?

George He gets stage fright.

Allan He's scared of a lot of things.

George That's true. But he's not had an easy life. He was bullied when he was young.

Allan We were all bullied when we were young.

George Yeah – but for him it started in the maternity ward. His mother rejected him. Even the nurses didn't want to know. The other babies used to gang up on him and steal his pacifier. Nineteen years later and his mother's still got post-natal depression. You can't blame her. The only friends he's ever had have been in this place and we don't much like him either.

Rose I think he's alright.

George Rose, there's nothing alright about Specs. Why are you pretending otherwise?

Rose I'm just trying to be kind.

George If you want to be kind, you'll get back to the scene and let him get back to the wings. That's what he likes. It's being out of sight, isn't it, Specs?

Specs Yes, George.

George Right then. Shall we take it from the top?

Allan Do we have to?

George Okay. We'll take it from the middle.

Allan Suppose we take it from where we left off?

Rose Wait a minute. Wait a minute . . .

George What is it now, Rose?

Rose Can I ask you something?

George Can't it wait?

Rose No. It's something I don't understand.

George (*exasperated*) Go on.

Rose It's about this handbag.

George The handbag.

Rose Yes.

George What about it?

Rose I was just wondering how big it was. I mean, how would you fit in?

George Well, it was a big handbag. In those days, women had big handbags.

Rose Those days.

George When the play was written.

Rose When was that?

George I don't know. Ask Specs. He was the one who found it.

Rose Specs?

Specs Eighteen nine—

His stammer is so bad, he can't finish the date.

George (*interrupting*) It doesn't matter when it was written. It was a long time ago.

Allan And it's by Oscar Wilde.

George (*pleasantly surprised*) That's right.

Allan He wore a green carnation. He was Irish. He wrote plays. And he was queer.

Rose He wasn't a queer. He was gay. There's nothing wrong with that.

Allan I know his sort.

Rose There's no need for negative stereotyping.

Allan His name was Oscar Wilde and he liked boys. He liked working-class boys. He took them back to his place and he took advantage of them. What am I supposed to call him?

Rose A homosexual. From the Greek.

Allan From the Greek . . . what? What he did or what he called it?

Specs Both.

Allan It makes me sick. If you ask me, they shouldn't have allowed him out to write comedies. They should have put him in jail.

Specs They— (*Trying to tell Allan that they did.*)

Allan (*angry*) What, Specs?

Specs Never mind.

George Getting back to your entrance, Allan . . .

Rose Wait a minute. You haven't answered my question. I don't see how you could have got into the handbag, no matter how big it was. Maybe if it was a suitcase . . .!

George What?

Rose And even then, they'd never have been able to carry you.

George works out what's going on.

George Rose. You haven't understood a single word of this play. Have you?

Rose Yes, I have.

George No, you haven't. When I'm found in the handbag, I'm a baby. That's the whole point. I'm not big. I'm small. I'm a baby.

Rose A baby.

George Yes.

Rose How old?

George I don't know. A couple of months.

Rose Is the handbag done up?

George I don't know.

Rose Because if it's done up, it could be very dangerous. You could suffocate.

Allan That's true.

George Well, obviously I haven't suffocated because if I'd suffocated I wouldn't be here and there wouldn't be any play.

Rose Even so . . . it would be a horrible thing to do, to put a baby into a handbag, to seal it up and leave it in the dark. It would be so scared and it wouldn't be able to breathe. And then to leave it in a railway station, on its own. How could anyone do that?

George It's a comedy!

Rose It's not funny. It's horrible!

George The handbag wasn't done up, Rose. It was just an accident. (*Pause.*) The baby crawled into the handbag when nobody was looking – and it enjoyed being there. Playing with the lipsticks and the tissues and whatever stuff women carry in their handbags. It was having a whale of a time. If it had been given any choice in the matter, it would have spent the whole rest of his life in the handbag except that the old gentleman, Mr Cardew, found him and pulled him out. And so he survived. Here I am. I'm still alive. That's the whole point of the play.

Rose Survival.

George Yes. It's a play about survival.

Allan I still think we should send a copy to the NSPCC.

A bell rings in the outside corridor. A hard, institutional sound. Everyone freezes.

George Did you hear that?

Allan I think we all heard it, George.

George Do you know what it means?

Allan You have a lot of bells here, don't you?

George You've noticed.

Allan It's hard not to.

George That's the nine o'clock bell.

Allan Wouldn't it be easier to have clocks?

Rose They don't trust us with clocks. There was an unfortunate incident involving a minute hand.

Allan When was that?

Rose Nobody could tell. Not exactly. It was before you arrived.

George That was the nine o'clock bell. We're in the middle of Act One. We've got another whole act to go. And now we've only got thirty minutes left. What are we going to do about that?

Allan You can cut some of my stuff, if you like.

George We can't cut your stuff. The play won't make any sense.

Allan It doesn't seem to make much sense to anyone anyway. Forgive me if I'm stepping out of line, but to be honest with you, I'm not sure you've made the right choice.

George The right choice. What do you mean?

Allan This play.

George Why not?

Allan You tell me. Why are you doing it?

George Doing it in what sense?

Allan Putting it on. Performing it.

George *The Importance of Being Earnest*.

Allan Yes.

George Because Specs found it. It was in the library.

Specs I—

Allan Is that the only reason?

George It's one of the reasons.

Allan But wouldn't you say, really, taking everything into consideration, that Oscar Wilde, as well as being a disgusting old pervert, is also a load of cobblers?

George *The Importance of Being Earnest* is not a load of cobblers, Allan. It's a masterpiece. It's immortal. It's one of the greatest comedies in the English language.

Allan How do you know?

George It says so in the introduction.

Allan Does it make you laugh?

George What?

Allan You said it's a comedy. Tell me one line that makes you laugh.

George Well . . .

Allan Knock, knock . . .

George It's not like that.

Allan Oscar.

George It's witty.

Allan Oscar Wilde, knocking up little kids. It's not witty. It's repulsive.

Rose I've got funny lines.

Allan Have you?

Rose Yes.

Allan Tell me one funny line.

Rose What . . . now?

Allan Tell me one funny line.

Rose Well . . .

Allan Come on, Rose.

Rose Wait . . .

Allan There aren't any.

George There are lots.

Rose (*bursting out as Lady Bracknell*) To be born, or at any rate, bred in a handbag, whether it had handles or not, seems to me to display a contempt for the ordinary decencies of life that reminds one of the worst excesses of the French Revolution.

A pause. Nobody laughs.

George There you are! That was great!

Allan You thought that was funny?

George Yes.

Allan You're not laughing.

George Well, I've heard it before.

Allan It wasn't funny.

George It was out of context.

Allan Okay, Rose, you tell me. Since you're the one falling about with mirth, what's so funny about that line?

Rose I think it's funny that she's got bread in the handbag.

Allan Bread in the handbag? You think she's got a loaf of bread in the handbag? She hasn't got anything in her handbag.

Rose She's got a baby.

Allan You don't get any of it, do you. You don't
   understand a single word! What about the French
   Revolution? What was that about?

Rose Why are you picking on me? I never learned dancing.
   I don't know . . .

Allan I'm not picking on you. I'm with you. I don't get it
   either. I don't even get the plot.

George It couldn't be simpler. It's a comedy.

Allan So what's it about?

George You want to know what it's about.

Allan That's what I said.

George Well, it's obvious. Specs! You tell him . . .

Specs (*fluent*) The play may be superficial but relishes it,
   a triumph of surface over substance, a distillation of
   theatre that ultimately defines theatre itself. Here –
   appearance, style and narrative are treated as essence
   not just by the protagonists but by the author whose
   voice, a *deus ex machina*, binds the action in a totality
   that is unmistakably his.

Allan Where did you get that from?

Specs (*miserably*) The introduction.

Allan The introduction. (*Pause.*) Did you understand
   what you just said?

Specs No.

Allan A *deus ex machina*. What's that?

Rose A day in a machine. (*Realising.*) It's like being here!

Allan Come on, Specs. Why don't you explain it to me?
   Why don't you just tell me the story?

George If you ask Specs to elaborate, we'll be here all
   night.

Allan Then you tell me.

George The story.

Allan What's it about?

George The story.

Allan Yes.

George You ought to know it by now.

Allan I do know it. I just want to hear it from you.

George Right. (*Pause.*) I'm Jack Worthing. Alright? Jack. I have a fake brother called Ernest who doesn't exist and that's the name I also call myself. Sometimes I'm Jack. Sometimes I'm Ernest. You're my best friend and your name is Algy. And you're a real friend. Someone I can trust. Not someone who'd lead me to do something that I'd regret for the rest of my life. And I'm in love. I'm in love with your cousin, Gwendolen, who's really nice and not a slut, but she doesn't like me as Jack, she likes me as Ernest. You're in love with Cecily who's also a nice girl, like Gwendolen, but you also call yourself Ernest and Cecily has always dreamed that she'll meet someone called Ernest so she falls in love with you. Lady Bracknell is your aunt with the funny lines which are funny if they're delivered properly and she's also Gwendolen's mother and she doesn't want me to marry Gwendolen, and I'm Cecily's gardener and I don't want her to marry you.

Allan I'm not sure I'm any the wiser.

Specs Not gardener.

Rose What about the handbag?

George What?

Specs Guardian.

George What about the handbag, Rose? It's leather with long straps.

Allan Well, I'm glad that's sorted.

George Right. So now – can we get started? Are you ready to make your entrance?

Allan Absolutely.

George Specs – give him his cue.

Specs opens the play and reads out the cue without stammering.

Specs (*reading*) Algernon, from the other room, strikes up the 'Wedding March'. Jack looks perfectly furious and goes to the door: 'For goodness sake don't play that ghastly tune, Algy! How idiotic you are.'

The music stops and Algernon enters cheerily.

George Thank you.
Specs That's— (*He can't finish the sentence.*)
George Now get lost.

Specs leaves.

So, I think we get it now, Allan. We hear you playing the piano and then you come in.
Allan Playing the piano.
George No. You stop playing the piano and then you come in. Otherwise you'd look pretty stupid, wouldn't you?
Rose We did all this yesterday.
George And the day before. (*To Allan.*) How can you have forgotten? You wait for the music. Do you want to hear it?
Allan (*calling*) Specs!

From offstage comes the sound of a wedding march, played on a xylophone.

Rose That's not a piano.
George I know it's not a piano. We don't have a piano here.
Rose (*nodding – in explanation*) Pianos have got piano wire.
Allan That makes complete sense.
George I don't think it really matters. All that matters is that I hear a musical instrument being played . . .
Rose It could be a trombone.
George It could be anything. And I call out. (*As Jack Worthing.*) For goodness' sake don't play that ghastly tune, Algy.

The music stops.

It stops. And then . . .

Allan (*as Algernon*) Didn't it go off alright, old boy? You don't mean to say Gwendolen refused you?

George Right. That was excellent. That was perfect. I really think we're getting somewhere.

Rose About this handbag . . .

George Rose . . . we've done all that.

Rose No. There's something else.

George What is it?

Rose Why does the handbag have to be leather?

George Oh God.

Rose Why is it leather?

George Do you really want to know?

Rose Yeah.

George Do you have to know?

A pause. George searches for the answer.

It's just written that way.

Rose You could change the line.

George You can't change the lines!

Rose Why not?

George Because it's Oscar Wilde. If you changed the lines, it wouldn't be funny any more.

Rose Why can't it be a plastic handbag?

George They didn't have plastic handbags when the play was written.

Rose Why not?

George It wasn't in fashion. Nobody wore plastic. In society, nobody would have been seen dead wearing plastic, not even dead people. It just wasn't the thing.

Rose I just think we ought to think about the cow.

George What cow?

Rose The cow that made the handbag. Why should an animal have to die just to make a fashion accessory?

George Look. . .this is *The Importance of Being Earnest.* Not *The Importance of Being a Vegetarian*. I mean, we've been rehearsing it for weeks . . .

Allan Months.

George Isn't it a bit late to be bringing it up now?

Two more characters enter. Irene, who plays Gwendolen, is a very tough Glaswegian girl. Not attractive. Kinsey, who plays Lane (the butler) has a similar background to George. In fact the two of them grew up together.

Irene For Christ's sake, George.

George Irene . . .

Irene What's happening?

George We're getting there.

Irene What are you doing?

George We've got a problem with the scene. Nothing to worry about. We're sorting it.

Irene You've been sorting it for a very long time.

George We're working on it.

Irene How long am I supposed to wait out there?

George Two pages. Two minutes a page. Four minutes.

Kinsey You can tell he's the one with the maths GCSE.

George Just wait another four minutes. We've got a hitch.

Irene I'm fed up waiting. I've been waiting all fucking day. I've just been sitting there, fucking waiting.

Kinsey She's angry.

George I can see that.

Irene I'm angry.

Rose You're not meant to be angry, Irene. That's why they send us to anger management.

Irene Actually, anger management really pisses me off. You need anger to live in this place.

Rose What's wrong with this place? I like it here.

Irene No you don't, Rose. They fill you with pills. You only think you like it.

Rose It's the same thing.

Irene What?

Rose Thinking I like it. And liking it. What's the difference?

Irene The difference is that it's a fucking hallucination.

Rose I like the hallucination.

Irene That's what's wrong with this place. Don't you see? Are you so thick you don't see it? Every day they're trying to turn us into something we're not.

George Do we have to have this conversation now?

Kinsey (*ignoring him*) You've got it wrong, Irene. They're untying the knots and they're trying to turn us into something.

Irene That's very clever, Kinsey. You really fancy yourself, don't you? Anyone would think you'd had an education.

Kinsey I've had a re-education.

Irene It's not the same thing.

Allan She's got a point.

Rose At least he isn't self-harming.

Kinsey No. I let other people do that for me.

Irene Are you having a go at me, Rose?

Rose No. I wouldn't do that.

Irene Because if you're having a go at me, we can step outside.

Kinsey You haven't stepped outside in eleven years.

Irene But one day I will – and you'll be the first person I'll meet there.

Kinsey I'm not going anywhere.

Irene I'll tell you what I hate about this place. They're trying to patch us together with their medicine and their methods. But I'm not going to let them do it to me.

Kinsey You like being a total screw-up.

Irene Fuck you, Kinsey . . .

Rose I don't like that sort of language. It's wrong.

Irene (*continuing*) If you're so clever, how did you end up here? How did you even end up being called Kinsey? It's not your name.

Kinsey It is my name.

Irene It's the name that they gave you. But it wasn't the one you were born with. Not the one your parents gave you.

Kinsey I lost my parents.

Irene You mean your parents lost you. And as quickly as they could.

George Irene . . .

Irene (*to George*) What was it that the newspapers called the two of you, George? You and Kinsey? Do you want to remind me?

Rose We never talk about that. You know we're not meant to talk about that.

Irene They had a name for you too, Rose.

Rose They didn't know me.

Irene They knew what you did. After that, they didn't *want* to know you. Nobody did. They still don't.

Rose One day I'll be out of here and I'll tell them the truth.

Irene Just make sure they haven't eaten.

George Why don't we get back to the play?

Allan We were talking about the handbag.

George sees this as a way of getting back into the rehearsal.

George That's right. Rose asked about the handbag. Rose? I think you had an interesting point.

Rose I don't see why it can't be plastic.

Irene Oh Jesus!

George (*to Irene*) Can I answer her?

Irene Go ahead.

George It's an interesting point, Rose. But the baby would die in a plastic handbag. It wouldn't be able to breathe. Even if the handbag was open, its little lips would get stuck to the side and that would be the end of it. You don't want to put a baby in a plastic handbag. It has to be leather. Alright?

Allan You know, the more I think about it, the more I wonder if this is the right play . . .

George That's because you don't understand the plot.

Allan So maybe you can help me.

George I've already done that. I've told you.

Allan You didn't tell me what happens at the end.

George (*thrown*) What?

Allan The end. What happens at the end?

George Why are you asking that?

Allan Because I want to know.

George You've never asked before.

Allan I'm asking now.

George You know perfectly well. We don't know what happens at the end. We don't have the last pages.

Allan We've lost some pages.

George Yes.

Irene How many pages?

George Act Three.

Allan We don't have Act Three?

George No.

Allan None of it?

George No.

Irene Fuck.

Kinsey I thought it all ended a bit abruptly.

Allan What happened to Act Three?

George It fell out. When they removed the staples, some of the pages fell out.

Allan Quite a lot of pages.

George Yes.

Rose We're not allowed staples. None of the books have any staples. They're pointy and they're made of metal so they take them out.

Irene Stupid bastards.

Allan So what happened to the pages?

George We looked for them but we couldn't find them.

Allan Doesn't that somewhat defeat the purpose?

George No. It doesn't matter what happens in the end. Oscar Wilde didn't work that way. He just wanted you to have a good time. And when you're having a good time, you don't want it to end.

Rose I think they live happily ever after. They get married and they have their own place to live and a job . . . and maybe one of those new Minis with leather seats and a sun roof.

Allan And they go down the boozer Friday nights, get pissed, get into punch-ups and vomit over the kerb?

Rose It sounds lovely.

Allan I'm beginning to wonder if performing this play is really such a good idea. I mean, think of the audience. What are we going to do when halfway through –

George Two-thirds.

Allan – two thirds of the way, we just stop.

George They'll forgive us.

Kinsey That'll make a change.

Allan The play is an antique. The jokes don't work. It's missing half the pages. And it was written by a pervert.

George Anything else?

Allan Well, yes. Since you mention it. I don't think it's relevant.

George Relevant? Who says it has to be relevant?

Allan Well, it might help. It might make the experience more enjoyable. So tell me, George. Your starter for ten. *The Importance of Being Earnest*. What's the connection? To us.

Rose That's a good question.

Allan Because I'll tell you something. It certainly isn't cucumber sandwiches and girls called Gwendolen and marriages and handbags.

171

George It's a masterpiece! It's a much-loved English classic!

Kinsey By an Irishman.

George Don't start that again.

Allan I wouldn't go and see it. Who does? Can you tell me that? What's the actual point.

George It's simple, Allan. People love it.

Allan The play?

George The theatre. They love it. It doesn't matter what's on. Chekhov. Stendhal. Andrew Lloyd Webber. Going to the theatre . . . it's a big deal. Mums and dads, they get a babysitter for the kids –

Rose (*alarmed*) Babysitters.

George – and they go off together up to London's West End. There are loads of theatres all in a row and everyone dresses up. They're shown where to park by a kindly traffic warden and in they go in their suit and tie, programme, box of Black Magic, and then the lights go down and suddenly it's like they're in a different world. Algernon Moncrieff's flat in Half-Moon Street. The room is luxuriously and artistically furnished. The sound of a xylophone is heard in the adjoining room.

Rose A piano.

George It depends on the production.

Allan And people pay for this?

George It's culture. Of course they pay for it. A good seat in the stalls can cost fifteen quid and you may still have to put another ten pence in for a pair of binoculars – but they don't mind. It's worth it.

Allan I wouldn't go if you paid me.

Irene Yes, you would.

Allan Yes, I would. But I wouldn't enjoy it.

George You'd love it. A quick gin and tonic at the interval, served in the comfort of the crush bar, then the second half –

Kinsey – three if you've got the whole play –

George – applause, encore, lights up and out for dinner at your local Aberdeen Steak House, three courses served with a fine wine. That's what it's all about. That's an evening out.

Irene It's still a rubbish play. If I met someone like Gwendolen I'd want to nut her.

Rose You shouldn't say that.

Irene Oh give it a break, Rose. Have you got anything to say that doesn't come out of the rule book?

Rose The rule book is there for a reason.

Irene Gwendolen makes me want to throw up. She wouldn't have lasted two minutes on my estate. She'd have been killed just for her name.

Allan You still haven't answered my question, George. Why did you choose this play?

George Alright. I'll tell you. There were two plays in the library. *The Importance of Being Earnest* and *Julius Caesar* and if you think this one is irrelevant, you should have read the other one. It was full of Romans.

Rose My mum went to Rome.

George Ancient Romans. In togas and things.

Allan Did it have any jokes?

George No. But it had a murder.

Rose We don't want to do that sort of play here.

Allan Who got murdered?

George Julius Caesar. They stabbed him over and over.

Irene That sounds more like it.

Allan Why?

George It was very complicated. They didn't like him.

Allan Was it a gang?

George Yes. A gang. With knives. They wait for him in the market and then they do him over.

Rose You mean . . . like a video nasty?

George It is a bit like that.

Rose Not suitable.

George I wouldn't have said so.

Allan *Julius Caesar*. I can't say I ever saw it. And I used to watch a lot of video nasties . . .

George You know, I'm not sure . . .

George is about to explain the nature of Julius Caesar. *He is interrupted.*

Allan I used to watch them all the time. When I was a kid. I lived down the road from my local Blockbuster and the manager took a shine to me. He used to take me into the back room to show me these dirty films . . . not that you get very dirty films at Blockbuster. Smutty more like, though still capable of affecting an impressionable mind.

Irene It was porn.

Allan I preferred the action films. *Die Hard. Scream Two.* Little did I know that they might one day furnish me with the title of my own autobiography. But the best news was when Blockbuster started renting computer games. Now I could enjoy the violence in the privacy of my own room.

Rose *Zelda: Warrior Princess.*

Allan I preferred *Doom* and Lara Croft. They were great. I mean, the graphics were really in your face. Only my stepdad . . . he was dead against them. He used to go on and on about them. All the shooting. All the killing. People getting mauled by lions and sliced up by monsters . . .

Kinsey You couldn't make a computer game of *The Importance of Being Earnest*. I mean . . . you could. But who'd want to play it? Eat another fucking cucumber sandwich and advance to the next level. It would never work.

Allan My stepdad used to say that one thing would only lead to another. The blood-splatter and the sound effects. They made it more and more realistic until in

the end it almost felt like the real thing and who could
blame you if you decided that you wanted . . . you
know . . . if you wouldn't actually prefer the real thing.
It was only one small step.

Irene Are you saying you're here because of computer
games?

Allan No. I'm not saying that. My stepdad didn't want
me to play violent games. He used to search me every
time I came back from school. I had a PlayStation but
he personally chose all the software. *Civilisation. The
Sims.* Stuff like that. He'd search my room . . . he was
worried abou my long-term development. Anyway,
one night he came in unexpectedly and caught me red-
handed. I'd just managed to get my hands on *Grand
Theft Auto* and there I was blasting away, left right
and centre. And there he was, standing at the door.

Rose What did he do?

Allan He beat me up. Put me in hospital for two days.

Rose Was that when you ran away?

Allan I wouldn't even have been able to walk away after
that. I could only just about manage to limp to school.
I ran away three months later, as soon as I was able.

Rose To London.

Allan Yeah.

Rose What's London like?

Allan London?

Rose Yeah.

Allan It's big.

Rose It's got pigeons. And the Millennium Wheel. I'd
love to go on the Millennium Wheel.

Irene What's the point of going on the fucking Millennium
Wheel? It'll only take you back where you started.

Allan I was labouring under the mistaken belief that the
streets of London would be lined with gold. But they
weren't. The streets were lined with creeps and weirdos.

Rose Where did you sleep?

Allan That was difficult. The police were always moving you on. I was only eighteen. In the end, I found a place near Victoria Station.

Kinsey Victoria Station. Well, well, well. Maybe there's a connection after all.

Rose The handbag! It was left in the cloakroom at Victoria Station.

Allan I got to know the station very well after I came to London. I was found by a great many gentlemen of a charitable and kindly disposition and many of them did, indeed, take me to the cloakroom.

George We don't want to know about this.

Irene I do!

George It's not relevant.

Allan It's the play that's not relevant. I vote we don't do it.

George What?

Allan Let's take a vote on it. I say we junk it.

George But we've been working on it for months.

Irene I don't care. I think he's right.

George We can't have a vote. Half the cast isn't here.

Allan That is their vote, George. They're not here because, all in all, they'd prefer to be on medication. That's their commitment.

Kinsey We're all committed.

George If we had a vote, I'd win. I want to do it. Specs wants to do it. Kinsey wants to do it. Rose wants to do it.

Irene I don't want to do it.

George That just leaves two of you.

Allan Specs doesn't want to do it.

George Yes, he does.

Irene Then let's hear him say it.

George You want to hear him say it?

Irene Yes.

George (*calling*) Specs!

Allan Here we go again.

A pause. They wait for Specs.

Kinsey Anyone fancy a game of Scrabble while we're
waiting?
Irene I hate fucking Scrabble.
Kinsey I can't understand why. You're so good with the
four-letter words.

Specs appears.

Specs Yes, George?
George Yes or no, Specs. Do you want to do this play?
Feel free to nod.

Specs nods.

George There you are.
Allan You haven't thought this through, George. It's a
terrible play. It's a horrible play. We're all going to
make complete idiots of ourselves.
George No, Allan. You're the one who doesn't see it.
When it's done properly, it's a brilliant play. It's hilarious.
Allan When it's done properly . . .
George We just haven't got there yet. That's what we're
working towards. I can show you. I can show you. Do
it, Specs.
Specs Me?
George Show them. (*To the others.*) Sit down. Watch
him. This is how it's done.

*George, Kinsey, Allan, Rose and Irene sit down. Specs
is centre stage.*
George Right.

*A pause. Then, unexpectedly, Specs provides a
faultless, virtuoso performance, acting all the parts at
high speed, changing voice and character, making the
play live.*

Specs (*Cecily*) Here is Ernest.

Specs (*Algernon*) My own love. (*Offers to kiss her.*)

Specs (*Cecily*) A moment, Ernest. May I ask you – are you engaged to be married to this young lady?

Specs (*Algernon*) Of course not! What could have put such an idea into your pretty little head?

Specs (*Cecily*) Thank you. (*Presenting her cheek to be kissed.*) You may.

Specs as Algernon kisses Specs as Cecily.

Specs (*Gwendolen*) I felt there was some slight error, Miss Cardew. The gentleman who is now embracing you is my cousin, Mr Algernon Moncrieff.

Specs as Cecily breaks away from Specs as Algernon.

Specs (*Algernon*) Oh!

Specs (*Cecily*) Are you called Algernon?

Specs (*Algernon*) I cannot deny it.

Specs (*Cecily*) Oh!

Specs (*Gwendolen*) Is your name really John?

Specs (*Jack*) I could deny it if I liked. I could deny anything if I liked. But my name certainly is John. It has been John for years.

Specs (*Cecily to Gwendolen*) A gross deception has been practised on both of us.

Specs (*Gwendolen*) My poor wounded Cecily.

Specs (*Cecily*) My sweet wronged Gwendolen.

Specs (*Gwendolen*) You will call me sister, will you not?

Cecily and Gwendolen embrace each other. Specs does this by embracing himself

George There you are. He's astonishing. He's a virtuoso.

Kinsey Maybe he should do it as a one-man show.

George Don't you start, Kinsey. We're not doing it as a one-man show but we are doing it. That's been decided. So now get offstage and let's get back to the first scene.

Kinsey Wait a minute. Wait a minute. You never gave me a vote.

George You did get a vote. You voted to do it.

Kinsey No, George. This was all your idea. I did it because you told me to.

George That's not true. That's not me. I wouldn't do that.

Kinsey You made the decision, George.

George No.

Kinsey Well, I've changed my mind. I don't want to do it. I'm voting against it.

Rose I can't keep up with this.

Irene It's a draw. Three all. I'm going to bed.

George Wait! What do you want, Kinsey?

Kinsey Well, I wouldn't have minded a decent part, for a start. I'm the butler. I just bring on the muffins and the cucumber sandwiches. And they don't even exist. It's embarrassing.

George They're imaginary. They're imaginary cucumber sandwiches. That's part of the drama.

Rose Are they in triangles?

Kinsey Rose . . .

Rose Or little squares? That's how I used to do them. Natty used to love them. We'd go down to the bottom of the garden and we'd have a little picnic in the daisies. Little Natty and me. We'd have little, tiny cups of tea out of a doll's house cup and I made sure the water was never scalding hot or anything like that. I put the knife away. That's why I wanted to do this play. Because it reminded me of the picnics . . . the cucumber sandwiches. And when I imagine them, they're always cut into squares.

Kinsey (*to George*) You see what I mean? This is total bullshit.

Irene I'm with you there.

Allen That's it, then. Three against three. That's not good enough.

Irene The end. Curtain. Fuck off.

George Wait a minute. Wait a minute. Kinsey, let me talk to you about this.

Kinsey We've talked enough, George.

George Just the two of us. Alone. You and me.

Kinsey You and me?

George Like we used to be. Just for a moment.

Kinsey You want to talk.

George Yes.

Kinsey I can do that.

George Thank you, Kinsey. (*He turns to the rest of them.*) Alright, everyone? Did you get that? We're going to take five.

Rose Five what?

George Five minutes, Rose. It's a technical term.

Kinsey Five minutes alone.

George One on one.

Rose doesn't understand this either.

Please.

Everyone leaves. As they go, Allen mutters to Kinsey.

Allen You tell him . . .

Kinsey and George are alone. A pause.

George Why are you doing this? What do you want?

Another pause. Kinsey is savouring the moment. He has the upper hand

Kinsey Let's talk about motivation.

George What?

Kinsey I think you heard me, George. You never gave me any time during rehearsals. So let's talk about motivation.

George Now?

Kinsey That's right.

George Your character is a butler, Kinsey. He doesn't have motivation. He gets paid, which is the next best thing.

Kinsey That's not what I mean. That's not what I had in mind.

George What then?

Kinsey I'd be interested in your motivation for casting me.

George Casting you?

Kinsey As the butler. As Lane.

George You want a bigger part.

Kinsey I don't want any part at all. But since Allan is complete crap and doesn't want to do this and keeps coming on at the wrong time, I would like to know, just out of interest, why you didn't cast me as Algernon.

George You weren't right for Algernon.

Kinsey You think Rose is right for Lady Bracknell?

George There's nothing wrong with Rose.

Kinsey Lady Bracknell is a respectable, witty doyenne of Victorian society. Rose is completely thick.

George It's a different interpretation.

Kinsey I should have played Algernon. Algernon and Jack are lifelong friends.

George That's why you're wrong for the part.

Kinsey Ah. (*Pause.*) I could have acted.

George I couldn't.

Kinsey It would have been nice, a bit of comic banter between us.

George It wouldn't work.

Kinsey You didn't want to give it a try?

George Not any more.

Kinsey I was the best friend you ever had, George.

George That's what I thought, once. But you led me right up the garden path.

Kinsey We went up the garden path together.

George But it wasn't a garden path, was it? It led us here. Unless this is the only garden in the country where they put the hydrangeas behind razor-wire.

Kinsey You still blame me. (*A long pause.*) How much of it do you really remember? It was a long time ago. Do you ever think about Ashurst?

George Not if I can help it.

Kinsey You and me. We were inseparable. Same school. Same street. Same brand of cigarette. You remember that? Ten Marlboro Lite from old Mr Harris on the corner? You get his attention, I nick 'em. And the ice-cream van. The chime of the bells on a hot summer day. Running in front of it to see if we could fake an insurance claim. And going up the garden path, since you mention it. Breaking into the conservatory.

George You were a year older than me.

Kinsey But you were the smart one. The director. You remember the bicycle rides? Ashurst. Findon. And then down the A24 to Worthing.

George I don't want to talk about Worthing.

Kinsey And then, of course, you must remember coming here . . .

George I remember that.

Kinsey I never thought they'd send us to the same place. Do you ever wonder why they did that? Perhaps it was therapy.

George Or punishment.

Kinsey I was twelve when I came here. I didn't understand what was happening. I didn't understand any of it. I remember they unlocked this door. We went in and they locked it behind us. And right in front of us there was another door. They unlocked it, we went through and then they locked it behind us. We came to a third door. Unlock, go through, lock it again. And then – I couldn't believe it – there was another door. 'What's this?' I asked. 'This is the front door,' they said. That was when I knew I was in trouble. (*Pause.*) Do you think they'll ever open those doors again, George? Is that your motivation? Be a good boy, put on a play, they'll look at you in a new light and let you out?

A pause.

George They might.

Kinsey They won't.

George I'm different now.

Kinsey New name. New number. Same old George.

George No.

Kinsey Still trying to blame me.

George It was your idea.

Kinsey You're never going to leave here. You should be glad.

George No.

Kinsey Because you know what would happen if you walked through all those doors? There'd be a crowd waiting for you outside. All the journalists and photographers. They'd snap you. They'd snap you in half . . .

George They've forgotten me.

Kinsey No one will ever forget you.

George They've forgiven me.

Kinsey You think so? Personally, I've never thought of journalists as the forgiving sort. And then there are the parents and the relatives, lining up to give you a good kicking. And then, waiting patiently in line, the rest of the world. 'You're slime. You're evil.' They'd rather you didn't exist.

George They don't know me. I've changed. And when I get out of here, I'll be someone else.

Kinsey The face of Satan.

George It was red-eye. That was all.

Kinsey A lethal injection, George. You remember that? Free with the *Daily Mail*. See page two, three, four, five, nine, ten, sixteen. They were even trying to kill you on the sports pages.

George I was eleven years old!

Kinsey That's no excuse.

George One day, they'll let us go.

Kinsey You think so? And what about the rest of them . . . the rest of your cast? You really think they're going to let Rose out? Give her a job in a crèche, perhaps. Count Dracula to supply the character reference. Or Irene. Let her go back to her family – or what's left of them – in Glasgow. Allan. Specs. There are two people who'd be much happier walking the streets and I'm sure the streets would be much happier having them. Do you really see it happening? Don't you see what you are?

George Have you finished?

Kinsey Not really.

George The bell will be going.

Kinsey Well, no one else is.

George I want to go on with the rehearsal. I need your vote.

Kinsey And I need you, George. I need you.

A pause. George waits to see if Kinsey will object. He doesn't. George calls.

George (*calling*) Allan. Irene. Rose. Specs.

Allan, Irene, Rose and Specs come back onstage.

George We've had a discussion. We've hammered a few things out.

Rose (*urgent*) It wasn't my hammer!

George We've decided . . . we've put a lot of work into this. We all have. So we're going to continue.

Irene Shit.

Allan Kinsey, you're a wanker.

George So that's it, then. The decision has been made.

184

Kinsey Whose decision?

The moment of truth for George.

George Kinsey wants to continue. Don't you, Kinsey.
(*Pause. Then, to Kinsey.*) Colin?

Kinsey What did you call me?

Rose Colin.

Irene Is that your name?

Kinsey It was my name. In Worthing.

Rose That's not allowed.

A pause. Then back to business.

Kinsey Maybe he's right. We've got nothing else to do.

Allan Okay. Just tell me one thing.

George What?

Allan Why *are* we doing this? Why are we bothering?

Irene Yeah – because frankly, between you and me, I
can't think of a fucking reason.

George How can you ask this now, after all this time?
We've got the costumes. We've got the set. You've
learned your lines . . . many of them in the right order.
We've spent weeks. Months. How can you ask this now?

Allan Better late than never.

Irene I still say we stop. I still say we pack the whole
thing in.

George No! We've voted.

Rose I might have changed my mind.

George What? (*He turns to Irene.*) Have you talked to
her?

Rose I don't know. I *think* it's a good idea.

George (*to the others*) There you are!

Rose But a lot of the things I think are good ideas turn
out to be not good ideas after all. That's the trouble.
Like the time with me and Natty. I thought it was a
good idea but that's how I ended up here and if there's
one thing I've learned, it's not to have good ideas.

Allan So you're against it.

George No. She's for it.

Rose No. I'm against it.

George She doesn't know what she's saying. She doesn't understand a single word that comes out of her lips.

Allan Then her vote doesn't count. She's disqualified.

Rose Let's talk about this tomorrow!

Irene Let's pack it in now.

George No. Wait. You don't see the importance. You don't see – one more week – how it could be. Listen to me. In a week's time, we'll have an audience. They'll come in through that door – and the door behind it – and they'll sit down and they'll watch us. And just for an hour, an hour and a half, they'll enjoy what we do. They'll see us eat the cucumber sandwiches and the muffins and they'll laugh at our jokes and they won't be afraid that something horrible is going to happen. On the contrary, it's Oscar Wilde. They'll know it's going to be hilarious. And even if they never find out what happens on account of our having mislaid Act Three, they won't mind. They'll forgive us. Think of that. They'll have been enjoying our company. A cultural experience. They'll have enjoyed us for what we are.

Kinsey Not who we are. Who we're dressed up and pretending to be. Lane the butler.

Allan Algernon.

Irene Gwendolen.

Rose Lady Bracknell.

George But that doesn't matter. That's the whole point. While we're standing here on this stage, that's who we are. If we do the play. Let me ask you, Allan. Who would you prefer to be? Algernon Moncrieff, wealthy bachelor with a flat in Half-Moon Street? Or Specs?

A pause.

Kinsey And when it's over?

George It doesn't matter. It will have been a start.

A pause.

George Specs?

Specs hurries off the stage.

George There he is. He's back in the prompter's chair. He'll help us if things go wrong.

A pause. The others consider.

Irene Alright. Fuck it. Let's do it. But just get a move on this time.

She leaves. Kinsey glances at George, then follows. George, Rose and Allan are left on the stage as they were at the start.

George Allan?

A pause.

Allan I never had any control over anything I ever did. I'm not a bad person, you know. I'm not. But when certain things happen to you, when they happen to you all your life, you're bound to explode. You can't help it. But I was never in control. I told them that, but they didn't believe me. Not then. Not now. Not ever.

George Specs will give you your cue.

Allan Will he?

George Yeah. He'll help you.

Allan (*resigned*) Right.

Allan leaves the stage.

Rose I feel nervous. Where are we going to begin?

George Back at the beginning. Where we were.

Rose Right.

George Do you want your line?

Rose No. I've got it.

A pause. Then the two of them return to character.

Rose (*Lady Bracknell*) Now to minor matters. Are your parents living?

George (*Jack Worthing*) I am afraid I really don't know. The fact is, Lady Bracknell, I said I had lost my parents. It would be nearer the truth to say that my parents have lost me . . . I don't actually know who I am by birth. I was . . . well, I was found.

Rose (*Lady Bracknell*) Found?

George (*Jack Worthing*) The late Mr Thomas Cardew, an old gentleman of a very charitable and kindly disposition, found me, and gave me the name of Worthing because he happened to have a first-class ticket for Worthing in his pocket at the time. Worthing is a place in Sussex: it is a seaside resort.

Rose (*Lady Bracknell*) Where did the charitable gentleman, who had a first-class ticket for this seaside resort, find you?

George (*Jack Worthing*) In a handbag.

Rose (*Lady Bracknell*) A handbag?

The bell rings. The same, officious bell we heard earlier. The three of them freeze. We hear slamming doors. Locks turning. The grim sounds of a maximum security installation. Nobody moves.

Fade out.

The End.

Production Notes

A Handbag developed from Anthony Horowitz's experiences of giving talks to children and young adults in institutions and prisons around Britain. He discovered that they did not conform to the media stereotype but were articulate, sensitive and individual. As a visitor to these institutions, you cannot ask the children what they did that brought them there. Eye-contact becomes hugely important: avoiding and making eye-contact can be a powerful status tool; especially in places where the young people are not allowed physical release, the little tics, gestures and moments of eye-contact become all important.

Anthony set out to write a comedy that was also sad. The play asks the question, can a child ever be considered 'evil'? For Anthony there is no such thing as an evil child. Even with the most monstrous act there must be room for redemption and a way forward. At the heart of the play is the theme of connection – of people not connecting to each other, desperately wanting and needing to connect, and feeling alienated.

The play was written in three months. Originally all six characters were male, to reflect the fact that in some institutions girls and boys are segregated, but as a writer Anthony found a cross-gender cast more dynamic. His most difficult task was choosing the least appropriate play they could be performing within an institution. When he finally hit upon Oscar Wilde's *The Importance of Being Earnest* the rest fell into place. All the references, themes and cross-references in the play come from a single scene in *The Importance*.

Other inspirations for the piece included the film *Scum*, the book and film of *Lord of the Flies*, the Channel 4 drama *Boy A*, and Venables and Thompson in the Bulger case.

The institution is intentionally vague and based more in fiction than in fact to allow these children to have the space to themselves without physical intervention or adult presence. What sort of institution it is and the atmosphere of the place are left to the individual company to discover.

CHARACTERS

The piece has just six characters so that each gets his or her moment: it is not designed for a large company. Ideally it will also use a cast of the right gender for the characters.

The characters are all between eighteen and twenty-two years of age. They might not know it, but all will be in this institution for life. There will be difficulties if you try to play the characters younger than they are, considering the experiences they have been through that are mentioned in the text.

Three of the characters are totally dependent on books. George relies on *The Importance of Being Earnest*, Specs is tied to any book and Rose utterly depends on the rulebook to guide her. The books are their safety and support and offer them a path. If you took the rule book away from Rose she would be lost. In this world the rule book is a PC way of behaving for young people who have committed heinous crimes.

George is perhaps the most self-aware of all the characters, which means he has the most to lose, whereas Specs is perhaps the most damaged. Therefore his moment of release where he acts out the plot of *The Importance of Being Earnest* is a huge moment for him.

It is important to have an idea about what the characters have done, and certainly Anthony knew when he was writing the play. But how detailed you make their pasts and what you decide is entirely at the discretion of the director. It's vital to note that *why* they did what they did is more important than *what* they did.

When writing, Anthony saw Rose as possibly being Afro-Caribbean in origin, George as middle to upper class and Irene as Glaswegian and from the Projects.

The characters have new names because this is meant to bring down an iron curtain between the past and present. In this institution there is a focus on escape from, not atonement for, the past.

DESIGN

It is necessary to create the sense of the institution as a set of solid walls beyond the imaginary/makeshift world of the Oscar Wilde drawing room. That real world has to be as solid as the Wilde world is imaginary.

There could be a raised area or stage where the characters plan to perform the show and even makeshift wings to create more of a sense of proper theatrical staging. However, when Irene and the others enter from another room they should have been unable to watch or hear the foregoing dialogue.

Doors are a big thing. The outside world is so far away and cut off for these children; they all desperately want to reach the outside but are trapped behind a series of impenetrable doors that render the outside almost mythical.

PERFORMANCE NOTES

If you give too much away at the beginning of the show then the audience will miss the discovery of this being an institution and the characters having no idea about the Wilde play they are attempting to perform. Don't forget the surprise elements you discovered when reading the play and allow the audience the same process of discovery.

Energy and intention in speaking the lines is paramount. Try to discover the thoughts and why the characters are speaking rather than just what they are saying.

If the swearing is a problem then Anthony would prefer it to be softened at the director's discretion than for the play not to be performed at all.

One worry that came up from the workshop was how to achieve the stutter for Specs. The vocal coach told us there are different forms of stuttering which accord to the location of articulation. Some people have problems with 'w' and 'm' words (like *what*, *why*, *my*), which means they trap the sound at the front of their mouths. Some get stuck with tongue-tip words (*don't*, *try*, *let*), and others get stuck on back-of-tongue words (*can't*, *god*).

For Specs it might be best to try the stutter with tongue-tip or lips words. To achieve this, try saying the word and then tense up the mouth when it is in that position – discover how difficult it is to say the word 'George' if your tongue is tense and stuck to the roof of your mouth.

Doing a stammer in theatre is about creating a physical block, practising that block so you develop the muscle memory, then re-finding the truth of what you are saying so it sounds both technically accurate and truthful.

The play demands and can withstand deep emotional exploration, so we played a series of games to help release the actors and demonstrate how a director can inspire and lead that process. These included finding the physical gesture that represents the character's worst fear and playing a scene between characters where, instead of using the lines, the actors could only use the text 'me' or 'you', thus identifying when the characters are concerned with themselves, and when they are reaching out to each other.

The danger of this play for a director is that it will become too static, as there is so much dialogue. To combat this, be very clear about the characters and their own physical worlds – what drives them and how they react to events. Try using games that explore eye-contact, status and physicalising the connection between the characters. For example, try a scene where one of the characters has to get eye-contact with the others, and they are seeking to avoid it. The relationships between them and the dynamics of the group are a vital part of the play and need to be explored both psychologically and physically.

From a workshop led by Raz Shaw,
with notes by Gemma Fairlie

HEARTBREAK BEAUTIFUL

Christopher William Hill

Christopher William Hill's stage plays include *Lam*, *Song of the Western Men*, *Icons*, *Death to Mr Moody*, *Inglorious Technicolour* and *Blood Red, Saffron Yellow*. He was librettist for the opera *The Murder of Charlotte Dymond*, and wrote the play *Multiplex* for New Connections. For radio he has written *Killing Maestros* (Best Script, BBC Radio and Music Awards, 2003, and the Peter Tinniswood Award), *Accolades*, *Suing Mr Spargo*, *Pundits* and *Love Me, Liberace*. He has written two series of the Radio 4 comedy *Tomorrow, Today!*; *Lambeth Palace* and *Marmalade for Comrade Philby* will be broadcast in 2009. He is currently under commission to Plymouth Theatre Royal, Hampstead Theatre and the Almeida.

Characters

GIRLS	BOYS
Ellie	Dan
Amber	AJ
Fat Kylie	Dazza
Fit Kylie	Tristan
Nessa	Headwound
Megan	Tyler
Jade	Troy
Amy	Griff
Saskia	Fudgecake
Bex	Callum
	Lewis
	Oscar

An empty space. Upstage, a trophy cabinet, containing a well-polished golden athletics trophy. A whistle blows and the cast appear, dressed in school sports kit. They stand at the sidelines, and remain on stage throughout the play. All sports equipment should be mimed, and any other props should be carried by the actors.

Dan and Tristan step forward.

Dan So . . . what do you want me to say?
Tristan I don't know. Start at the beginning.
Dan The beginning?
Tristan If you want.
Dan I go to a crap school.
Tristan I know that.

He smiles.

Dan You've got everything at St Oggs . . . new gym, swimming pool . . . track . . . we've got jack, yeah?
Tristan Jack?
Dan Jack-shit.
Tristan Right.

The whistle blows. The boys run on. Troy and Tyler watch as the girls enter.

Troy Not bad legs.
Tyler No tits.
Fit Kylie Eff off.
Dan It's like the Neanderthals, yeah . . . some of our lot, they're crawling *back* into the primordial swamp.
Tristan That bad?

Dan I'm serious. Mr Walker . . . he's the arsehole that thinks he runs the school, yeah? He tried to bring back cricket. The stumps got nicked and the cricket bat is now Exhibit A in a case of aggravated assault.

Tristan laughs.

It's not funny. The school's been condemned . . . we screwed up OFSTED . . . We were a designated Sports College but they spent all the money on computers and interactive whiteboards. In every class we've got like two kids that are borderline illiterate. They put up a sign for lunchtime literacy classes, but none of them could read it.

Tristan You're joking?

Dan We make shit schools look good.

Whistle.

Megan Pick team captains.

AJ runs a circuit around the stage.

Dan But there's AJ, yeah? Golden balls . . . and golden legs . . . and golden arms . . . golden bloody everything.

Tristan Your brother?

Dan Yeah, my little brother. And he's, like, good at all sports, you know? An all-rounder.

Tristan He's a good sprinter.

Dan The best. You know, when he's focused. I know he could win the county championship cup . . . if he really tried. But nobody's beaten it in twenty years. It's just stayed in the trophy cabinet . . . the one trophy we've got. Everything else got won by some other school . . . or got nicked. Mr Walker's well proud of that cup.

Whistle.
The boys line up.

Griff Well?

Troy Not Lewis, he's so gay.

Tyler Griff, bruv . . . pick me!

Griff Tyler.

Tyler Yeah, man.

He steps forward.

Fudgecake Me, me!

Griff Dazza.

Fudgecake Me!

Griff Headwound.

Fudgecake What about me?

Griff What about you?

Fudgecake If you don't pick me, you're going to dent my self-esteem. And when that happens . . . I eat. And if I eat I'll get fat –

Tyler *Fatter.*

Fudgecake You'll be responsible for contributing to the obesity epidemic.

Beat.

And *then* you'll be sorry.

Griff No I won't.

Lewis Pick me and I'll ask my sister if she'll let you feel her up.

Griff Your sister's well fit.

Lewis Exactly.

Fudgecake bites into a chocolate roll.

Fudgecake When I get to seventy stone and Sky 3 come round to make the documentary, I'll tell them it was your fault I got fat.

Griff Who cares?

Dan Seriously, *primordial.*

Megan enters bouncing a basketball. She shoots a hoop.

Troy You throw like a girl.
Megan I am a girl.
Tyler Prove it.
Megan Freak.
Dan I mean . . . we're crap at most sports.
Headwound Scrum down.

*The cast form a large and shapeless rugby scrum.
Callum appears from beneath, desperately holding the
ball to his chest.*

Callum I don't know what I'm doing. I don't fucking
know what I'm doing.

*Before he has a chance to run, the scrum reforms and
dives on Callum, who yelps as he disappears from
view. Lewis appears, talking on his mobile.*

Lewis Come on – answer the fucking phone . . .

*Griff is talking on his mobile on the other side of the
stage.*

Griff I gotta go . . . gotta call waiting. Yeah?
Lewis Griff – ball's coming your way.
Dan He's got a lazy eye and no depth perception.
Griff What?

*The ball hurtles through the air and catches Griff on
the side of the head, knocking him to the ground.*

Tristan As bad as that?
Dan I shit you not. But then there's AJ . . . and it's like the
hand of God picking him from the line-up of humanity.
And he's good at all sport . . . just picks it up . . .

We see a montage of different sports.

Athletics . . . football . . . rugby . . . basketball . . . hockey
. . . everything. Even rock-climbing.

AJ steps forward.

Griff Taking in slack.

He does so.

AJ That's me.
Griff Climb when you're ready.
AJ Climbing.
Griff Okay.

He climbs.
  Whistle.
  A group of teenagers enter, dressed in hoodies. Their 'leader', Oscar, stops and takes off his hood and watches Lewis, a fellow hoodie, with interest.

Lewis (*dreamily*) I think I'd like to try a bit of rock-climbing.

Oscar advances menacingly on Lewis.

Oscar You like sport . . . admit it.
Lewis No I don't.
Oscar Look at him. He's a traitor.
Lewis I don't . . . I like reading and drama and . . . sudoku . . .
Saskia I expect he likes football as well.
Lewis I don't. It's all lies. *Lies.*
Dan They hunt in packs . . . at St Barts. The geeks. Oscar Shelburne . . . he's their leader . . .
Tristan Do geeks have leaders?
Dan They do at St Barts. They all dress in hoodies . . . so no one starts on them. So they look dead hard. But underneath . . . pure geek. From their sensible shoes to their orthodontic braces.

Lewis runs off, upset. Ellie pushes through the crowd and nervously removes her hoodie. She smiles, revealing a gleaming pair of braces, which seem to glint in the light. AJ watches her, transfixed.

Oscar (*calling*) Ellie.

Troy and Tyler turn.

Troy Oi, look.
Tyler Brace-face!

They laugh, and Ellie pulls up her hood and disappears into the crowd. AJ and Oscar are clearly disappointed. Amy enters and smiles at Dan.

Amy Alright, Dan?
Dan Alright.
Amy You going to English?
Dan Yeah. You?
Amy Yeah.
Dan Cool.
Amy Yeah.

Beat.

You know what we're gonna be doing?
Dan Same as usual. You know . . . 'Remember five things from last lesson.' Cos he can't remember sod-all and he wants us to remember it for him.
Amy (*giggling*) You're so funny.
Dan No I'm not.

She laughs again.

Can you stop doing that?
Amy Doing what?
Dan Laughing like that?

Amy laughs again.

That'll be a 'no', then.

Headwound steps forward. He wears a baseball cap and medallion.

Troy Alright, gangsta?
Amber Gangsta? He's not even black.
Tyler You're so racist.
Headwound Alright, Fat Kylie?
Fat Kylie Alright, Headwound? Stay over at my place later. Mum's got her new prescription, she'll be out flat all night. I will be and all, if you know what I mean?
Troy Result!

Headwound smacks him.

Amber Are you coming for netball practice at lunchtime?
Fat Kylie Mum doesn't like me taking part in competitive sports.
Nessa Only cos she knows you're shit at them.

Fit Kylie enters.

Fit Kylie Alright?
Nessa You're in early.
Fit Kylie Yeah, it was an ugly *Jeremy Kyle* . . . they were all mingers.
Fat Kylie They're always mingers on *Jeremy Kyle*.
Callum Mum says *Jeremy Kyle* breeds guests in some caravan park in Norfolk . . .
Fit Kylie Who asked you?
Nessa You heard about Jade Nicholls?
Fit Kylie She had to have her stomach pumped.
Fat Kylie Bacardi Breezers.
Fit Kylie Her nan bought her a six-pack for her sixteenth.
Dan If it wasn't for drink and drugs the whole school could be really good at sport.
Tristan What about AJ?

Dan I'm trying to make sure he doesn't get mixed up in all that, you know. But it's hard . . . when he had a girlfriend like Amber.

AJ You hand in your coursework?

Amber No. I'm like, 'The dog ate it,' right? And he was like, 'Yeah, and I'm the sodding Pope.' So I'm like, 'Right, Your Holiness,' getting me phone out –

AJ Your phone?

Amber Click to file-manager, click to photos. 'That's the dog, sir,' – click – 'That's me feeding the coursework *to the dog . . .*'

AJ What did he do?

Amber Internally excluded me, the prick. And with photographic evidence and all.

AJ Harsh.

Amber Yeah.

Whistle.
   School track, evening. AJ and Dazza kick a football around.

Dan They were never right for each other . . . I mean, he never listened to me. I always have to look out for him . . . make sure he's not getting led astray, you know?

Tristan (*smiling*) So you're a control freak?

Dan picks up the football.

AJ We were having a kick-around.

Dan Yeah, and now you're not. You're supposed to be warming up. Drop and give me ten.

AJ and Dazza drop and perform the press-ups. The Kylies and Nessa enter and watch. Fat Kylie has her hair scraped back tightly – a 'Croydon facelift'.

Fit Kylie Oi, Dazza?

Dazza springs up and jogs over to the girls.

Dazza Alright, Kylie?
Fat Kylie Dazza.
Dazza Kylie.
Nessa Kylie says you look well fit.
Dazza Which Kylie?
Nessa Both of them.
Fit Kylie Shut up, Nessa.
Fat Kylie Yeah, shut up.
Dazza I am fit. I'm an athlete.
Nessa No, they mean . . . 'fit' fit.
Dazza Oh. Right. *Fit.*
Fit Kylie Shut up.
Fat Kylie Yeah, Nessa, shut up, yeah?

Dazza flexes his arm.

Dazza Feel that.

Fit Kylie squeezes Dazza's bicep.

Fit Kylie (*teasing*) Nothing there.
Fat Kylie I wanna squeeze.

She squeezes Dazza's other arm.

Cool.
Nessa Get a room.
Dazza What are you doing later?
Fat Kylie / Fit Kylie Burger King.
Dan Dazza?
Dazza Yeah, okay . . .
Dan Give me two laps.
Dazza See you later then, ladies.

He salutes them. Fat Kylie laughs, Fit Kylie stares at her.

Fit Kylie What?

Nessa Dazza and Kylie sitting in a tree . . . F–U–C –
Fat Kylie Shut up.

Dazza jogs off.

AJ (*to Dan*) You coming too?
Dan What? Burger King? I don't think so.
AJ Why not? I'm going.
Dan No you're not. You're supposed to be maintaining a healthy diet.
AJ It's just Burger King.
Dan They say 'go large' for a reason . . .

We cross back to Nessa and the Kylies.

Fit Kylie Dazza's so fit. And he's like so into me. I've been reading *Sugar*. It's in my stars.
Nessa You will meet a tall, dark arsehole?
Fit Kylie What do you reckon, Kylie?
Fat Kylie He's alright. Nothing special.

Fat Kylie tightens her hair band and cries out in pain.

Fit Kylie Why do you do that with your hair?
Fat Kylie I dunno. Just to make myself look good.
Fit Kylie It's not working.
Fat Kylie What?
Fit Kylie You look like a horse in a wind tunnel.

Whistle.

Dan Don't get me wrong . . . I'm really proud of AJ. He's like a school celebrity – he's always in the local papers. But it's like . . . nobody knows it's because of me . . . all the training I do with him. I'd like a bit of that. People noticing me.

Tristan smiles.
  Boy's shower. Headwound flicks Tyler with his towel. Tyler yelps.

Troy They say he's got three nipples . . . AJ.

Headwound Bollocks.

Troy Nipples.

Headwound No, I mean, 'Bollocks, he hasn't got three nipples.'

Troy I stood in the shower and counted them.

Tyler You see, that's why people call you a poof.

Troy Who calls me a poof? I'll fucking do 'em.

Headwound I call you a poof.

Troy Alright, well I'll make an exception.

Tyler Poof.

Troy I just said he had three nipples. I didn't say he had three *beautiful* nipples.

Tyler You don't know when to shut up, do you?

Troy Do what?

Beat.

You think it's like a sign of great inner strength or something?

Headwound What?

Troy Having three nipples?

Tyler No, I think it's a sign of being a complete freak.

Dan stares at Tyler.

What you looking at?

Whistle.

Tristan So . . . no girlfriend?

Dan (*awkwardly*) I tried, yeah? AJ and Dazza . . . they were always trying to set me up.

Dazza What about Stacey Collins?

Dan Don't fancy her.

Dazza Melody Smith?

Dan Too freaky.

Dazza Maggie Strivens?

Dan No. She's gone all *High School Musical.*

Three girls dance across the stage.
Whistle.
Canteen lunch queue. Dazza, AJ and Dan wait in
line, looking out towards the canteen servery.

AJ What is that?
Dazza Stroganoff.
AJ Looks like someone's puked in it.
Dazza That's what Stroganoff looks like.

He smiles at an unseen dinner lady.

Yeah, the Stroganoff.
AJ Stroganoff . . .
Dan Salad.
AJ Chips with that, please.
Dan You don't want chips.
AJ I *do* want chips.
Dan What's the point training every night if you're just
going to fur up your arteries with that crap?
AJ They're my arteries.
Dan Yeah. Very grown up. Have a salad.
AJ (*to Dazza*) I swear to God that salad was here last
week.
Dazza What?
AJ I recognise the fly . . . there, see? Suffocated under the
cling-film.
Dazza Minging.

They take their food and move further down the lunch
queue.

Bex Alright, Dan?
Dan Bex.
AJ (*whispered*) Go on then . . . ask her.
Bex Ask me what?

Dan (*embarrassed*) I was just gonna say . . .

Bex What?

Dan You're really pretty.

Bex You think?

Dan Yeah. I mean . . . you know . . . you're no munter.

Dazza (*quietly to AJ*) He so wants to get his end away.

AJ You reckon?

Dazza (*quietly to Dan*) Look, bruv . . . I know you're desperate and everything. But *Bex*?

Dan Why? What's wrong with her?

Dazza She's a little bit klepto.

Dan You're joking?

Dazza Go on then . . . ask her why she's got a bag full of spoons.

> *Bex overhears and glares at Dazza, embarrassed.*
> *Whistle.*
> *Fit Kylie, Fat Kylie, and Nessa smoke outside.*

Fit Kylie What are we gonna do?

Fat Kylie Smoke some more?

Fit Kylie Revision?

> *They stare at her.*

Joke.

Nessa *Jeremy Kyle?*

Fit Kylie I'll be Jeremy.

Fat Kylie You were Jeremy last time.

Nessa (*enthusiastically*) I'll be the nutter from the trailer park.

Fit Kylie (*to Fat Kylie*) And you can be her fat mother with the steroid addiction and the transgender boyfriend.

Fat Kylie Piss off.

Fit Kylie (*as Jeremy Kyle*) So tell me what you told our researchers, Nessa.

Nessa I had sex with my brother.

Fit Kylie Is it because of the painful divorce of your mother and father, and your inability to accept that your fat addict mother is now having a relationship with a man who up until six months ago was still a woman?

Nessa No . . . it's cos I was off my tits on Ritalin.

Fit Kylie (*to camera*) Don't boo her, audience, she's only fifteen.

Nessa Laugh at me and I'll knife you, yeah?

Fit Kylie In a gang, are you?

Nessa Yeah.

Fit Kylie Think it's 'cool' to carry a knife?

Nessa Hell yeah.

Fit Kylie I'll get you help with Graham after the programme . . .

Nessa For what?

Fit Kylie For sex-addiction, incest and psychotic tendencies.

Nessa Cool.

Fat Kylie puts her arm around Nessa.

Fat Kylie The system failed her, Jeremy, not me. That's why she slept with her brother, Tyrone.

Nessa I shagged him cos he's dead fit.

Fat Kylie Sick.

Fit Kylie Coming up . . . the all-important DNA results. We find out if Tyrone is uncle *and* father to Nessa's eleven children.

Whistle.
 Dazza runs past.

Fat Kylie / Fit Kylie Hi, Dazza.

Dazza Hi, Kylies.

Dan (*to Tristan*) They used to call Dazza 'Jaffa', because of an accident in Year Eight . . .

*School gym, three years earlier. The cast perform
awkward forward-rolls, as Dazza attempts to do the
gate vault.*

Dazza's doing the gate vault . . . and he slips . . .

*Dazza falls onto the lower bar, crushing his testicles in
the process. He runs round in a circle, squealing in pain.*

Dan And Mr Whiting, he's like . . .
AJ Stop screaming, Dazza. Pain's for losers.
Dazza But I smacked me bollocks on the gate vault, sir.
Fit Kylie Shut up, yeah?
Dazza I'm not going to be able to have kids now, am I?
Fit Kylie Look in the mirror, it was never gonna happen.
Dan That's why they called him Jaffa.
Tristan Jaffa?
Dan You know . . . seedless.

Tristan smiles.
    Whistle.
    Oscar reads a book.

Lewis Did you watch *Big Brother* last night?
Oscar Mum says television was sent by the devil.
Lewis We got ours from Currys.
Saskia So what do you do instead?
Oscar Read, mostly.

Oscar flicks through the pages of his book.

Oscar It's all part of my plan . . . to win over Ellie
    Martin. *Hamilton of 4B.*
Lewis Who?
Oscar He has a mortal enemy called Ginger Carruthers,
    in the Fifth Form. So their sports master arranges for
    them to have a boxing match. And from that day on,
    they're inseparable chums. And everybody gives
    Hamilton of 4B the respect he so richly deserves.

When she witnesses my heroic pugilistic triumph, Ellie
will finally realise she's deeply in love with me.

Lewis What's a 'chum'?

Oscar It means . . . it means they're very special friends.

Lewis Gay?

Oscar No, not *gay*.

Headwound enters with Troy and Tyler.

Precisely on time . . . piece by piece my plan falls into
place.

Troy What?

Tyler What did you say?

Oscar Excuse me . . . Headwound?

Headwound turns.

Yes, sorry to bother you. I just wondered if it would be
possible to have some sort of . . . fight. If it's not
inconvenient?

Headwound You wanna do what?

Oscar I want to box you.

Tyler You want to hit him?

Troy You want to hit Headwound?

Oscar Yes.

Headwound What?

Oscar I mean . . . no. I mean, well, yes . . . but like a
sportsman.

He shakes Headwound by the hand.

Headwound What are you doing?

Oscar I'm shaking your hand.

Headwound I can see that. Why?

Oscar It's what they do.

Headwound What who does?

Oscar In the book.

Troy What book?

Oscar *Hamilton of 4B.*
Troy Gangsta.
Headwound I can handle myself, bruv.
Oscar Come on then, put them up.
Headwound Put what up?
Oscar Isn't that what they say?
Headwound Look, I don't want to fight you.
Tyler You've got to fight him.
Troy He called you a pussy.
Oscar I didn't.
Headwound Don't make me punch nobody.

Oscar jogs on the spot.

What's he doing now?
Tyler I think he's warming up, bruv.
Oscar Jab . . . hook . . . straight . . . uppercut.
Troy He knows his moves.
Oscar I've researched extensively.
Headwound Look, I don't wanna fight you.
Oscar Why not? Afraid I might beat you?
Headwound No, I'm afraid I might smash your face in and get done for GBH.

Ellie enters.

Oscar Ellie, look. I'm boxing . . . for you! I'm boxing Headwound!

He lunges at Headwound, who neatly sidesteps. Oscar overreaches and pulls a muscle. He cries out.

Troy Nice one, Headwound.
Tyler Cool.
Headwound What? I didn't do nothing.

Oscar slumps to the floor, writhing in agony.

Tyler Let that be a lesson to you.

Troy Right?

They exit.

Saskia What happened?
Oscar I appear to have pulled a groin muscle
Saskia Has to be a first time for everything.

She smiles.
Whistle.

Fit Kylie Got my period, Miss.
Fat Kylie On the blob.
Amy Period.
Megan Period.
Amber Period.
Callum Period.

The girls stare at him.
Whistle.
Track. Afternoon. Amber watches as AJ performs warm-ups. He walks backwards and forwards over the same stretch of the running track.

Amber What are you doing?
AJ Training. Why?
Amber Cos it's so *boring*.
AJ Go if you want.
Amber Trying to get rid of me?
AJ No.

He scratches the back of his hand.

Amber What's wrong with your hand?
AJ Nothing.

Amber takes his hand.

Amber They're well red . . . What've you done to them? Eczema or summin'?

AJ No.

Amber So what then? There's gotta be something wrong with them.

AJ It's just . . . you know, yeah?

Amber No. That's why I'm asking.

AJ When I get stressed and stuff . . . if I've got a race or . . . I just wash them . . .

Amber You just *wash* them?

AJ Over and over . . .

Amber What? Like you're a mentalist?

AJ No.

Pause.

Mum was gonna phone Denise . . .

Amber Who's Denise?

AJ On *This Morning.* See if I needed counselling and . . . you know.

Amber So it's not like a . . . disease?

AJ No.

Amber (*disappointed*) Right.

AJ That's a bad thing?

Amber You gotta disease, you get benefits and shit.

AJ What?

Amber I mean . . . if you're sick in the head, that's still *like* a disease. You could be psychotic or summin'.

AJ Just cos I scrub my hands?

Amber You *scrub* them?

AJ It's only –

Amber You're really screwed up. You should see a doctor, or Jeremy Kyle, or summin'.

AJ You think there's something wrong with me?

Amber Don't you?

AJ I'm asking what you think.

Amber I don't like thinking much.

AJ Don't like *thinking* . . .?

Amber Dad says it messes your head up.

AJ He'd know.

Amber You saying my dad's a twat?

AJ Yeah.

Amber He lets me smoke in the house.

AJ (*ironically*) Sorry, yeah . . . he's a great dad.

Amber I just mean . . . if there was something wrong with your brain . . . a little bit psycho –

AJ I told you, I'm not –

Amber I'm just saying . . . if you were . . . you could be on Disability Benefit and everything.

AJ Like that's a good thing?

Amber It is a good thing. You can stay at home and look after the kids.

AJ Whose kids?

Amber Duh . . . our kids.

AJ You're not –?

Amber No . . . I'm thinking, you know, the future?

AJ Right.

Amber Next year . . . year after . . .

AJ What?

Amber Mum says I'm not getting any younger.

AJ You don't think everybody's got the perfect person for them . . . you know, *somewhere*?

Amber I think you've been watching too much shit TV.

AJ You read all those crappy magazines . . . 'Find the Perfect Guy', yeah?

Amber There's no such thing as a perfect guy.

AJ Yeah, cheers.

Amber Get over yourself.

AJ What, so you put up with what you got?

Amber Yeah, and as long as he's not a complete skank you just get on with it.

AJ Get on with what?

Amber Duh. Have babies.

AJ So if I'm at home on Disability, who's gonna pay for the kids? Disability Benefit won't cover it.

Amber I'll get a good job –

AJ How? You're gonna get shit GCSEs.

Amber It's not just about exam grades.

AJ No?

Amber It's about flashing my tits round so the boss gives me a job anyway . . . they'll be bigger then, my tits.

AJ How?

Amber Mum's friend . . . pervy Steve . . . he's getting them for me . . . eighteenth birthday present, yeah?

AJ So you got the job, yeah . . . what happens when they work out you're shit at it?

Amber I might be good at it.

AJ What sort of job is it?

Amber Secretarial . . . or something with animals.

AJ Vet?

Amber Butcher or something. Mum's friend, the lesbian one with the body-piercing, she works in an abattoir, got enough money to buy a Harley and marry her girlfriend from the Ukraine. That'd be cool . . .

AJ What, a Ukrainian girlfriend?

Amber Twat. A Harley. Then I'll have a really dramatic accident at work and sue – 'no win, no fee'. I'll be like that fat bloke on telly, who slips in oil at work, breaks his wrist and gets five grand . . .

AJ Who?

Amber The ugly one in the advert. Ask me, I don't think he fell . . . reckon he did it over-wanking.

AJ laughs.

I can see us ten years from now, yeah? When we're like old and nearly thirty, yeah?

AJ God.

Amber No, listen . . .

AJ I am listening.

Amber We'll have a girl and a boy . . . Britney and Justin.
Like thingy Timberlake, you know?

AJ Justin?

Amber Yeah. And we'll sit at home watching *Jeremy
Kyle* and *This Morning* . . . only we'll switch over
when Dr Chris is on cos he's always on about fingering
yourself to check your prostate and dodgy plastic
surgery where your nipples drop off . . . Then we'll do
Loose Women, and I'll put on fish fingers or Pot
Noodle for lunch . . . then we'll have a cuddle in the
afternoon with the lights off so you can't see my
stretch marks –

AJ Stretch marks?

Amber From the babies, duh . . . and the KFC meal-deals.

AJ I like Pizza Hut.

Amber Yeah . . . we'll do KFC one night, Pizza Hut the
next.

AJ Yeah?

Amber Yeah. KFC, Pizza Hut, KFC, Pizza Hut, KFC –

AJ I get it.

Amber I'll be a right fat cow, but you'll still love me and
you won't knock me round, even if I'm leathered on
Bacardi Breezers and WKD . . .

AJ You've thought it all out?

Amber Oh yeah, we'll be together for ever.

AJ (*uncertainly*) Cool.

Amber Could say it like you meant it.

AJ God . . .

Amber What?

AJ You do my head in sometimes.

Amber You what?

AJ Ever think . . . you've learnt everything about the
world all slightly wrong?

She looks at him blankly.

No . . . I forgot. You don't like thinking.

Beat.

I'll see you around, yeah?
Amber You're dumping me?

Beat.

AJ Yeah. I'm sorry.
Amber Let's talk about it.
AJ Do what?

Amber takes out her mobile.

Amber I've got *Jeremy Kyle* on speed-dial.

Whistle.
  Bus stop.

Fit Kylie (*as Jeremy Kyle*) We need to hear more . . .
Amber And he dumped me, yeah?
Fit Kylie The DNA results show that AJ . . . is a complete tosser.
Amber It was like . . . meant to be and everything.

A bus roars past.

Fit Kylie Well stop, yeah . . .

She gives the bus driver the finger.

That's the second bus that didn't stop.

She loosens her shirt.

Fat Kylie What are you doing?
Fit Kylie Gonna flash my tits, yeah?
Fat Kylie (*ironically*) We want him to stop.
Fit Kylie You saying my tits aren't worth stopping for?
Fat Kylie Only if he's got a magnifying glass.

Whistle.
  Track. Night. AJ sprints on stage, Dan times him with a stopwatch.

Dan It's a new PB.

AJ The crowd go wild.

Dan What's wrong?

AJ Nothing's wrong.

Dan Doesn't look like there's nothing wrong.

AJ I split up with Amber.

Dan Good.

AJ Good?

Dan You've got to be single-minded. Got to keep your eyes on the prize.

AJ That's what Dad used to say.

Dan flicks through his athletics magazine.

Dan You're second in the county rankings . . . just behind Tristan Summers from St Oggs.

AJ Yeah, I know . . . again, the crowd go wild.

Dan You could take it seriously.

AJ I am. Look . . . serious face.

Dan If you're just gonna piss around –

AJ Okay. Alright.

We see Tristan run a lap of the stage. Dan watches.

Dan Tristan's great. His technique . . . when the starting pistol goes and he's straight off the starting block . . .

AJ But he's at St Oggs, they've got all the facilities . . .

Dan (*watching Tristan*) His focus . . . his determination. His *legs* . . .

AJ stares at him.

I just mean . . . the power, you know.

AJ starts to warm up, performing a series of leg stretches. He jogs off, passing Ellie who laughs nervously.

Ellie Whenever he comes past I always make a complete tit of myself.

Oscar watches, irritated.

Oscar You know, I'm as capable of having a fulfilling sexual relationship as the next man.

Ellie What?

Oscar I was talking to Mother the other day. 'Oscar,' she said, 'I think it's high time we sat down to discuss the birds and the bees.' I said, 'Mother, I'm fully cognisant when it comes to the hows and whys of *fucking*.'

Ellie You said the f-word to your mum?

Oscar I said I'm not being rude, I'm being *historical*. It's all about etymology. She said, 'You mean the study of insects?' I said, 'No, Mother, that's *entomology*. Even someone with an IQ of 130 or less knows *that*.'

He snorts.

'Fucking' is a word of pure Anglo-Saxon origin.

Ellie Anyone ever told you you're a bit creepy?

Oscar What?

Ellie You know . . .

She demonstrates with a shiver.

Oscar Poor Mother, she has such a naive understanding of the natural world, I'm not entirely sure she doesn't believe that the birds and bees are indeed responsible for populating the planet. It seems a miracle I was born at all. I can only assume that Father's penis fell into her while she wasn't looking.

Ellie So you know all about sex?

Oscar Yes, I do have internet access. But then I began hypothesising. What if it *were* possible to interbreed the birds and the bees? I could create a super race of bird-bees.

Ellie A what?

Oscar As large as conventional birds, but with stingers and poison sacks. They'd have little electronic collars, so I can program their destinations before they fly off on their diabolical missions. Or parrots . . . then they can *tell* people why they've arrived to kill them.

Ellie What?

Oscar Imagine? Our very own army of bird-bees. Together we'll be invincible.

Oscar throws himself at Ellie.

Ellie What are you . . . doing?

Oscar This was meant to be.

Ellie What was?

Oscar Kiss me.

He kisses Ellie.

We were destined to be together for ever.

Oscar makes a pass at her; they join at the braces, locked together in an embrace.

Ellie Ah! My braces!

AJ enters. He stands patiently. Ellie turns, trying to pull away from Oscar and spots AJ.

AJ!

Pause.

AJ You can stop snogging him, you know.

Ellie No.

AJ No?

Ellie No, I can't.

AJ What are you doing?

She tries to pull away, but their braces remain linked.

Ellie It's not what you think.

Oscar Yes it is.

Ellie Shut up.

Oscar It's exactly what you think!
Ellie Oscar . . .
Oscar We're in love!

Ellie kicks Oscar in the shin, he bends down to rub his leg, dragging Ellie with him.

Ellie Ow . . .
AJ It's okay. It'll wait. See you later, yeah?

AJ runs off.

Ellie AJ . . . come back!
Tristan So what happened?
Dan We had to get someone from Design Tech to separate them.

Whistle.

Amy Period.
Megan Period.
Callum I haven't got a period.

Beat.

Because I'm a boy.
Amber Period.
Fat Kylie I've not got a period, if you know what I mean, Miss, yeah?
Fit Kylie You *what?*

Whistle.
  Corridor. Fit Kylie turns on Dazza.

Fit Kylie You cheated on me?
Dazza Well . . . you know . . .
Fit Kylie How many times?
Dazza Twenty –
Fit Kylie *What?*
Dazza Twenty-six?

Fit Kylie You *counted*?
Dazza Only the good ones.

Fit Kylie smacks Dazza on the arm.

Dan Turns out they spent the night in a sleeping bag
together, off their heads on a bottle of Lambrini Fat
Kylie stole from the offie. Course, then Headwound
finds out that Dazza's been having it away with Fat
Kylie.

Whistle.
School corridor.
Dazza enters, anxiously. Troy and Tyler run on.

Troy Where you been, bruv?
Dazza (*anxiously*) What's Headwound say?
Tyler There's good news and bad news, man.
Troy He's going to beat the crap out of you, bruv.
Dazza And there's good news?
Tyler Least you're a good runner.
Troy Innit.

They run off, laughing.

Dazza I'm a dead man.

He runs off in the opposite direction.
Whistle.
Fit Kylie vents her anger, talking so fast it's almost impossible to hear her.

Fit Kylie And I nearly slapped her, yeah, innit?

Nessa goes to speak but is interrupted.

I gave her the dirty stare, yeah?

She demonstrates.

And I was like, 'Do I fucking know you? You know what?
Fuck off, get out of my shadow, bitch.'

Beat. Nessa stares blankly.

You know what I'm saying?

Nessa No. Can you say it again?

Whistle.
    Boys' changing rooms. The cast converge, forming a chanting mob. Dazza backs away as Headwound advances on him.

Headwound You impregnated Fit Kylie?

Dazza It was an accident, man.

Mob Fight, fight, fight . . .

Headwound No, it's not a *fight*. I love you man.

Dazza You what?

He hugs Dazza. Beat. The mob is momentarily thrown.

Mob Gay, gay, gay . . .

Whistle.
    Nessa, Amber and the two Kylies stand outside Burger King.

Fit Kylie I'm going to paint my bedroom pink and get a cot. I even nicked some stuff from Mothercare. You got to plan ahead.

Fat Kylie I'll get a council flat or something, yeah? They always give you a place if you've got a kid.

Nessa What about your mum?

Fat Kylie What about her? She's loving it. 'Always knew you'd get banged up young.' So I'm like, 'It's fucking genetics then, innit?' Can't fight genetics. Mum got a flat, I'll get a flat . . . it's like *tradition*.

Amber They'll never let you keep it.

Fat Kylie Who?

Fit Kylie They'll take the baby away.

Fat Kylie I'll look after it. Feed it and stuff.

Nessa Feed it what?

Fat Kylie I won't feed him breast milk.

Fit Kylie It's a 'him' now, is it?

Fat Kylie I won't do breast – not natural, is it?

Nessa What?

Fat Kylie Not having him grow up with some tit fetish . . . I'll give him yogurt.

Nessa For God's sake . . . Listen to yourself.

Fat Kylie Then when he's on solids . . . I don't know . . . potatoes are vegetables, aren't they? Three packs of crisps and two packets of Skittles and that's his five-a-day.

Nessa Crisps?

Fat Kylie Yeah, it's potato, isn't it? It *is* a vegetable.

Fit Kylie Duh.

Nessa How can you be doing Food Technology and know so little about food?

Fat Kylie looks off-colour.

Fit Kylie You okay?

Fat Kylie Feeling a bit funny.

Whistle.
Sports track. AJ performs leg stretches, Dazza smokes a cigarette.

AJ So he was okay?

Dazza He didn't pound my head in, did he?

AJ But why?

Dazza He says he's not ready to be a dad . . . and he's saving up for a Nintendo Wii.

The Kylies enter.

Fit Kylie / Fat Kylie Alright, Dazza?

Dazza Yeah?

Fit Kylie It's well good news.

Dazza That Headwound didn't put me on a life-support
machine?

Fit Kylie No, not that.

Fat Kylie It's twins.

Dazza What is? Who's having twins?

Fit Kylie We both are.

Dazza Man, my sperm's really jumping!

Dan Turns out, falling on the gate vault . . . it hadn't
affected Dazza's ability to procreate. He got both
Kylies pregnant, Fat and Fit Kylie. And with four kids
on the way, his mind wasn't really on running.

The Kylies exit as AJ enters.

AJ So you're giving up athletics?

Dazza Yeah, bruv. Till I get my first wage cheque I'm
potless.

AJ What are your mum and dad gonna say?

Dazza Dad said if I ever brought a gay guy home with
me, or I was going out with someone, you know . . .
black or Asian, he said he'd kill me. Fucking Nazi.

He smiles.

Don't know what he's gonna be like when he finds out
I've got two girls pregnant at the same time. Who
would've thought my sperm would be so . . .

AJ So what?

Dazza Dunno . . . can't think of the word.

AJ Virile?

Dazza Yeah.

Pause.

There's some kind of fish, or something . . . in Australia.
When they're mating, they say the sperm and egg
trail's so long you can see it from outer space.

AJ Sick.

Dazza The Kylies . . . they're in their second trimester.
AJ Their what?
Dazza You wanna see the scan pictures?
AJ Not really.

Dazza fishes the pictures out of his pocket.

Dazza Here.
AJ Yeah, she looks pretty nice – big nose.
Dazza That's the placenta or something.

Dan enters. AJ carries on warming up.

Dazza Alright, bruv?
Dan Why aren't you warming up?
Dazza I can't stay.
Dan Why not?
Dazza It's the Kylies. I'm gonna be a good dad . . . and that means giving up everything I enjoy doing.
Dan Like athletics?
Dazza Yeah. I've got a good job . . . you know, Shoe City. Good prospects for promotion and twenty per cent discount on formal brogues.
AJ On what?
Dazza It's a kind of shoe.
Dan Right.
Dazza You know . . . I'm gonna have four kids to support.
Dan Sure.
AJ Here they come.
Dan What?
AJ The Kylies.

The Kylies enter and adopt pregnant poses.

Fat Kylie / Fit Kylie Alright, Dazza?
Dazza Bollocks. Gotta go. Yoga.

He runs off.

See ya.

AJ and Dan are left alone.

AJ Just me then.

Whistle.

Tristan So what? You were jealous of AJ and Ellie getting together.
Dan It just got in the way of training. That's all.
Tristan That's all?
Dan What are you? Sigmund fucking Freud?

Whistle.
  Ellie and AJ awkwardly confront each other.

Ellie So what do we do now?
AJ You could give me a love-bite –
Ellie Okay.

Pause.

AJ I mean, you know . . . if you want, yeah?
Ellie What do I – ?
AJ Oh, right . . .
Ellie Cos I haven't –
AJ That's okay –
Ellie You know, ever –
AJ No worries . . .
Ellie There's a diagram on the wall in the Girls' toilets.
AJ Cool.
Ellie So I suppose . . . mouth on neck?
AJ That sort of thing . . .
Ellie Right.
AJ I suppose.
Ellie Okay . . . so do I suck or blow?

She moves her mouth towards his neck. AJ pulls away.

AJ That diagram in the toilets . . . you sure it's for a love-bite?

Ellie What . . . ?

The penny drops.

Oh.
AJ I think you just bite.
Ellie I can do that.
AJ Cool.
Ellie Like this?

She bites him on the neck.

AJ Not so . . .

AJ cries out in pain.

Ellie What?
AJ Ah!
Ellie Sorry . . . sorry . . .
AJ No . . . it's okay.
Ellie Oh God . . .
AJ What is it? What's wrong?
Ellie Your neck . . .

AJ holds out his hand – it's covered in blood.

AJ It's blood . . . I'm bleeding.

He slumps into Ellie's arms.

Ellie Oh God . . . no . . . no . . .

Awkwardly, Ellie lowers AJ onto the ground.

Headwound (*entering*) What's wrong with him?

He bends down.

Is he dead?
Ellie Course he's not dead. He just . . . cut his neck, that's all.
Headwound Did what?

He sees the blood.

Oh God . . .
Ellie What?
Headwound Blood.

He passes out, lying on the ground next to AJ.

Ellie Oh, great.

Frustrated, she shouts out.

Anyone else?

She kneels on the ground and rolls AJ into the recovery position, as Dan enters. He watches Ellie silently.

Please don't die . . .
Dan What've you done to him?
Ellie (*startled*) Dan . . .
Dan What are you doing?
Ellie I tried to kiss him and . . . Look, it doesn't matter.

Beat.

I'm putting him in the recovery position. You know, so he
   doesn't choke on his tongue.
Dan It's not him swallowing his *own* tongue that I'm
   worried about.

AJ comes round.

AJ What . . .
Ellie Don't get up too quickly . . .
AJ What happened?
Ellie (*quietly*) I kissed you and you passed out.
AJ What?
Dan She kissed you and you passed out.
AJ Must've been a good snog.
Ellie I'm still picking bits of skin from my braces.
AJ What?

Ellie It was a joke.

She turns her head and pulls something from her braces.

Dan Are you okay?

AJ sits up.

Ellie Not too quickly.

AJ notices Headwound lying on the ground.

AJ What's up with him?

Dan helps AJ to his feet.

Dan It's like it's contagious.
Ellie Ha.
Dan You need some fresh air.

*They help AJ off. Oscar enters and discovers
Headwound lying prone on the ground.*

Oscar (*hushed*) Griff.
Griff (*entering*) What?
Oscar Look.

He motions to the horizontal figure of Headwound.

Griff What's happened to him?
Oscar Who cares? At last my foe is vanquished.

*He stands triumphantly, with one foot on
Headwound's stomach.*

Griff You think you should be doing that?
Oscar Photograph me.
Griff What?
Oscar Photograph me.

Griff takes out his mobile phone.

Griff Smile.

Headwound slowly comes round.

Oscar Just get on with it.

He smiles for the camera. Griff takes a picture and Oscar swiftly removes his foot.

Headwound What happened?
Oscar You . . . passed out.
Headwound What are you doing with your phone?
Oscar Nothing.

*Awkwardly, Griff hides the phone behind his back.
    Whistle.
    Oscar and Griff run off, pursued by Headwound.
Afternoon football match.*

Lewis Mark your man!

AJ dribbles the ball past the defence and kicks towards the goal.

AJ He shoots . . .

Beat.

He doesn't score.
Lewis Ref!
Griff Foul!
Troy Are you *blind*?
AJ The reverse pass, the Cruyff turn . . .

AJ lines up a shot and scores.

Get in!

*He turns his shirt inside out and runs round the pitch.
Dan watches in silence.
    Whistle.
    Cheers from AJ's team. They run up and hug him.*

Troy Good game, guys.

The football players disperse. AJ spots Dan.

Dan I was waiting.
AJ Yeah, okay . . .
Dan Four o'clock, you said.
AJ Sorry.
Dan Sorry?

Dan takes a letter out of his pocket.

The letter came.
AJ Great.
Dan You could sound more enthusiastic.
AJ Great!

Dan hands the letter to AJ. He holds the letter, then stuffs it into his pocket.

Dan You're not going to read it?
AJ Yeah . . . Later, okay?
Dan You don't want to know what it says?

AJ shrugs.

Dan You've been selected for English Schools.

AJ turns as the whistle blows.
    He runs a lap of the stage and sits on the floor.
    He lies back, very still. Ellie enters. She leans over AJ, checking to make sure he's still breathing. AJ suddenly sits up, gasping for air.

AJ What are you doing?
Ellie I thought you were dead.
AJ Well, I'm not.

He breathes.

See?

He smiles.

Ellie Sorry.

AJ So what would you have done if I was dead? Kiss of life?

Ellie Not if you were dead. I would have called an undertaker.

AJ Yeah. Cool. Thanks.

He lies back.

If I just lie here on the ground . . . for long enough . . . something'll happen, right?

Ellie I suppose.

AJ It might be cool, or it might be shit . . . but something'll happen.

Ellie Yeah.

AJ What?

Ellie I don't know. Something.

AJ holds out his arm, Ellie takes his hand.

AJ No . . . my pulse . . .

Ellie What?

AJ Take my pulse . . .

Ellie does so.

Fast, is it?

Ellie Normal.

AJ How d'you know?

Ellie Here, take mine . . .

She holds out her arm. AJ takes her pulse.

See?

AJ What?

Ellie It's the same.

AJ Maybe we're both dying.

Ellie stares at him.

Well, we might be.

Ellie Mum says we're dying from the day we're born . . . cell by cell . . .
AJ Can't wait to meet your mum.
Ellie What?
AJ Sounds like a right laugh.

Ellie hits AJ.

Ow. That hurt.
Ellie It was supposed to.

Pause.

AJ I never thought I'd live past sixteen.

Ellie laughs.

What? I'm serious.
Ellie Seriously?
AJ Seriously serious.

He smiles. A cheer goes up. AJ and Ellie follow the distant track event.

I always wanted to be a runner. Even tried to get that careers computer program to tell me I should be an athlete. I said I wanted to spend time outside and have exercise and shit.
Ellie What did it say?
AJ It said I should be a gravedigger.
Ellie Seriously?
AJ Seriously.

Ellie takes out a tube of Bonjela.

AJ What's that? Lip balm?
Ellie Bonjela . . . for my ulcers.
AJ Nice.

Self-consciously, Ellie rubs the Bonjela on her gums as AJ lies on his back staring up at the sky.

Ever thought what death'll be like?

Ellie Whose death?

AJ Your death . . . my death . . . everybody's?

Ellie Not really.

AJ I do.

Ellie Great.

AJ You'll be lying there . . . you know . . . all the machines and shit, beeping away . . .

Ellie You're looking forward to it?

AJ Not looking forward . . . just reckon you get that moment, yeah . . . that sort of heartbreak beautiful moment.

Ellie That what?

AJ You know . . . where everything makes sense. Everything you've done in your life . . . it all kind of flashes up in front of you. And it's . . . it's kind of cool.

Ellie Cool?

AJ Cos you only see the good bits . . . all the shit bits, you just don't see them. But the good things – they're all squished into one . . . *ball*, I suppose. And it's beautiful. As you die . . . all you can see in your head . . . it's the stuff that *matters*. And it kind of blows your mind.

Ellie Is this because of your dad?

AJ What?

Ellie Look, nothing. Sorry.

AJ No. It's okay.

Pause.

He was cool, Dad.

Ellie I wish I'd met him.

AJ flashes up film on his mobile.

AJ That's him.

Ellie He's . . . lying very still.

AJ Yeah. He's dead.
Ellie He's what?
AJ Not really.

Ellie laughs, relieved. AJ flashes up another film.

That's him dead.
Ellie (*shocked*) Eww!

She stops herself.

Sorry.
AJ Alright. Not everyone wants to see someone's dead dad.
Ellie I do. I mean, you know . . . if you want to show me, I want to see it.
AJ Cool.

He lies on his back again, looking up at the sky. A low hum as a plane passes high overhead.

Where do you think they're going?
Ellie Who?
AJ In that plane. America?
Ellie Wrong direction.
AJ What would I look like if I was on that plane and fell out?
Ellie The doors are pressurised. You can't fall out.
AJ But if I did?
Ellie You can't.
AJ If I did though? If there was a bomb . . . and I got blown through the door and fell right here?

Smiling, he sits up and takes a sachet of tomato ketchup out of his pocket.

Ellie What's that?
AJ Ketchup.

He rips open the sachet and smears the ketchup round his mouth.

240

Ellie What are you doing?
AJ Photograph me?
Ellie What?
AJ Like I was dead . . .

He stands up and throws his mobile to Ellie.

Like I fell out the plane and just landed here.

He drops to the ground and strikes a 'dead' pose.

Ellie You're sick.
AJ Or like this . . .

He gets into a different, even more ridiculous pose.

Come on.
Ellie I'm not photographing you.
AJ Or like this . . .

*He lies still and contorted on the ground as Dan
enters.*

Dan Kissed him again?
Ellie Ha.

AJ sits up.

Wanting to be different just makes you like everybody else.

Whistle.
AJ sits up and holds his hand to his chest.

Dan That's when AJ started getting chest pains.
Tristan And you still made him train? Why didn't you
get him to see a doctor?
Dan I didn't know he was getting chest pains, did I?
Tristan He didn't tell you?
Dan No. He didn't fucking tell me.

Whistle.

*Sports track. Training night. Ellie bends over,
performing a warm-up exercise.*

Ellie Who's that?
AJ Where?
Ellie In the tree?
AJ Phil the Perve.
Ellie He's got a camera.
AJ Yeah.

He calls out.

Alright, Phil?
Ellie You talk to every perve sitting up a tree with a
camera?
AJ Show him your bum, it'll make his day.
Ellie What?
AJ Smile for the camera.

He smiles and poses.

Now piss off, or I'll call ChildLine.

Pause.

So?
Ellie So what?
AJ You gonna kiss me or not?
Ellie Kiss you?
AJ Unless you find me physically repulsive or –
Ellie Alright.

They kiss.

So . . . was that okay, or . . . ?

AJ smiles.

What? Did I do it wrong . . . cos if I did it wrong, tell me
and –
AJ No.

Ellie What?

AJ It's just . . .

Ellie Oh God.

AJ You taste . . .

Ellie I've haven't eaten all day . . . unless you count Wrigley's Extra as food . . . I've been building up to this . . .

AJ It's not that, it's – you taste . . . Bonjela-ey.

Ellie In a good way or a bad way?

AJ kisses her again.

Good way?

Whistle.

AJ We're staying in a Travelodge . . . for English Schools. You can come if you like?

Whistle.

Dan So Mr Walker hires a coach to take us to the English Schools athletics meet . . . and Amber's there. And she's still pissed off with AJ for dumping her, so she's all over me, trying to make him jealous . . .

Amber Come on, Dan, we can sit at the back of the coach and do French kissing and shit . . .

Dan Maybe I just don't fancy you.

Amber Yeah, right. Like *that's* possible.

Dan I'm serious.

Amber What?

Dan I'm just saying –

Amber Saying what? Saying I'm a minger?

Dan No.

Amber Cos that's what it *sounds* like you're saying.

Dan I'm not.

Amber What . . . are you gay or something?

Dan does not respond quickly enough and Amber picks up on this.

It all makes sense. You watch what you eat. You're always down the gym. You're either very sporty or very, very gay. Which is it?

Whistle.
Outside Little Chef. Ellie enters.

Ellie They're not doing pancakes.
AJ No?
Ellie They said the microwave's packed up.
AJ Right.
Ellie They do a Yorkshire pudding with a curried beef filling?
AJ Don't fancy it.
Ellie No.
AJ What do you think of your room?
Ellie It's nice.
AJ Phoned your mum?
Ellie She said if we're going to 'do it' we have to use condoms.
AJ Filthy cow, your mum.
Ellie She's just learnt from previous mistakes . . . i.e. me.

Whistle.
AJ holds his chest.

Are you okay?

Dan enters. He glares at Ellie.

Dan You're here.
Ellie Apparently.
AJ She's got a name.
Dan Remember, no sex. It saps your energy.
Ellie He's worse than Mum.
AJ (*irritated*) We're not *having* sex.

244

Ellie We're not having pancakes either . . . the microwave's packed up.

Dan What?

Ellie It doesn't matter.

Dan I want some high knees and heels kicks – then two laps of the track, right? Just to get used to it.

AJ You coming, Ellie?

Ellie Yeah. In a minute.

Irritated, AJ runs off. Ellie stares at Dan.

Dan What?

Ellie You think he should be doing that?

Dan Doing what?

Ellie So much training.

Dan (*sarcastically*) Well, yeah . . . because he's got a race tomorrow. I mean, I thought that was why you were here?

Ellie You know he's been getting chest pains?

Dan Look, you don't understand the mind of an athlete.

Ellie Right, so you're a psychologist now?

Whistle.

Dan The whole school was there . . . to watch AJ compete. Not that they were all into sport . . . just meant dossing around for a day.

A half-hearted Mexican wave from the crowd at the athletics stadium.

Amber She's such a minger . . . Ellie Martin. What does AJ even see in her?

Nessa It's not just about looks.

Amber Yeah, but on the inside . . . she's a minger on the inside. And that's worse. Much worse. I'm not going to say what I think of her.

Nessa No.

Amber I'm not going to stoop to that level.
Nessa Fine.

Ellie enters.

Amber You're a bitch, Ellie Martin.
Ellie What?
Amber You heard.

Whistle.

Tristan So why d'you do it?
Dan Do what?
Tristan Coaching.

Dan takes the trophy from the cabinet.

What do you think about? When you watch him compete?
Dan I think . . . what would it be like without AJ? What if it was me out there, winning the trophy?

The crowd lift Dan up onto their shoulders, and he holds the trophy aloft.

And the crowd . . . they'd all be cheering.

The crowd cheer.

Tristan Then what?

Dan is dropped to the ground. The runners take their positions on the track.

Griff On your marks. Set.
All Bang!

AJ clutches his chest.

Ellie AJ . . . AJ!

The crowd surges forward, and AJ and Ellie disappear from view. Voices are heard, lost in the surging crowd.

Callum Give him some air.
Troy Why'd you say that?
Callum They always say that, don't they?

The crowd subsides.

They've took him in to hospickal.
Oscar The word is 'hospital'.
Troy Putting the dick in dickslexic.
Oscar The word is actually 'dyslexic'. Which
unfortunately makes a complete nonsense of your
attempt at witty riposte.
Tristan What did he say?
Troy Don't know. If I did I'd probably have to beat the
shit out of him.
Oscar (*quietly*) Yes, Oscar. That's right. Confound them
with your superior knowledge of the English language.
Amber 'Oscar'?

Oscar is momentarily thrown.

Oscar Yes?
Amber Oscar what?
Oscar Shelburne.
Amber Oscar *Shelburne*?

She laughs.

You even sound like a geek.

Oscar takes out a pen.

Oscar What's your address?
Amber Why?
Oscar I'll need an address so I can pre-program the killer
bird-bees.

Amber suddenly leans over and kisses Oscar.

Why did you do that?

Amber Just wanted to see what it would be like with a geek.

Oscar (*ironically*) And? I'm waiting with bated breath.

Amber Where'd you learn to snog like that? Read that in a book, did you?

Oscar Yes.

Beat.

I think it's important that you know something.

Amber What?

Oscar The stories about my being rather under-endowed in the genitalia department –

Amber That you're hung like a crane fly?

Oscar Yes, that.

Amber Well?

Oscar They're all absolutely true.

Amber It's what you do with it, though, isn't it?

Oscar Precisely. I have an IQ of one hundred and fifty. So . . . it might not be big, but it *is* clever.

They kiss.
  Whistle.
  Outside the hospital.

Dan You still here?

Ellie I wanted to see how he was.

Dan They're still doing tests.

Ellie What's wrong with him?

Dan If they knew that they wouldn't be doing tests, would they?

AJ enters.

AJ I've got to have an ECG.

Dan A what?

AJ You know . . . they stick things to your chest to read your heartbeat.

Ellie Right.

Beat.

So you're not going to die then?
AJ One day.

Beat.

Not yet.

Ellie smiles.

Dan You think it's my fault?
AJ Don't you?
Dan I know I've been pushing you a bit.
AJ A *bit*?
Dan But you've got this . . . talent.
AJ What if I haven't, though?
Dan But you can *prove* it.
AJ What if I don't want to?
Dan What?
AJ What if I don't want to know?
Dan You have to.
AJ For fuck's sake.

Pause.

You never get to that point where, you know . . . when
you start thinking . . . life's a competition and the
prizes are shit?

*The crowd parts revealing the now empty trophy
cabinet.*

They reckon it's a torn muscle. They just want to make
sure.

He stares at the empty cabinet.

Dan Look . . . I'm sorry.

Pause.

Forgiven?
AJ You're a bit of a wanker sometimes.
Dan In a good way?
AJ Can you be a wanker in a good way?

He smiles.

Dan Twat.

He punches AJ on the arm.

Dead arm.
AJ Fucking hell.

Whistle.
Fit Kylie, Fat Kylie and Dazza at yoga class.

Fit Kylie Mum would freak out if she knew I was here.
She thinks yoga's a mortal sin.
Dazza It is the way you do it.
Fit Kylie Would you stop perving down my top?
Fat Kylie So what did you say to your mum? Tell her
who the daddy is?
Fit Kylie She thinks the baby was sent by God.
Dazza The love god.
Fit Kylie / Fat Kylie Get over yourself.
Dazza Okay, okay.
Fit Kylie / Fat Kylie And stretch . . .

They stretch.

Shit.
Dazza What's up?
Fit Kylie / Fat Kylie I think my waters have broken.
Dazza Triffic.

Whistle.

Dan So that was it. The Kylies had their babies . . . I got stuff sorted out with AJ. You know, like . . . happy ever after, yeah?

Tristan approaches Dan.

Tristan You talk a lot, don't you?
Dan Yes.
Tristan Shut up.

He kisses Dan. Dan smiles. Megan blows the whistle and the cast disperse.

The End.

Production Notes

Why did you write the play?

CHRISTOPHER WILLIAM HILL The play really centres on my relationship with my brother. He is nineteen and a county athlete and I am, well . . . not! Our mother died early last year and that has altered the balance of our relationship.

In many ways the play is about Dan and AJ finding different ways of coping with the huge emotional rift that has taken place in their lives, in this case the death of their father. When someone dies there is a massive gap and there has to be a realignment of roles in order to make up for that loss. For AJ training gives him structure, order and discipline. And similarly for Dan, training his brother (although he is not an athlete himself) gives him a sense of purpose and is a way of honouring their father's memory. Sport gives sense to the non-sense of death.

THE DAN AND TRISTAN NARRATIVE

The play could be a memory play – Dan telling the story of AJ to Tristan . . .

JEREMY SAMS Dan wants to tell the story, but on the other hand he doesn't. The story comes out in fits and starts. There are moments when Dan becomes just as out-of-control as every other character in the play. Look, for example, at how Dan speaks when he is with Tristan in comparison to how he talks to Amy. This suggests that there are times when someone else is in control of the narrative.

Something you could investigate is who is in control of the narrative and what changes about the play and the staging when different people take charge.

How would you show who is in charge of the story?

JEREMY The act of telling this story is hugely courageous for Dan. There's a sense of catharsis and Tristan rewards this intimacy with a kiss at the end. And of course it's a love story. It's full of all different sorts of love. Was that in your mind?

CHRISTOPHER Of course. There have been a few queries about the kiss at the end – to be honest I had almost forgotten it was there. I never meant it to be a particularly big deal. It is a play with a couple of gay characters in it, not a 'gay play', and the kiss at the end could be a peck on the cheek or a kiss on the lips, but most importantly it's a thing of love. The Dan and Tristan relationship certainly didn't come from a political perspective. I could have done a more traditional 'boy falls in love with girl' story, but somehow that seemed a bit too neat.

JEREMY That was a delightful surprise for me, that they were in love.

CHRISTOPHER It's good to show that gay men are capable of it too! And part of my intention with that relationship is that it should be somehow commonplace. It is a mark of how far we have come. When I speak to young people now they are much more open about who is gay and who is straight – it has become much more part of the fabric of everyday life than it was when I was at school. Which can only be a good thing.

JEREMY There is of course an issue of how you might rehearse the kiss if for any reason the actors are not comfortable with it. I always try and engineer a situation where as few other people as possible are in the room. Ideally just the director and the people involved – this goes for rehearsing any scene with intimate content.

Questions to ask: Dan and Tristan

- What is the relationship between Tristan and Dan?
- How long have they been together?
- Have they slept together?
- What is the purpose of Dan's story? What is his objective?
- Why does Dan decide to reveal these events to Tristan at this moment? If there was a scene before the play started what would happen in it? Perhaps you could improvise this scene.

Is Dan the narrator throughout? Or does the play gather its own momentum?

JEREMY In some ways the answer to this is up for grabs but the one thing I would say is that there is an intimacy in this revelation. That's very important.

SCHOOL TRIBES

But the play isn't just about Dan and AJ. It has a real sense of community and life to it.

JEREMY It features a whole crowd of people who are trying to have relationships guided by rules they have learnt off the telly. There is a horrendous absurdity to that trend of behaviour. They are trying to make sense of the world with information that is often flawed. AJ has the wonderful line: 'Ever think . . . you've learnt everything about the world all slightly wrong?' That was very striking to me. And also creates much of the comedy of the evening. 'I've got *Jeremy Kyle* on speed-dial . . .' and 'Mum was going to phone Denise . . . on *This Morning*' are other good examples.

CHRISTOPHER Yes, it certainly is a comedy, I intend it to be lots and lots of fun!

Which schools do the characters attend?

I have left who goes to which school pretty fluid. It is perhaps something you can work on with your actors. But some are decided for you – it is made clear in the opening scene that Tristan and Dan go to different schools. But I would urge you to make decisions that make the most sense for your production.

Is there a class divide?

I didn't really have class in mind when I wrote the play. I guess Oscar is the most traditionally middle class; he is certainly bookish and well-spoken. What I was more concerned with was the tribal nature of schools – that was more in my thinking than the idea of class.

There are specific groups in the text, the geeks (of which Oscar is one), the jocks (AJ and Dazza) and the 'it' girls (both Kylies, Nessa, Amber). There seems to be pressure on this generation to define who they are at an early age – to sum themselves up in a soundbite.

CREATING THE GROUPS

Play around with the idea of the different groups that occupy the text.

- Does the group have a leader?
- What is the status within that group?
- What are the 'rules' of the group?

Is there scope for changing the sex of the characters?

CHRISTOPHER Generally yes . . . It's not something that worries me particularly. As long as it makes sense within the confines of your production. And of course there are opportunities for doubling which could enhance the sense of it being an ensemble piece – a story told by a collective – if that's the way you want to go.

I am keen not to give the 'answers', but rather to allow people to interpret the text with their own companies and spaces in mind.

SPORT

CHRISTOPHER I wanted to write a play that put sport onstage. I thought it would be a really interesting thing to see – certainly one that I haven't seen very often. And I find the links between theatre and sport fascinating.

JEREMY I watch a lot of football and I am always struck by the echoes between that and theatre. Both are essentially dramatic performances and both have those surges of energy: moments of calm followed by a sequence of highly dramatic activity.

CHRISTOPHER I certainly wanted the text to have a similar kind of bounce to that of say basketball. It should have a kind of sporty echo. But also I suppose sport was something I witnessed from afar and almost envied. As a non-sporty gay guy growing up in Cornwall you always thought, 'If only I was that little bit fitter, stronger, faster, wouldn't it all be easier?'

People who play competitive sports have a rule book. They know exactly what they are doing – or seem to. They put on their PE kit, run out onto the pitch, know the rules of the game and, perhaps more importantly, they know who they are. And I guess for me that was something I was quite jealous of. I always had this sort of constant fear of people walking up to me and asking, 'How's it hanging, Chris?' and I'd always think to myself, 'Gosh, yes . . . how is it hanging?' I didn't quite know.

On the rugby pitch I was always as far away from the ball as possible – stuck right out on the furthest wing, with that constant terror of the ball heading towards me. It was like the ball was approaching in slow motion. It must have been a hilarious scene. That's where the scene with Lewis on the mobile phone and Griff getting hit by the rugby ball comes from.

When rehearsing the sports that are played onstage it is a good idea to get your cast to play the sport for real.

- Play a game of football.
- Get the actors to get the feel of that sport into their bodies.
- Then take the ball away. Get them to keep the game going.
- Take the game inside.

JEREMY It is amazing how the ball becomes the least interesting thing in the little stadium you have created.

THE PRODUCTION AESTHETIC

JEREMY Chris notes in the opening stage directions that the sports equipment should be mimed and that the cast should be onstage at all times. What was your thinking behind that?

CHRISTOPHER Sports have a natural and essential energy and fluidity to them and I wanted to emulate that onstage.

If you are worrying about getting off to do a costume change, or if you drop a ball and it rolls off into the audience, then that natural rhythm is interrupted. I thought having everyone onstage and having mimed props would give the production an elegant simplicity and enable snappy dialogue and smooth scene transitions.

JEREMY I spend a lot of time in rehearsal making scene changes as elegant and integral as possible. It should never feel like the narrative has stopped to allow the scene change to happen. Think about how scenes might dovetail. Set up the incoming scene before the established scene has finished. Getting people on and beginning scenes is never the problem – it's getting them off cleanly that is the challenge.

When you are directing at the Olivier, it is such a large space that people have to enter running – it's not a bad note for this play. And because it has sport as one of its central ideas it's perfectly legitimate.

THE STYLE OF PLAYING

What is the metaphor? Christopher suggests that all the actors are in PE kit, in which case the metaphor is a school gym where scenes appear and disappear. This will affect the costume. It is probably not the kind of play that can sustain elaborate costume changes, so whatever costume you decide on must make sense in each scene.

Who creates the scene and with what? There is a version where the acting company create everything, including the sound.

Who is telling the story? Dan or the collective of actors? How will this alter the production aesthetic?

Is it a memory play? This will affect how people get on

and offstage. Does Dan literally create the picture, bringing people on and offstage? Think how this will impact on the play's fluidity.

JEREMY I always try to decide the simplest way I can make a moment onstage happen and work on from there.

Christopher punctuates the play with blasts on the whistle. It is a brilliant device to indicate the change of scene, location or character. It acts like a screen wipe, immediately altering the atmosphere of the scene and signalling change.

Look at the rhythm of where the scenes are broken up by the whistle.

- What effect does it have?
- Who blows the whistle?
- Megan blows the whistle at the end of the play. What does this indicate?
- What happens if Dan has the whistle?

This is something that you could play around with. The whistle could be like the conch – the person that blows it therefore being in control of the incoming scene.

JEREMY It is interesting that there are no teachers or parents – in fact no adults in the play at all. Even the dinner lady and the PE teacher are invisible. Was that deliberate?

CHRISTOPHER Yes, it's very much from the teenagers' perspective. The whole play is seen from their point of view, as it were, although the style of their speech does alter – when they are in the formal context of the PE lesson, for example.

JEREMY That's true, and it gives the language an authenticity and a veracity which is hugely refreshing. But at the same time it is clear that the play is not naturalistic. We are never in danger of playing soap opera. Although the speech is colloquial in some respects, the text as a whole has a theatricality to it. The language has a heightened musicality and a bounce which lifts it out of kitchen-sink naturalism into something more playful and inventive.

Where is the play set?

CHRISTOPHER There is inevitably quite a lot of Cornwall in it, simply because that was where I grew up. But I think people should feel free to allow whatever their natural accent is to impact on the script. There is an interesting thing about language and dialect and how homogenous it is becoming; there is a kind of morphing of accents that has come about which is generational rather than regional.

THE PLAY AS A MUSICAL SCORE

When reading the play aloud it is evident that it has a distinctive pattern. There are moments of high-octane, high-energy performance where the dialogue should bounce and fizz along, and then there are two or three big scenes where the play should really 'sit down' and we should be concerned with the emotional weight of the exchange. What is striking about the text is that there are moments when the characters try to work out the world with the information they have been given. They share their thoughts and feelings in a very complete way, and it is imperative that the production honours these scenes and these emotions.

AJ and Amber. It would be easy to trivialise this scene (pages 216–20) or to play it as pure, fast-paced comedy.

You could play AJ as not interested and Amber as not very bright. But what happens if you embrace the legitimacy of their positions? AJ is interested in Amber – after all, they are having a relationship which doesn't finish until the end of this exchange.

- Try the scene as if AJ's objective is to get Amber's help or support. What effect does this have?

The scene should have great heart to it, whereas if AJ is always trying to get rid of Amber the danger is that the scene becomes trivial.

- See what happens if Amber finds AJ's symptoms fascinating.
- Try and find a positive reading. See what happens if everything Amber says is good news.

Amber's vision of the future shouldn't necessarily be a negative one; she is canny, and although her ambitions don't perhaps match our own or indeed AJ's, we should go easy in our judgement of the character.

It is also significant that both AJ and Amber are expecting a different scene – the scene that we do see is coloured by what they wanted to say.

Analyse the scene:

- What does AJ expect to happen?
- What does Amber expect to happen?

You could improvise a scene where they both hear exactly what they wanted to. Explore what each character's perfect outcome to the scene would be.

- Who is pushing and who is pulling?
- Who is attacking and who is defending?
- Who is in control? And at what points?

Spot the moments where the mood changes – these are sometimes called the 'events' of the scene.

- What are the moments of unity between the two characters? The things that both find funny, or agree on.

It is important that we invest in the reality of these emotions which are as real to teenagers as they are to adults.

AVOIDING CARICATURE

There is a danger of caricature with the play. The characters exist on the very edges of reality, but if you play these scenes with absolute reality then you avoid this trap.

JEREMY look after 'Chekhov' moments and the 'Catherine Tate' moments will look after themselves!

There are sections of the play that are quite clearly non-naturalistic, physical, choric events:

- The trophy moment.
- The scrum.
- The montage of sports.
- The *High School Musical* moment.

JEREMY The moment when 'high-school-musical style dancers cross the stage' should not be the first time this type of action occurs within the play. Part of the challenge of the piece is establishing a metaphor which supports this kind of happening.

It is important to choose a mode of storytelling and stick to it. If you decide that the ensemble creates everything then use that language throughout the play. You have to hold your nerve as a director!

REHEARSING THE SPORTS MONTAGE

What are the possibilities? The stage directions indicate 'We see a montage of sports' . . .

- Who takes part?
- Does everyone take part in each sport? Or do you divide the group, two or three people representing each sport?
- Are the images we see frozen tableaux?
- Do they move into a frozen image?
- What is AJ's role within the montage? Does he participate?
- What is the objective of the montage?

JEREMY Look at the rhythm of the text that Christopher has written.

'Athletics . . . football . . . rugby . . . basketball . . . hockey . . . everything. Even rock-climbing.'

Establish the music of the text and then dance to the music. It would be wrong for the montage to get in the way of the pace of the text thus far.

CHRISTOPHER it is one of the things that sets up the pace for the later dialogue.

JEREMY There is no definitive directorial concept and that's not what I'm trying to give you. What I would say is that we view this sequence through Dan's eyes – he is our lens, so it is important that AJ is the star. There needs to be a sense of his triumph.

Keeping the pace of these sections earns us time elsewhere to really investigate some of the characters and engage with them as they try to decipher the world.

JEREMY One of the most integral parts of this script is its musicality. My advice to directors is to try and get a bird's-eye view of the play – make some early decisions on the essence of your show, what it is and what it isn't. Identify which bits need to go fast, where it is busy and where it can decelerate a bit. Write it down and put it somewhere safe. Once you are in rehearsals you get so involved in the minutiae of the production it is difficult to look at the whole. When you feel that you might have lost perspective, have a look at what you've written. It's amazing how revealing those initial thoughts can be.

From a workshop led by Jeremy Sams,
with notes by Naomi Jones

THE HEIGHTS

Lisa McGee

Originally from Derry, Northern Ireland, Lisa read Drama at Queen's University Belfast. She was writer on attachment at the National Theatre, London, in 2006. Her plays include *Girls and Dolls* (Stewart Parker Award Winner, Susan Smith Blackburn runner up, Irish Theatre Award nominee), *Jump!* (Exchange Theatre, New York), *Seven Years and Seven Hours* (Rough Magic Theatre Company commission) and *The Young Man with the Cream Tarts* (Sneaky Productions, Belfast). Television includes *The Things I Haven't Told You* (Tiger Aspect/BBC), *Totally Frank* (Endemol/Channel 4). Lisa is creator and lead writer of the IFTA award-winning television series *Raw* (Ecosse/RTE). She is currently working on a film adaptation of her stage play *Jump!* (NI Screen/Hotshot films) and a new season of *Raw*.

Characters

Jacob
narrator, male, seventeen

Lillie Lee
female, seventeen

Dara
female, sixteen

Boyle
male, fifteen

Webb
male, sixteen

Jimmy
Dara's brother, male, seventeen

Bizzy
female, sixteen

The Nice Woman
female, forties

The Glass Girl
female, baby

Pat
or 'Fat Pat', male, forties

Matt
or 'Fat Matt', Pat's twin, male, forties

Mother
of Pat and Matt, female, sixties

Sampson the Shopkeeper
male, seventies

Television Presenter

In memory of my friend Christopher Webb

ONE

Darkness. A shadow appears.

Lillie I make up stories. That's what I do. Sometimes they're funny. Sometimes they're sad. Sometimes they're wonderful. Sometimes they're terrible. But they're always just stories.

TWO

Night. Lillie's bedroom.
Lillie lies in bed. Dara stands at the foot of the bed aiming a gun at her. Jacob appears. He looks at the bedroom before continuing downstage. He speaks directly to the audience.

Jacob Most people, if they woke up in the middle of the night to find a stranger standing at the foot their bed, aiming a gun between their eyes . . . well, most people would do one of three things, I think. They would either scream, faint or try to escape somehow. Not Lillie . . . Lillie sat bolt upright, smiled at her intruder and simply said.

Lillie Hello. Can I help you?

Jacob Lillie wasn't like most people. Lillie lived here. Here on The Heights estate.

Lights come up revealing a street and a large run-down tower block.

There's never anything to do up here. There's nothing to do and nowhere to go. We all just sit around waiting for something, for anything to happen. It never does. Nothing ever happens on The Heights.

THREE

The street.
Dara and a group of boys race onto the street. Dara is holding an old gun.

Boyle Give it back, Dara!
Dara In a minute, I said. Fucking relax.
Webb Where'd you find it?
Boyle Moses gave me it.
Dara Where'd he get it?
Boyle I dunno. He found it, I think. Give us it, Dara.
Webb Moses just gave it to you?
Boyle I bought it off him.
Dara You paid money for this piece of shit, Boyle?
Boyle It's not a piece of shit.
Dara The thing must be a hundred years old.
Webb How much did you pay for it?
Boyle Twenty.
Dara Pence I hope.
Boyle Piss off. Quid.
Dara He robbed you, Boyle.
Boyle You know fuck all about guns.
Dara I know enough about Moses.
Webb What do you need a gun for, Boyle?
Boyle I just liked the look of it.
Dara You liked the look of this rusty piece of shit?
Boyle Give me it back now, Dara, I'm serious.
Dara Oh, he's serious now!
Boyle I'm not gonna ask again.
Dara What are you gonna do then?
Boyle I swear to God, Dara, if you were a fella . . .

Dara You'd fuck me, I know.

Boyle lunges at her. Webb steps in between them.
Dara backs away, laughing.

Boyle Tell her to give it to me.
Dara I'm not gonna break it.

Jimmy enters.

Dara Jim Bob!
Jimmy (*to Dara*) Ma's looking for you.
Dara Let her look.
Jimmy What's going on?
Webb Boyle bought a gun.
Jimmy Fuck me – I'm impressed.
Boyle I'm glad someone is.
Jimmy I told Moses he would never get rid of that thing –
    bastard proved me wrong.
Boyle Piss off.
Jimmy Give us a look at it then.
Webb Dara! Throw!
Boyle Dara, do not throw.

She throws the gun to Jimmy. He catches it.

Jimmy Jesus . . . it's not light, is it? That's a beauty, Boyle –
    they don't make them like they used to, do they?
Boyle Ha ha!

Jimmy throws it to Webb. Webb catches it.

Stop it.
Webb Though, Jimmy, I'd say this thing could still do a
    lot of damage.

Webb throws it to Dara. She catches it.

Dara Yeah, if you threw it at someone . . .

271

Jimmy Or force-fed it to some poor bastard.

Dara throws it to Jimmy.

Boyle Dickheads.

Jimmy throws it to Webb again.

Jimmy We're dickheads, are we?

Webb pulls Boyle towards him. He gets him into a headlock and points the gun at his head.

Webb Say that again, fuckwit. Let me hear you say it again.

Dara laughs.

Jimmy Come on, Webb.

Boyle pushes Webb off.

Boyle Hilarious. As much as I'm enjoying the gun-related humour – it's mine, and I want it back now, please.
Webb Yeah, you're right. Sorry.

Webb approaches Boyle to give him the gun. At the last moment he snatches it away and throws it to Dara.

Dara Sucked in!
Boyle Wankers. You're all wankers. A collection of wankers, that's what I'm looking at. That's what I have before me. You are the elite of the wanker world.

Bizzy walks onto the street reading a book. Dara doesn't see her and walks backwards with the gun.

Dara Aw, you want it back? You want it back, Boyle? Here.

Dara throws the gun to Jimmy. As she does so she walks backwards into Bizzy causing her to drop her book.

Dara Fuck, sorry.

Bizzy You're alright.

Dara picks up her book and hands it back to her. The boys continue to argue amongst themselves.

Dara Reading again, Biz?
Bizzy There's no law against it.
Dara It's dangerous, though. I mean, look what just happened – lucky one of us wasn't injured.
Webb Dara!

Webb hurls the gun at Dara. She catches it.

Bizzy Reading's dangerous but playing catch with a loaded weapon, that's perfectly safe, is it?
Dara This? This isn't a weapon – this is a historical artefact. It doesn't even work –

Dara raises the gun in the air.

Boyle Don't, Dara . . .
Dara And it's not loaded.

She fires the gun. A loud bang. She laughs.

Shit!
Boyle What did I say?

Boyle runs towards her and takes the gun from her hands.

What did I tell you?
Jimmy Relax, Boyle – nobody died.
Dara Holy shit. (*To Bizzy.*) You alright?
Bizzy Yeah. Fine. I'm fine.

Jimmy hits Boyle across the head.

Jimmy What are you doing, walking about with a loaded gun? Prick.

Bizzy looks to a flat in the tower block behind them.

Bizzy Look. The Countess is at her window; you got her attention anyway, Dara.
Dara What?

Jimmy realises what Bizzy is referring to. They all look up at one of the windows in the tower block behind them.

Jimmy So she is.
Webb She creeps the fuck outta me.

Jimmy gives the flat the finger. Boyle points his gun towards it.

Boyle You're next, Snow White!

The boys and Dara all run off, laughing. Bizzy sits down on the pavement and continues to read her book.

Jacob Lillie lived on the sixth floor. She never left that flat. Never really left her room. She was so sick, you see. Allergic to the sun, at least that's what everyone said. Apparently if her skin saw daylight she would swell until she was three times her original size – then she would just drop dead. So Lillie never came outside. She just sat at her window all wrapped up looking down on the street. Occasionally people down here would shout things up at her. They'd shout 'Dracula' or make the sign of the cross with their fingers – original stuff, groundbreaking material. Most of the time, though, she just got ignored . . . But that all changed because, well . . . Dara had an idea.

Dara and the boys are gathered on the street again. Boyle is playing with his gun, the others are messing around with a ball. Bizzy sits with her book as before.

Jimmy It's a stupid idea.
Dara Says who?

Jimmy Me. Just then. Did you not hear me?

Webb She'd fucking freak out, though, Jim.

Jimmy Nah, you're better keeping away.

Boyle It would be funny, Jimmy.

Dara (*to Jimmy*) They think I should.

Jimmy Oh well, if the intellectual heavyweights think
you should, go ahead . . . don't listen to your brother.

Boyle (*re gun*) I want this back, though, Dara.

Jimmy She won't need it. She's not doing it . . .

Dara Don't tell me what I can and can't fucking do, Jimmy.

Bizzy (*quietly*) I think you should listen to him.

Dara What? Who asked you?

Bizzy I don't think you should do it, that's all.

Webb (*to Bizzy*) Just you read another chapter, limpet.
(*Beat.*) It'll be a laugh, Dara.

Bizzy It won't, though – not for her. It'll be frightening.

Webb That's the point, fuck-features.

Dara It's just a joke, Bizzy.

Jimmy (*to Webb*) If you're so keen, why don't you get up
there and do it yourself, big man?

Dara Aren't you listening to me, Jimmy? I said I'm doing it.

Boyle You tell him.

Webb Good woman, Dara!

Dara I just need to wait until it gets dark first.

FOUR

Lillie's bedroom.
    *Lillie lies in bed. Dara stands at the foot of the bed
staring at her. She has the gun in her hand. She points it at
her. Lilly stirs in her bed. She opens her eyes. She sits up.*
    She stares at Dara. Silence.

Lillie Hello. Can I help you?

Dara doesn't respond. She simply stares back at her.

Can I help you?

Dara I don't know.

Lillie Are you planning to kill me?

Dara No. No, of course not.

Lillie I only make the assumption because . . . well, you're pointing a gun at my head.

Dara looks at the gun. She lowers it.

Dara I'm sorry.

Lillie It's okay.

Dara I'm so sorry.

Lillie The thing is . . . if you were – planning to kill me I mean – well, I wouldn't mind. Honestly I wouldn't.

Dara Are you mental?

Lillie You broke into my room in the middle of the night and pointed a firearm at me while I slept. Yeah, I'm the mental one.

Dara It was . . . it was supposed to be a joke.

Lillie I don't get it.

Dara Yeah, neither do I, not really. Not any more.

Lillie It wasn't a joke, Dara.

Dara How do you know my name?

Lillie shrugs.

We wanted to scare you. It was a joke.

Lillie I don't think it was. I think it was an excuse. You didn't want to scare me: all you really wanted was to see me, to look at me – to observe the freak in her natural environment. That's the truth of the matter, isn't it?

Dara No.

Lillie You don't need to lie. It's fine.

Dara If I had wanted to scare you I wouldn't have managed it.

Lillie I don't scare easily.

Dara You knew I was coming.

Lillie How could I possibly have known that?

Dara You knew. You knew I would come sooner or later. I see you. Every day I see you sitting in here staring out at me.

Lillie And every day I see you. I see you standing *out* there staring *in* at me.

Dara This was stupid. I'm sorry. I really am.

Lillie Don't be.

Dara What's your name?

Lillie You don't know my name?

Dara I've never heard anyone use it. Out there . . . well, they call you the Countess, you know, like . . .

Lillie Dracula, yeah, I get it. (*Beat.*) My name's Lillie. Lillie Lee.

Dara Well, I think I should go now. (*Beat.*) It was nice to meet you, Lillie Lee.

Dara walks towards the window.

Lillie Don't go, Dara. Stay.

Dara Why?

Lillie Stay and talk to me. Stay and tell me everything . . . tell me anything.

Dara I can't. Nothing ever happens. Not really. There's nothing out there. I don't have anything to tell you, Lillie.

Lillie That's okay. Just make it up.

Dara sits on the end of Lillie's bed.

FIVE

The street.

Jacob I knew Lillie. Not many people can say that. Before Dara there was me. Though it was all over before it even really started. (*Beat.*) One day last summer I was just hanging around the street as usual, hoping for something to break the boredom, hoping for a miracle, and I got one. It was just a little thing, but it was miraculous all the same. A piece of pink notepaper floated past my shoulder and landed on the pavement. I picked it up and read what it said.

Lillie Once there was a nice woman.

Jacob Once there was a nice woman.

Lillie The nice woman had lots of nice things, but she wasn't happy.

Jacob It was the first line of a story.

Lillie Because it didn't matter how many nice things she had. She was still all alone.

Jacob So I went back there every day.

Lillie What she really wanted was a baby.

Jacob I went back to that exact same spot every day and every day the next line of the story would float down from her window.

Lillie So the nice woman hoped and wished and prayed.

The Nice Woman appears.

Nice Woman Please God. Please give me a baby. I'll love it, I'll look after it. I promise. Please God, please.

Lillie One day there was a knock at her door. She opened it and screamed with delight – a cradle sat on her step. She looked inside and there she was – her very own beautiful baby girl.

The Glass Girl appears and goes to the Nice Woman.

However, she wasn't like other babies; this little girl was
different, she was special. This little girl was made
entirely from glass. She had little glass hands and little
glass fingers, little glass feet and little glass toes, a little
glass mouth and two little glass eyes . . . even the hair
on her head was glass. The nice woman didn't mind at
all. She looked at her and said . . .

Nice Woman You're the most beautiful thing I've ever
seen. You're perfect.

Lillie But she knew she had to be careful. She was so
frightened her little glass girl might break that she
made her lie still in a room full of feathers –

Nice Woman It's safe in here. Nothing can hurt you in
here.

Lillie The nice woman sat beside her and read her
stories, but she never touched her.

Nice Woman I might damage you, without meaning to.
I never want to damage you.

Lillie One night the little glass girl had a terrible dream –

The Glass Girl screams in horror.

It was a strange dream, too, for although she'd never seen
the ocean, she dreamt she was drowning in it. She
screamed and cried – she was so scared that the nice
woman put her arms around her without thinking –

Nice Woman There, there, shhh now, shhh.

Lillie She comforted her until the little glass girl wasn't
frightened any more. They lay back together on the
fluffy white feathers. A while later, sunlight poured
into the room. The nice woman opens her eyes. She
must have fallen asleep. She's warm and wet. She looks
down at her body – and for a moment she's confused.
The fluffy white feathers have all turned red. They
stick to her skin. Horrified, she realises they're soaked
in blood – her own blood. Her arms and legs are
decorated with hundreds of tiny cuts, her body is

covered in the smallest shreds of glass. The little glass
girl is gone. The nice woman starts to cry . . .

Nice Woman All I did was fall asleep.

Lillie She whispers: 'Poor poor nice woman – she held
her little glass girl too tightly –'

Nice Woman Now I'm all alone again.

Jacob When I'd collected all the lines – when I'd pieced
the entire story together, she invited me to visit. So I did.

SIX

Lillie's bedroom.
*Lillie and Jacob sit at the window, staring down onto
the street.*

Lillie Everybody wonders what I do up here all day.
How I keep myself occupied. How I stop myself from
going mad. The truth is I make up stories. That's what
I do. Sometimes they're funny. Sometimes they're sad.
Sometimes they're wonderful. Sometimes they're
terrible, but they're always just stories.

Jacob You're good at it – you're really good.

Lillie You've only read one.

Jacob I liked it though.

Lillie I have hundreds, thousands, hundreds of thousands.

Jacob Hundreds of thousands?

Lillie You don't believe me?

Jacob No, I believe you. It's just . . . well, that's a lot of
stories.

Lillie I have a lot of time on my hands.

Jacob I suppose.

Lillie It's like a prison . . . this room.

Jacob It's not much better out there, you know, Lillie.
I mean, there's a pub that we're too young for, a club

that we're too old for – sitting on the street drinking
cider is as exciting as it gets.

Lillie At least there's people out there.

Jacob They're not very interesting, Lillie.

Lillie At least you have people you can talk to, Jacob.

Jacob Doesn't your ma talk to you?

Lillie Yeah, of course. There's never anything new,
though. I think we might have used up all our
conversation – now we're just repeating ourselves.
(*Beat.*) She'd go mad if she knew I had you up here.

Jacob Why doesn't she let you have friends, Lillie? Why
doesn't she let people visit?

Lillie She's afraid I'll catch something.

Jacob laughs.

Jacob I should be offended, but I've a feeling she's right.
(*Points down at the street below.*) You could probably
catch something from Boyle just by looking at him.

Lillie No, she's okay . . . She means well – she thinks
she's looking after me. I mean, she is looking after me.
I just wish . . .

Jacob What?

Lillie Nothing.

A silence.

Jacob So how do you get your ideas, then . . . for the
stories?

Lillie From this window. I sit at this window and I look
out at people – I imagine things about them – about
their lives . . .

Jacob Like what?

Lillie Like secrets they might be hiding, that type of thing.

Jacob I see. So which of them have you written a story
about?

Lillie A few of them. But mainly that one.

She points down to the street.

Mainly that girl who's always with the boys.

Jacob Dara.

Lillie Dara? Is that her name?

Jacob Yeah. Dara lives two doors down from me – I know her brother Jimmy. He's in my class. He's in my class when he bothers to turn up. He's okay, but Dara . . . I don't know, I never really –

Lillie covers his mouth with her hand.

Lillie Don't. Don't tell me anything. I don't want to know.

Jacob removes her hand and holds it for a second. She pulls it away and goes back to looking out of the window.

Jacob Have you ever written about me?

Lillie Not yet. I probably will . . . Although . . .

Jacob Although what?

Lillie I think you'd make a better narrator, Jacob.

Jacob How do you mean?

Lillie doesn't answer. She returns to her window.

Lillie Do you notice how Dara's always running about? She's always moving. Always needs to be doing something, to be going somewhere, and she's always talking. I think she's afraid to be still. Because stillness means silence. People like Dara hate silence – they always want to fill it. Silence scares them.

Lillie turns to Jacob. He stares out of the window. He hasn't really been listening to what she's said. A long silence follows.

Lillie You're not afraid of it though, are you, Jacob?

Jacob Sorry?

Lillie Silence. (*Beat.*) What's wrong?

Jacob What? (*Beat.*) Sorry, I was just thinking . . .

Lillie Right.

Jacob Don't you want to know what I'm thinking about?

Lillie I already do.

Jacob Really?

Lillie You're thinking, this is boring now. For a while it was fine but the novelty has worn off. You're thinking you'd rather be out there with the others.

Jacob No!

Lillie It's okay.

Jacob I love coming here, Lillie.

Lillie You don't have to.

Jacob I want to.

Lillie Promise?

Jacob I promise. (*Beat.*) I love coming here . . . being with you.

Jacob looks at Lillie. Lillie smiles at him, then quickly decides to change the subject.

Lillie If you could have a superpower, what would it be?

Jacob What?

Lillie Any superpower.

Jacob I . . . don't . . . I'm not sure.

Lillie Just pick one.

Jacob What's the point?

Lillie It's a game.

Jacob I don't want to play.

Lillie Pick one, Jacob!

Jacob Flying.

Lillie Flying?

Jacob The ability to fly – that would be my superpower.

Lillie That's a terrible choice – the ability to fly. Why would you choose that?

Jacob I . . . I don't know. I . . .

Lillie That's an awful choice, Jacob. (*Beat.*) Do you know what mine would be?

Jacob No.

Lillie Time control. The ability to rewind, fast forward or freeze time. That's a good one, isn't it? That's better than flying. Admit it, Jacob.

Jacob I suppose.

Lillie I mean, you could travel to the past, visit the future and pause the present. Imagine all the things you could see . . .

Jacob Lillie . . .

Lillie Just imagine . . .

Jacob Lillie, I don't want to imagine any more.

Lillie What?

Jacob I don't want to imagine, I don't want to pretend, I don't want to play games.

Lillie What do you want?

Jacob I want you to tell me something real.

Lillie stares at him for a moment.

Something true – a memory – something that actually happened to you. Something real.

Lillie I . . . can't think of anything.

Jacob Try.

Lillie I don't want to.

Jacob Please, Lillie . . .

Lillie Why?

Jacob I need you to.

Lillie Why do you need me to?

Jacob You talk all the time without really saying anything. Every night I leave this room feeling I know less than I did the night before . . . and I hate that.

He cups Lillie's face with his hand.

Lillie Jacob . . .

Jacob Tell me something real.

Lillie I can't.

Jacob kisses Lillie. She kisses him back for a moment, then pushes him away.

Jacob What's wrong?

Lillie You shouldn't have done that. (*Beat.*) I think you should leave now.

Jacob And I did. I left. I hoped that she would ask me to come back. She never did. Anyway, soon her new playmate would arrive.

SEVEN

Lillie's bedroom.
  Lillie in her bed, Dara looking out of the window.

Lillie What else?

Dara Nothing else.

Lillie That couldn't be it.

Dara I'm telling you it is.

Lillie If I came over there I bet I'd find something else.

Dara Webb and Boyle are playing football. Jimmy is hitting Dave the debt . . .

Lillie You said he was shouting at him . . .

Dara He was the first time you asked, now he's hitting him.

Lillie What else?

Dara Mags is drying out mats on her balcony.

Lillie Still? She was doing that yesterday.

Dara These are different ones . . .

Lillie How many mats does she have?

Dara Fucking shitloads by the looks of it.

Lillie Where does she put them all?

Dara Oh . . .

Lillie What? (*Beat.*) What is it, Dara?

Dara One of the Fat Twins has just got up.

Lillie Which one?

Dara Pat.

Lillie Is he the one with the glasses or without the glasses?

Dara With.

Lillie Lazy bastard.

Dara Lazy fat fucker.

Lillie Lazy fat dirty brute. (*Beat.*) What's he doing?

Dara Pulling his curtains – Jesus . . .

Lillie What?

Dara (*disgusted*) He's standing at his window with no fucking shirt on.

Lillie He's disgusting.

Dara Yeah . . .

Lillie He makes me sick.

Dara I can't see the other one. I can't see Matt.

Lillie Oh, he'll be there somewhere – he'll make an appearance. You don't see one without the other – they might as well be Siamese. You'd think they'd get sick of each other . . .

Dara No . . . not Fat Matt and Fat Pat.

Lillie They both turn my stomach.

Dara I don't know them. Bizzy does . . . she says they're alright.

Lillie Bizzy?

Dara She's my friend.

Lillie The one that's always reading.

Dara Yeah, that's her. Yeah, Bizzy says they're okay – that they're harmless.

Lillie I don't care what Bizzy says.

Dara I'm sorry. I thought . . . I just thought you might be interested.

Lillie I'm not.

Dara Okay.

An awkward silence for a moment. Lillie goes and joins Dara at the window.

Lillie You know, Dara . . . sometimes I think that I'm the only real person. Sometimes I think that I've made everyone else up – all those people down there – I imagine that they're only in my head – that when I stop thinking about them they stop existing. (*Beat.*) Do you think I'm mad?

Dara No . . . of course not. (*Beat.*) Do you ever think that about me? Do you ever think I'm not real?

Lillie I have done. There are times when I know what you're gonna say before you even say it. It's like I know what you're thinking – it's like I see it coming.

Dara places her hands gently around Lillie's throat and then suddenly begins to choke her.

Dara Did you see that coming, Lillie?

Lillie struggles, and falls to her knees. Dara continues to choke her.

Did you fucking see that coming, Lillie?

Dara releases her grip, laughing. Lillie catches her breath.

Lillie Bitch. (*Beat.*) Fucking bitch.

She starts to laugh. She turns her neck towards Dara.

Did you mark me?
Dara No. Did you want me to?

Lillie nods her head.

We're not like the rest of them, are we, Lillie?
Lillie No. It would probably be easier if we were.

EIGHT

The street.
Bizzy sits on a wall, reading. Jimmy, Boyle, Jacob and
Webb sit on the pavement having a drink and playing a
game of cards. Dara walks past them.

Dara Alright.
Jimmy Ma's looking for you.
Dara Let her look.
Jimmy She's going mental. I can't listen to her. You get
yourself home – you hear me?
Dara I will . . . not just now though, okay?

Jimmy shakes his head. Dara starts to walk on.

Boyle Why don't you have a game, Dara?
Dara Na, I'm alright.
Webb Come on, Dara. We haven't seen you in ages. You
hiding on us?
Dara No. Course not. I've stuff to do, that's all . . .
Boyle It can wait, can't it?
Webb Sit down. Have a drink.
Dara Later, maybe.

Dara starts to walk on again. Webb smirks.

Webb Later, maybe . . . She can't tear herself away.
Jimmy Fuck up.
Dara What did you say, Webb?
Webb I just . . .
Jimmy Go on, say it. Go on, say it and it'll be the last
thing you fucking say.
Webb Nothing.
Dara What's going on, Jimmy?

Jimmy stands up and walks towards her.

Jimmy We know where you've been going, Dara, who you've been with. Everybody knows.

Dara And what of it?

Silence.

And what of it?

Webb You're spending a lot of time up in that thing's bedroom . . . that's all I saying.

Dara When really I should be down here drinking Laser and playing switch . . .

Boyle Poker.

Dara Shut up, Boyle.

Jimmy Shut the fuck up, Boyle.

Jimmy looks at Dara.

Jimmy I want you to stop going up there.

Dara You're serious?

Jimmy I'm serious.

Dara Why?

Jimmy People are talking about you. People are saying shit about you and about her . . . about you both.

Dara laughs.

Dara Jesus . . . Well, at least we've given them something to talk about. There's not exactly a lot else going on, is there?

Jimmy It's not funny, Dara.

Dara It is. It's a bit funny. (*Beat.*) What's the big deal? I go up there and I talk to her.

Jimmy That's not what people are saying.

Dara I don't care.

Jimmy Well, I do. It's embarrassing. You're shaming me. Is that want you want?

Dara Of course not.

Jimmy Promise me you won't go up there again.

Dara I can't.

Jimmy turns away from her. He addresses the boys.

Jimmy Come on. We're going.

Jimmy starts to walk away. The boys begin to gather their things and follow him.

Boyle Why?
Jimmy Because I said so, prick. Come on!

Boyle starts to gather up the cards.

Leave them . . .

Jimmy kicks the cards. They scatter over the pavement.

Leave them and come on.

Jimmy walks off. The boys follow. Dara watches. When they've gone she sees Bizzy sitting on the wall, reading.

Dara How's it going, Bizzy?
Bizzy Oh, you do remember my name, do you? I was starting to think you'd forgotten all about me.
Dara Not you too.
Bizzy Not me what?
Dara Everybody's talking about me, apparently.
Bizzy I've got more interesting things to talk about than you, Dara.

Dara smiles.

Dara I'm glad to hear it. (*Beat.*) New book?

Bizzy nods.

Any good?
Bizzy Haven't made up my mind yet.

Dara snaps the book out of Bizzy's hand.

Hey!

Dara Maybe I'll read it.
Bizzy I don't think you'd like it.
Dara You don't think I'd understand it, you mean.

Dara looks at the book.

Bizzy Dara . . .
Dara Hmm?
Bizzy What's she like? The Countess?
Dara Her name's Lillie.
Bizzy What's she like?
Dara She's nice.
Bizzy Really?
Dara She's, you know, funny . . . She's different, but contrary to popular belief she doesn't have two fucking heads and a tail.
Bizzy Take me to see her.
Dara No.
Bizzy Please. Take me. Take me to see her.
Dara She's not a painting in a museum, Bizzy.
Bizzy Just once.
Dara Not happening.
Bizzy Why not?
Dara She hasn't invited you.
Bizzy You could invite me, though.
Dara No.
Bizzy You said she was nice . . . If she's nice she won't mind.

Dara gives Bizzy back her book.

Dara Let it die, Bizzy.
Bizzy Fine.
Dara Look, I'll see you about. I have to go.

Dara leaves.

Bizzy (*under her breath*) Yeah . . . Of course you do . . .

NINE

Lillie's bedroom. Dara stands at the window staring out.
Lillie lies on her bed.

Dara Seriously, Lillie, this is strange. This is very strange.
It's been two days now and still no sign of Fat Matt.
They've never been apart for this long. Fat Pat's in
there all alone. What the fuck is going on?

Lillie What were you talking to her about?

Dara What?

Lillie The girl on the street. What were you talking to her
about?

Dara The girl on the street?

Lillie The book girl. The girl who's always reading. I saw
you talking to her earlier.

Dara Oh, Bizzy.

Lillie Yeah.

Dara Maybe he's gone to visit someone – but if he did,
surely Pat would have gone too. I mean, surely they
know all the same people.

Lillie What were you talking about?

Dara I dunno. I can't remember.

Lillie You were talking about me . . . weren't you?

Dara No . . .

Lillie You were . . . I saw her look up here. And you were
laughing.

Dara No . . .

Lillie Where you laughing at me, Dara?

Dara Don't be paranoid.

Lillie Were you laughing at me with her?

Dara Lillie, don't be ridiculous.

Lillie You come up here – you listen to my stories – you
pretend to be my friend, and all the time you're going
down there and you're laughing at me.

Dara That's not true. I would never laugh at you, Lillie.
Lillie I saw you.
Dara You saw me talking to her.
Lillie Talking about me.
Dara Not the way you think, Lillie, I swear. But if you don't believe me . . . If you want me to go . . .
Lillie No. No, I'm sorry.
Dara It's fine. Let's just forget about it, okay? Let's forget about it and get back to the matter at hand.
Lillie The matter at hand?
Dara Fat Matt. The mystery of the missing twin. Any theories?
Lillie Maybe Pat killed him.
Dara Why?
Lillie Maybe they had a fight about something.

TEN

Fat Pat and Fat Matt's place.
Fat Pat and Fat Matt sit beside their mother, who lies in her bed. She is very ill.

Jacob Matthew and Patrick were always fighting. For forty years they did little else. They lived on the first floor of block three with their mother and they tortured her with their constant arguing and bickering. When the poor woman's time came, she lay quietly on her deathbed and asked just one thing of them before she passed away . . .
Mother Boys . . . promise me you'll stop fighting. Promise me you'll look after each other and love each other.
Pat / Matt We promise, Mammy.
Jacob And they meant to keep their promise. Three years passed without so much as an angry word – they were

perfect gentlemen. Then one day they went into Sampson's shop to buy the newspaper.

ELEVEN

Sampson's shop.

Sampson Hiya Matt, hiya Pat. How are you?

Matt Not bad, Sampson, not bad.

Jacob Normally they bought the same thing on every visit.

Pat We'll have the *Daily Mirror*, two cans of Fanta, two packs of Maltesers, a Lion bar and a Twix please, Sampson.

Jacob But today Matthew's feeling adventurous.

Matt Will we buy a Lotto ticket, Pat?

Pat But we never buy a Lotto ticket, Matt.

Sampson You never know your luck, lads. What is it they say . . .

Jacob If you're not in you can't win.

Sampson If you're not in you can't win.

Pat You have a point there, Sampson.

Matt Will we get one, Pat?

Pat Do you think we should, Matt?

Matt I think we should, Pat, yeah.

Jacob Eventually, after hours of deliberation over numbers, the twins left the shop – lottery ticket in hand.

TWELVE

Pat and Matt's living room.

Jacob And later that evening tension and excitement filled the air as they settled down to watch the results.

Pat passes a plate of chocolate biscuits to Matt.

Pat HobNob?
Matt Cheers.

They watch the TV.

Voice of Presenter Which brings tonight's Lottery Jackpot Rollover to a grand total of . . . wait for it . . . ten million pounds, ladies and gentleman! What do we think about that?
Matt Jesus, but I hate that bastard.
Pat Me too, Matt.
Matt If there's one bastard I hate it's that bastard, Pat.
Pat Fruity Orange fucker. (*Beat.*) More tea?
Matt That would be lovely.
Pat Still though . . . if he was handing you a cheque for ten million . . .
Matt If he handed me a cheque for ten million I'd marry the bastard . . .

Pat passes Matt a cigarette. He then takes out a lighter.

Pat Light, Pat?
Matt Cheers, Matt.
Pat Imagine what you could do with that money.
Matt I'd buy a boat.
Pat A boat?
Matt Like a big yacht thing.
Pat What the fuck would you do with a yacht?
Matt I'd sail it.
Pat You don't know how.
Matt I'd learn.
Pat They cost a fortune, them things.
Matt We've ten million, Pat.
Pat I know. But still . . . think about it first, that's all I'm saying.

Matt I have thought about it.

Pat You have not – you're buying this yacht on impulse, that's what you're doing.

Matt I am not.

Pat You're out there throwing our money about like it grows on trees.

Matt No, I'm fucking not!

Pat Don't raise your voice to me! Remember what Mammy said.

Matt Sorry, Pat.

Pat You're okay, Matt.

Matt A yacht's a good investment, though.

Pat How?

Matt Cos you can live on it as well.

Pat I'm not living on a boat.

Matt Why not?

Pat I get seasick, Matt.

Matt Once you got seasick, Pat.

Pat Once was enough.

Matt You'd get used to it after a couple of weeks.

Pat Why should I have to? I'm not living on a boat and that's the end of it.

Matt Fine. Don't . . .

Pat I won't.

Matt Won't stop me.

Pat What?

Matt I'll take my five million, buy a yacht and live on it myself.

Pat Oh, will you now?

Matt I will.

Pat Is that how it is?

Matt It is.

Pat Well, I'll take my five million and buy a big fucking mansion.

Matt Good for you.

Pat And I'll put a big electric fence around it so you can't get in.

Matt I won't want in.

Pat Oh, you will. You'll want in when your big stupid boat sinks.

Matt Yacht!

Pat You'll come crying to me then: 'Let me in, Pat . . . Please, Pat . . . I'm sorry,' and I'll say, 'Fuck away off – I told you not to buy that boat.'

Matt Yacht . . . it's a fucking yacht and I won't need to come crawling to you. It'll be the other way round. You'll beg me to let you stay . . .

Pat Never.

Matt You will, you'll have to when your mansion burns down.

Pat My mansion won't burn down.

Matt It will. Your faulty electric fence will blow up and your house will burn down.

Pat There's nothing wrong with my electric fence.

Matt It's faulty!

Pat Shut your mouth.

Matt Everything will go up in flames.

Pat Shut up!

Matt You'll have nothing again.

Pat Stop it!

Matt Nothing, nothing, nothing.

Pat throws a punch, knocking Matt to the floor.
Silence.

Jacob Patrick only hit Matthew the once. That was all it took. He banged his head on the corner of the coffee table as he fell to the ground.

THIRTEEN

Lillie's bedroom.
  Lillie lies on the bed. Dara sits at the window as before.

Dara I don't know.

Lillie I'm only telling you what I think . . .

Dara I don't think Pat's the killing type.

Lillie Why not?

Dara I don't think he'd have the energy.

Lillie So what? Matt just disappeared, did he? Forty-odd years living in the same place, unemployed and overweight, and suddenly he decides to take himself travelling – suddenly he decides to get up and do something.

Dara If Pat did kill him, what did he do with the body? We've been watching his flat for days now – we'd have noticed him try to dispose of his clinically obese twin.

Lillie He must . . . he must still be in the flat somewhere.

Dara Bullshit.

Lillie I'd put money on it, Dara.

Dara You're not even joking, are you?

Lillie He's in there. I know it.

Dara You might know it, but you can't prove it.

Lillie I can if you help me.

Jacob Getting yourself into an unbelievably horrifying and slightly surreal situation is much simpler than you might expect.

FOURTEEN

Night. Pat and Matt's place.

Jacob You begin by taking a really stupid idea – like . . . I don't know, breaking into your neighbour's home while he's at bingo to look for the body of his murdered twin. Then you put that stupid idea into action.

Dara walks in. She begins to poke about.

And after thirty minutes of searching, when all you've managed to find is a bulk supply of Cadbury's Dairy Milk and a box of 'specialist' porn –

Dara looks in a box.

Dara Urgh! Dirty bastard!

Jacob – you're suddenly startled when you hear a key turn in the lock and realise your neighbour has come home early.

Pat enters, singing to himself.

Dara (*whispers*) Shit, fuck, balls, fuck, shit, shit, bollocks.

Jacob You run upstairs and hide in his bedroom – you plan to escape when the coast is clear.

Pat looks around his living room.

Pat What the fuck is going on in here?

Jacob Unfortunately for you, your neighbour isn't blind . . .

Pat looks around the ransacked living room.

Pat (*shouting*) I know you're in here. I know your still in here, you fucker. Come out, you slimy bastard – come out here and face me like a man!

Jacob Panic sets in. All you want to do is get out of there. You rush out of the bedroom only to be met by your now understandably angry neighbour at the top of the stairs.

Pat and Dara come face to face.

Pat And just what the hell do you think you're playing at?

Jacob You didn't mean it – you were just trying to push past him that's all. You didn't mean for him to lose his balance, you didn't mean for him to fall backwards, thumping his big, fat, heavy head on every stair as he went. And you stand there just looking at him, he's not breathing, he's not moving, you stand there and you think to yourself . . .

Dara Holy fuck!

FIFTEEN

Lillie's bedroom.
Dara and Lillie sit looking out of the window.

Lillie I can't believe you killed Fat Pat.

Dara Will you stop saying that, please?

Lillie Sorry.

Dara It was your fault anyway. 'I know there's a body over there, Dara.' (*Beat.*) Body, my hole.

Lillie You're the one that threw him down the stairs.

Dara I did not throw him down the stairs – it was an accident. Anyway, how could I have thrown him down the stairs? I mean, look . . .

Dara points out at the street.

Dara Look at the size of that coffin. What am I, the Bionic fucking Woman?

Lillie There's a big turnout, isn't there?

Dara Yeah, well, people round here love nothing better than a funeral. Sad bastards.

Lillie Who found him?

Dara Sampson the shopkeeper – he hadn't gone to pick up his newspaper. Pat always collected his newspaper.

A pause.

At least it's the funeral. At least it's over today. Once he's
in the ground that's it. There's nothing they can do . . .

Lillie Unless they dig him up again.

Dara Why would they dig him up again?

Lillie I dunno.

Dara Why would you say that?

Lillie No, you're right. Why would they dig him up?
I mean everybody thinks it was an accident.

Dara Was an accident!

Lillie Yeah. I know.

Dara Don't say things like that, Lillie – I am of a very
fucking nervous disposition at present.

*They watch the funeral procession for a few more
moments.*

Lillie What did it feel like?

Dara What do you mean?

Lillie When you watched him lying there. When you saw
him dying. What did it feel like?

Dara It was all so quick, Lillie. Though . . .

Lillie Though what?

Dara I'm sure I saw a little smile on his face – just before
he went. It was as though he was thinking, 'This is it,
I'm out of here, I'm finally leaving this shithole
behind.'

They return to watching the procession.

Lillie Isn't that your brother?

Dara Yeah, that's my brother and all his little bitches.

Lillie Is he still not talking to you?

Dara No.

Lillie All because of me.

Dara All because he's a prick, Lillie.

Dara notices something.

Sweet Jesus!

Lillie What?

Dara Look who's showed up!

Lillie Who?

Dara Standing behind my brother. Big guy. Big fat fella - looks a lot like the guy who's now lying in that coffin – only without the glasses.

Lillie realises.

Lillie Oh. I suppose I was wrong.

Dara You think?

Jacob I never did finish that story.

SIXTEEN

Pat and Matt's living room. The two brothers sit in front of the television watching the Lottery results. They are in the middle of a heated argument.

Pat You'll come crying to me then: 'Let me in, Pat . . . Please, Pat . . . I'm sorry,' and I'll say, 'Fuck away off – I told you not to buy that boat.'

Matt Yacht . . . it's a fucking yacht and I won't need to come crawling to you. It'll be the other way round. You'll beg me to let you stay . . .

Pat Never.

Matt You will, you'll have to when your mansion burns down.

Pat My mansion won't burn down.

Matt It will. Your faulty electric fence will blow up and your house will burn down.

Pat There's nothing wrong with my electric fence.

Matt It's faulty!

Pat Shut your mouth.

Matt Everything will go up in flames.

Pat Shut up!

Matt You'll have nothing again.
Pat Stop it!
Matt Nothing, nothing, nothing.

*Pat throws a punch, knocking Matt to the floor. Silence.
Matt lies on the floor for a second before sitting up
and clutching his head in agony.*

Pat I'm . . . Jesus, Matt, I didn't mean . . .
Matt What did Mammy say?
Pat I know . . .
Matt The one thing Mammy asked us to do, Pat.
Pat I'm sorry.
Matt What good is sorry? What good is sorry now? It's
ruined, Pat. We've broken our promise. Our poor
Mammy's dying wish.
Pat I shouldn't have lashed out. I shouldn't have lost my
temper.
Matt No, you shouldn't have.

Matt gets up and starts to walk out of the living room.

Pat Where are you going, Matt?
Matt I'm leaving, Pat. I can't even look at you. I can't
bear to be around you. I never want to see you again.
Jacob And he didn't. If Matt had known those would
have been the last words he would ever get to say to
his brother – he probably would have chosen different
ones.

SEVENTEEN

The street.
 Jimmy, Jacob, Webb and Boyle are playing football.
Dara walks past.

Jimmy She finally blew you out then, Dara?

Dara Fuck! Breaking your vow of silence are you, Jimmy?

Jimmy You're taking it well.

Dara What are you talking about?

Jimmy You don't know.

Dara Clearly I don't have a clue what you're slabbering on about. So are you gonna continue to spout shit at me or actually fucking tell me?

Jimmy Your friend the Countess . . .

Dara Her name's Lillie.

Jimmy She's got herself a new best friend. She's dropped you like you were on fire.

Dara What?

Jimmy She's been waving Bizzy over all morning. She's in there with her now.

Dara Bizzy's in Lillie's room. What? Now?

Jimmy Jesus, it's bad if someone with no other human contact gets bored listening to you, Dara.

Jimmy laughs. Dara rushes off.

Dara . . . Dara, get back here . . .

Dara Fuck off and die, Jimmy.

EIGHTEEN

Bizzy's flat.

Jacob The night that poor Fat Pat met his untimely death, Lillie noticed something which worried her ever since. From her window she watched Dara make her speedy exit out of Pat's front door and down the steps of the tower block, but she soon realised she wasn't the only one watching.

Bizzy walks out of her bedroom with a torch and a book.

Bizzy, who shared her bedroom with her three sisters, had come out onto her balcony to read by torchlight in peace and quiet.

Bizzy sits on the balcony and starts to read. Something at the other side of the tower block catches her attention. She watches.

At the time it was both intriguing and confusing . . . at the time it didn't make sense. It wasn't till a few days later that Bizzy understood, that she knew what happened that night . . . that she knew what Dara did. The thing is, Bizzy isn't sure if it horrified or excited her.

NINETEEN

Lillie's bedroom.
Bizzy is tied to a chair in the middle of the room. She's bound and gagged. Lillie points the gun at her. Dara enters.

Dara Lillie . . .
Lillie She knows. She saw you. She saw you run away. She knows what you did.
Dara You can't do this, Lillie . . .
Lillie I have to. She'll tell someone.
Dara She won't. You won't, will you, Bizzy?

A terrified Bizzy shakes her head.

Lillie Yeah . . . like she'd say anything else.
Dara I trust her.
Lillie You shouldn't.
Dara Put it down, Lillie.
Lillie I'm trying to protect you, Dara.
Dara I don't need you to protect me. Lillie, look at me . . .

Lillie looks at her.

Listen to me. This is mad. You're not gonna actually do it. I know that and you know that. Put it down.

Lillie lowers the gun.

Because they all know she's up here, Lillie. They all saw her up here. So if anything happens to her they'll know you did it, Lillie. They'll put you in prison . . .

Lillie I already am in prison.

Dara This isn't a game.

Lillie I know.

Dara Let's just put a stop to it.

Lillie Yeah, it's time to put a stop to it. I'm tired now. It's time for the ending, I think.

Lillie quickly aims the gun at Dara's head.

Bizzy, apparently before Pat died, he smiled. He smiled because he was leaving all this behind. He smiled because he was escaping, escaping all the boredom, all the monotony, all the shit – he was moving on.

She fires the gun, shooting Dara in the head. Dara falls to the floor. Then she turns the gun on herself.

Lillie Watch me, Bizzy. Watch me smile.

Blackout. A second gunshot sounds. In darkness Jacob and Lillie speak.

Jacob There's never anything to do up here. There's nothing to do and nowhere to go. We all just sit around waiting for something, for anything to happen. It never does. Nothing ever happens on The Heights.

Lillie I make up stories, that's what I do.

TWENTY

The street.
Dara, Jimmy, Boyle and Webb scuffle over the gun –
exactly as they did in their first scene.

Jimmy Give us a look at it then.
Webb Dara! Throw!
Boyle Dara, do not throw.

She throws the gun to Jimmy. He catches it.

Jimmy Jesus . . . it's not light is it? That's a beauty, Boyle –
they don't make them like they used to, do they?
Boyle Ha ha!

Jimmy throws it to Webb. Webb catches it.

Stop it.
Webb Though, Jimmy, I'd say this thing could still do a
lot of damage.

Webb throws it to Dara. She catches it.

Dara Yeah, if you threw it at someone . . .
Jimmy Or force-fed it to some poor bastard.

Dara throws it to Jimmy.

Boyle Dickheads.

Jimmy throws it to Webb again.

Jimmy We're dickheads, are we?

Webb pulls Boyle towards him. He gets him into a
headlock and points the gun at his head.

Webb Say that again, fuckwit. Let me hear you say it again.

Dara laughs.

Jimmy Come on, Webb.

Boyle pushes Webb off.

Boyle Hilarious. As much as I'm enjoying the gun-related humour – it's mine, and I want it back now, please.

Webb Yeah, you're right. Sorry.

Webb approaches Boyle to give him the gun. At the last moment he snatches it away and throws it to Dara.

Dara Sucked in!

Boyle Wankers. You're all wankers. A collection of wankers, that's what I'm looking at. That's what I have before me. You are the elite of the wanker world.

Bizzy walks onto the street reading a book. Dara doesn't see her and walks backwards with the gun.

Dara Aw, you want it back? You want it back, Boyle? Here.

Dara throws the gun to Jimmy. As she does so she walks backwards into Bizzy causing her to drop her book.

Dara Fuck, sorry.

Bizzy You're alright.

Dara picks up her book and hands it back to her. The boys continue to argue amongst themselves.

Dara Reading again, Biz?

Bizzy There's no law against it.

Dara It's dangerous, though. I mean, look what just happened – lucky one of us wasn't injured.

Webb Dara!

Webb hurls the gun at Dara. She catches it.

Bizzy Reading's dangerous but playing catch with a loaded weapon, that's perfectly safe, is it?

Dara This? This isn't a weapon – this is a historical
  artefact. It doesn't even work –

Dara raises the gun in the air.

Boyle Don't, Dara . . .
Dara And it's not loaded.

She fires the gun. Nothing happens.

Dara (*laughing*) See!
Jimmy I think Boyle actually just shat himself.
Boyle I did not.

*Boyle runs towards her and takes the gun from her
hands.*

Webb Give me twenty quid, I'll give you my belt, Boyle –
  it would do more damage than that thing.
Jimmy My sock would do more damage than that thing.

They all laugh except Boyle.

Boyle You're all such funny bastards, aren't you?

Bizzy looks at one of the tower blocks behind them.

Bizzy Look. The Countess is at her window again
Dara What?

Jimmy realises what Bizzy is referring to.

Jimmy So she is. Not that she needs an excuse to look at
  us. Creepy bitch.

*Jimmy gives the flat the finger. Boyle points his gun
towards it.*

Boyle You're next, Snow White!
Webb What the fuck do you think you're looking at?!
Dara Give it a rest.
Jimmy What?

Dara She's not doing any harm, is she?

The boys and Bizzy start to walk away. Dara remains staring intently up at Lillie's window.

Jimmy You coming, Dara?
Dara Yeah . . . I'm coming.

Dara follows them.

TWENTY-ONE

Lillie's bedroom.
Lillie stands at her window looking out at the street.

Lillie Sometimes they're funny. Sometimes they're sad. Sometimes they're wonderful. Sometimes they're terrible. But they're always just stories.

The End.

Production Notes

When approaching the text and your production the playwright thinks three words should be kept in mind at all times: *fun*, *creativity* and *lively*. She wants companies to take ownership of the piece and enjoy interpreting it in their own way. Possibilities are endless with *The Heights*, therefore it's not about making right or wrong decisions but about enjoying the play and making your decisions fit the logic of your production. These notes offer things to think about rather than rules.

THE TEXT

The Heights is about storytelling. Lillie is a storyteller – she admits to this in her first line and it is in storytelling that the text has its roots. Lillie writes stories, Jacob narrates them, Dara is a lead character in stories and Bizzy reads them. Lillie, entrapped in her room, watches the people below and makes up stories about them. She is the centre of the piece and all things come from her.

It is suggested by the playwright that Jacob is the only person Lillie actually ever meets – everyone else is imagined. But this is not set in stone, and companies should feel free to interpret their relationship as they wish. The play suggests that Lillie dropped notes from her window with the 'Glass Baby' story on, that Jacob found them, and that this is how they met. But Jacob becomes too 'real' for Lillie when he tries to kiss her and as this is something Lillie cannot control she distances herself from him again.

The gun going off in Scene One is the moment when all the stories begin. The repetition of that scene at the end is the 'real' version of events, but Lillie imagines the gun actually fired and the play springs to life from there. She has never met or heard Dara, or the other characters; she has only seen them from her window and imagined how they talk and what they say. She invents whole narratives for them and imagines what would happen if they met her. For Fat Matt and Fat Pat, characters living nearby, she imagines a whole history, their traumas and even Pat's death.

It is important to be aware that there is a fine balance between showing the audience that Lillie makes up stories and not giving away that everything has been made up by her. The mixture of fantasy and reality should be carefully handled so that there is fun to be had with the blurring of the two. The audience should ask themselves after the production which bits were real – if they watched it again could they see the clues and signs?

The playwright describes the play as a detective story – not about hiding the 'truth', but about being subtle in how you layer the clues, which are both in the script and which you create in the production. The replay of the final scene should be exactly the same as it was in the first up until the gun not going off, to heighten the fact that the play springs from that point. Something to think about is that it could be at the end of the play that you reveal how much of a storyteller Lillie has been.

Lillie is isolated by her illness; she does not go out and does not hang out with the gang who occupy the estate below. They live in different worlds with different atmospheres, Lillie is wrapped in cotton wool, and so safe that she craves danger and damage. Therefore her imagination is quite brutal and the imagined meetings with Dara have a morbid edge. Lillie's dilemma and loneliness are important, and the audience should care for her isolation and journey throughout the piece.

Jacob and Lillie's relationship offers a number of possibilities for the way the story is told. At times Jacob challenges, as narrator, to be the centre of the play, but it is Lillie who should always end up dominating. Jacob becomes her voice, watching and intertwining with the world she looks down on. There are some interesting choices to be made in how they interact and are placed onstage.

THE PRODUCTION

In performance *The Heights* has limitless possibilities, but it is important that there is some sort of logic to your production which matches the logic of the play. Lillie is the centre of the world and everything comes from her. How do you show this? With the use of a bed, books, paint, Plasticine, clothes? And why does she create those stories? Solitude, anger, escape?

Once you know what your tools are and the theme you want to explore, you can build your production around this, with all characters and stories starting from this point. The rules of the production should match the rules of the play. If your method is clay, how does that thread through the production? What do we see of Lillie creating things and when?

It is important to let the audience know that Lillie makes up stories without giving away the reveal that Lillie has created almost all the action. Find your tool and then use it subtly through the piece. It may be towards the end of the piece that you reveal the extent of Lillie's creativity.

A great deal can be achieved physically in *The Heights*, and experimenting with creating the more abstract moments, such as the death of Fat Pat and the Glass Baby story, may give some interesting results. Experiment with these – it is a good idea just to try things out quickly, to get a shape of them and start a conversation.

For example, can you create Fat Pat's character falling down the stairs through the actor not moving himself but being moved by others? Or try the whole thing through sound effects or props. Think about how Lillie creates her stories and see if Pat's death can be created with that tool. How can you make moments like these and the Glass Baby story stand out against the stories of the street? What is the relationship between the abstract and the naturalistic? Getting on your feet as soon as possible is a really good idea. However, remember always to keep the story you are telling as clear as possible.

The script has great energy and pace and is robust to many different ways of staging but there are some important things to consider.

Taking Scenes Ten to Twelve as an example: the setting shifts through different time zones and places very quickly. This should happen without any gaps. Jacob is the glue holding the scene together. Where does he move onstage? How can the different moments be layered and the evolution or Matt and Pat's life be clear? And where is Lillie during all this?

Think about layering the scenes over each other, either by actors moving or by using different parts of the stage. Fluidity is the key to the script and you should avoid blackouts and scene changes if you can. Objects link scenes in the script very well – or maybe it is through the use of your creative tool that Lillie tells her stories?

Although the script is robust, it does need good spatial control and focus. There is lots of split-focus in scenes, especially when you consider your placement of Lillie. Therefore be clear where you want the audience to look. Playing with the dynamics of the script will help this.

Think about what is important in each scene; be as specific as possible – a word, a character trait, a facial expression – and then play with the rhythm and speed of the text to see how you can focus audience attention on this one thing.

Where are the pauses and why? Try different things out: it's not about finding the right thing straight away.

Boyle, Webb, Bizzy and Jimmy are as you see them in the script, but it is important they have the energy of the street. This energy is different to that of Lillie's world, but also has similarities, as they are all stuck with nowhere to go. Their frustration manifests itself in different ways: think about how this happens.

Fat Pat and Matt are people whose lives Lillie imagines. Maybe she has heightened and abstracted their behaviour in some way – but how do we also make them real and touching?

Bring design elements in as soon as possible. The storytelling heart of the play links well with set, lighting and sound.

CASTING AND LANGUAGE

You can perform *The Heights* with a larger cast than is defined – feel free to make it work for the company that you have. There is a possibility of more than one person playing Jacob or Lillie, but make sure you are clear: when do they split? Why do they split? There are also ways of adding actors to the street gang, and to the Fat Pat and Matt and Glass Baby stories.

Characters can all be men or all be women. If your actors are all of one gender, you can have the characters also of one gender by changing their names. But if having men playing women or women playing men fits the style of the production you want to create, then that is fine.

You can change swear words, omit them completely or use something more locally appropriate. Some of the swearing is specific to Northern Ireland so won't necessarily translate easily. Accent should be fairly urban.

The gunshot is an important sound effect: keep it. The absence of the shot is the surprise at the end.

The end of the play is the pay-off. The moment the audience realise Lillie has made it all up is important.

From a workshop led by Rufus Norris,
with notes by Nathan Curry

THE SÉANCE

Anthony Neilson

Anthony Neilson's plays include *Welfare My Lovely*, *Normal*, *Penetrator*, *The Year of the Family*, *Heredity*, *The Censor* (winner of the Writers' Guild Award for Best Fringe Play, 1997), *Edward Gant's Amazing Feats of Loneliness*, *Stitching* (nominated for Evening Standard Most Promising Newcomer, 2002), *The Lying Kind*, *The Wonderful World of Dissocia*, *The Menu*, *God in Ruins* and *Relocated*. He also directed the UK premiere of John Adams's opera *The Death of Klinghoffer* (winner of a Herald Angel Award). TV commissions include *Deeper Still*, *A Terrible Coldness*, *Bible John* (*In Suspicious Circumstances*), the feature film spin-off of *Cracker*, and a two-hour *Prime Suspect* film. His feature film debut, *The Debt Collector*, which he wrote and directed, won the Fipresci (International Critics) Award at Troia International Film Festival.

Characters

Ryan

Sophie

Natasha

Mark

Andy

Jarjar

Phoebe

Ryan's parents' house.

A round table sits in the centre of the room.

Around its outer perimeter, squares of card have been stuck down, each one carrying a letter of the alphabet – except for two cards that sit opposite each other, one showing the word YES, *the other the word* NO. *Six chairs surround the table.*

Ryan is setting candles in a cluster in the centre of the table.

Two girls enter – Sophie and Natasha – clutching their Bacardi Breezers.

Sophie Is this it?

Ryan Sophie . . .

Sophie What?

Ryan I said – don't bring drinks in here.

Sophie Why not?

Ryan Cos they get knocked over, they get spilt –

Sophie Yeah right, cos I'm such a fucking spazz.

Ryan Yeah, but *you* bring them in and then *they* bring them in . . .

He indicates the others outside.

There was like, fucking chewing gum stuck to the sofa the last time.

Sophie Did Daddy spank you?

Ryan Fuck off.

He lights the candles.

Natasha Shouldn't there be numbers?

Sophie I thought you was getting a proper one?

Ryan From where? Fucking *Tesco's*?

Sophie There's shops that sell them. What about that hippy shop that sells the bongs?

Natasha Or a magic shop.

Sophie Yeah, that one in the arcades.

Ryan That's a joke shop. It sells plastic dogshit and nails through the finger and shit.

Sophie No, it sells magic stuff as well cos my brother got some tricks there.

Ryan It's not magic though, is it? It's something else.

Sophie Like what?

Ryan I don't know – the supernatural.

Natasha Paranormal?

Ryan (*shrugs*) It's probably bollocks.

Sophie Then what are we doing it for?

Ryan To find out.

Mark enters. He's got a can of cider in his hand.

Mark This it, yeah?

Ryan Oh for fuck's sake – I don't want drink in here.

Mark Shit, man, it's not even a proper fucking board.

Ryan Give me the can.

Sophie That's what *we* said.

Mark I thought you was going to get one online.

Ryan They were, like, thirty quid for the cheapest.

Mark We could've all chipped in.

Ryan Yeah, *right* . . .

Natasha That wax is going to go on the table.

Ryan Fuck.

He puts the candles out.

Anyway, Phoebe says it doesn't matter. She says it's about the people, not the board.

Sophie Yeah. but Phoebe's fucking mental.

Natasha Sshhh.

Sophie I think we should fit her up with Jarjar. He's a
  nerd as well.

Ryan Phoebe's not a nerd.

Sophie What is she then?

Ryan I don't know. She's not a nerd though.

Natasha I like her.

Ryan I like her too.

Sophie Sounds like it. Maybe it's you that wants in her
  knickers.

Natasha looks uncomfortable.

Mark You should put numbers on it.

Ryan Eh?

Mark What if it wants to say numbers?

Sophie She.

Mark Sorry – she.

Ryan She can spell them out.

Mark She can spell out 'Yes' and 'No', you put those.

Ryan Fucking hell – if you're so smart, you make the
  fucker. Where's the rest?

Mark They're having a spliff.

Ryan Oh right – do I not get a toke?

Mark You said not to bring it in.

Ryan Are they in the garden?

Mark They were.

Ryan Right, give me the bottles.

*He attempts to take the drinks from Sophie and
Natasha. Natasha surrenders hers but Sophie glugs
hers down first.*

Ryan And that as well.

Mark I'm drinking it, man.

Ryan takes the can and exits, followed by Mark.

It's like a fucking concentration camp here . . .

Mark exits. Pause.

Sophie They're all going to be stoned off their tits.

Pause.

Are you alright?

Natasha Yeah, I'm fine.

Sophie Andy behaving himself?

Natasha He's not spoken to me yet.

Sophie That's good, isn't it? Maybe he's getting over you.

Natasha Yeah. I suppose.

Sophie Yeah, I know what you mean. Remember when that guy Jason was really into me?

Natasha Jason?

Sophie Remember – drippy Jason.

Natasha Oh – yeah.

Sophie Yeah. I mean, he wasn't as bad as Andy but he was still, like, pretty much stalking me.

Natasha Was he?

Sophie Yeah, man. He used to hang about the bottom of my street waiting for me to come out; and then he was all, like, 'I love you, Sophie, I want to marry you.' I mean at least you and Andy went out for a bit. I didn't even hardly know him.

Natasha Yeah.

Sophie Yeah, but what I'm saying – he did it for about maybe a year, he was totally obsessed, and then he just stopped – I think he got fixated on Emma the Elephant, which is a fucking laugh. I heard he shagged her, did you hear that?

Natasha No.

Sophie What was I saying? Oh yeah, but like – I was glad he'd stopped but there was a little bit of me, I don't know . . . Like, I didn't fancy him. At all, right? But you got so used to it, it was funny when it stopped. I sort of missed it. D'you know what I'm saying?

Natasha Not for me. I just want it to stop.

Sophie Yeah, you think that now . . .

Natasha I'll always think that.

Sophie Yeah, but it's nice to be wanted, yeah? That's all I'm saying.

Natasha Honestly, I just want it to stop.

Pause.

I mean, I'm sorry I hurt him, but that doesn't mean he can just own me and stop me seeing other boys and stuff.

Sophie He's your best mate, though.

Pause. Natasha shrugs.

Is he not?

There is something almost hopeful in Sophie's tone. Natasha quickly shakes her head, 'Be quiet.' Andy enters. Sophie twigs.

Yeah, but anyway . . . that's what she said.

Andy looks at the table.

We were saying – it's not even a proper one.

Andy Proper what?

Sophie Proper thingy-board.

Andy Ouija.

Sophie What?

Andy Ouija board.

Sophie Yeah, whatever.

An awkward silence.

I don't even think we should be doing it, you ask me.

Andy Why not?

Sophie I don't know. It's just weird. It's messing about with stuff we don't understand.

Andy So's everything.

Sophie Yeah, but people go mental from it and shit. I heard about someone did a séance and he thought an evil spirit had got inside him and he jumped out a window.

Andy Isn't that *The Exorcist*?

Sophie What, the film?

Andy No, the musical.

Sophie Yeah well, I've not seen *The Exorcist*, have I?

Natasha Have I seen it?

Andy *The Exorcist*?

Natasha Yeah.

Andy Yeah.

Natasha Have I?

Andy We watched it. At my house?

She doesn't remember!

Andy Last Halloween.

Natasha Oh – yeah . . .

Andy Sorry it was so forgettable.

Natasha No, I remember. With the head turning round and the puking.

Sophie Is it scary?

Natasha More horrible than scary.

Andy What? You got me to put the light on in the toilet for you, you were so scared.

Sophie Maybe she was just scared of your toilet.

Sophie looks out at the garden. Andy addresses Natasha.

Andy Are you alright?

Natasha nods.

You're not talking much.

Natasha Me?

He indicates the table.

Andy You want to do this?

She shrugs.

Cos we don't have to if you don't want to.

Sophie They're all just getting wasted. It's just a laugh to them. Me and Nat were the only ones that even knew her.

Pause.

Natasha I didn't really know her. She used to get on the bus sometimes.

Pause.

Sophie It's just mental that she's not here any more. That she's someone we knew but now she's just, like – not on the planet, like . . . *anywhere*. And you know what? Just the week before, she said to me how she was thirsty all the time.

Pause.

That must have been it. The diabetes – that makes you thirsty. All the time she had this thing in her and she didn't even know it.

Andy I thought you said she was a slag.

Sophie I never said that!

Andy I think you did.

Sophie No I fucking didn't! Why would I say that?

Andy I don't know. I just remember you saying it.

Sophie When?

Natasha Andy . . .

Andy When?

Sophie When did I say Charlotte was a slag? Come on.

Andy I don't have, like, a date or a time . . .

Sophie No, cos I never fucking said it!

Natasha She didn't.

Andy shrugs.

Andy If you say so.

Sophie Andy, you take that fucking back! I never called her a slag!

Andy Fine . . .

Sophie I never called her a fucking slag and if I did it was a joke!

Sophie gets tearful.

Nat, tell him . . .

Natasha goes to comfort her.

Andy Fucking hell . . .

Natasha Shhh, it's okay. You didn't call her a slag.

Sophie I liked her. She was my friend.

Natasha I know. Sshhh.

Pause.

Sophie I just miss her, you know?

Natasha I know . . .

A voice:

Jarjar Is there anybody there?

A traffic cone pokes through the door, inverted and used as a loudspeaker.

You must not meddle with the spirits, you blasphemers! You infidels! You tempters of Satan!

Andy creeps up to the cone . . .

Jarjar You are meddling with things beyond your mortal understanding! You are . . .

Andy kicks it.

Oww!

Jarjar enters, holding his mouth.

That fucking hurt, you twat!

He attempts to kick Andy back, and a restricted chase ensues. Jarjar throws the cone at him.

Natasha Watch it!
Sophie Don't be such a pair of dicks.

Andy wrestles Jarjar to the ground, where he gets him in a headlock.

Jarjar I am a servant of the secret fire! Wielder of the flame of Anor, and you cannot pass!
Andy What? What was that, Jarjar? Jarjar-fucking-Binks!

Strangulated.

Jarjar The dark fire – will not avail you – flame of Udun!
Sophie Stop fucking about!
Andy What are you saying, Binksy boy?
Jarjar Go back to the shadow – you cannot pass!!

It begins to get a bit serious. Jarjar is getting red in the face.

Andy Say you're a wank.
Jarjar You're a wank.

Andy tightens his grip.

Andy No, say you're a wank!
Jarjar Fuck you.
Natasha Andy, leave him . . .
Sophie You're going to break something.

Pause. Andy lets go of him.

Jarjar You fucking hurt my mouth.
Ryan What's going on?

Mark and Ryan have returned.

Andy Nothing.
Sophie They were being gay.
Ryan What's that fucking cone doing in here?
Andy Sophie's upset about Charlotte.

Mark Who?

Ryan I'm telling you, man, I don't want any shit going on. If anything gets broken or fucked up in any way, I'm telling you, you can all fuck off.

Mark He's such a charming host.

Ryan Where's Phoebe?

Mark She's in the bog.

Jarjar Is she laying some cable?

Natasha *Aww* . . .

Sophie Don't be rank.

Jarjar What? It's *natural* . . .

Mark Girls don't shit, though.

Andy That's totally true.

Jarjar So how did *you* get born then?

Mark Genius.

Jarjar Thank you, thank you.

Mark That's comedy genius, right there.

Ryan Stop fucking about and sit down.

Natasha Where should we sit?

Ryan Does it matter?

Natasha Where's Phoebe sitting?

Ryan I don't know – Phoebe?

> *Pause.*

Mark I'm really ripped off that spliff.

Ryan So am I.

Jarjar I'm bing-bong-booed.

Mark Do none of you lay-dees want a smoke?

> *They look non-committal.*

Jarjar Girls are such girls.

Sophie Yeah, cos you're a good advert for it, Sackboy.

Mark It's not that strong, honest.

> *Jarjar gives an evil laugh.*

Sophie I know. I *have* had a smoke before. I just don't need to get stoned every day of my life.

Jarjar That's funny, because I do!

Mark Yeah, man!

They high-five each other.

Jarjar Wasters till we die!

Mark Wasters till we die!

Sophie Is that your thing, is it? 'Wasters till we die'? Cos that's pathetic if it is.

Jarjar Yeah, right. Have you got these in a size ten?

Again, they high-five.

Sophie Oh yeah, that's funny. Some of us have to get a summer job cos we don't get pocket money like little babies.

Jarjar Weed'll get you through times of no money better than money'll get you through times of no weed.

Sophie You're a fucking moron.

Mark Chill out, Sophe. He's just winding you up.

Phoebe enters with a canister of salt.

Jarjar Uh-oh – here's Evil Willow.

She starts to sprinkle it around the table.

Ryan Ho! What the fuck are you doing?

Phoebe What?

Ryan What the fuck are you doing flinging salt around?

Phoebe It's protection. You've got to do it.

Ryan Protection from what?

Jarjar Giant snails.

Phoebe Evil spirits.

Ryan No, no –

Phoebe It's got to be done.

Ryan Bollocks. How does salt protect you from evil spirits?

Phoebe It just does. It purifies.

Natasha That's why you chuck salt over your shoulder – to blind the devil.

Mark Yeah, man – we can hoover it later.

Ryan You mean I can.

Natasha I'll help you tidy up.

Andy Yeah. We'll all help.

Pause.

Ryan Right, well – not much then.

Phoebe is allowed to continue.

Sophie How do you know about all this stuff, Pheebs?

Ryan Her mum's a goth.

Sophie Is she?

Phoebe Used to be.

Sophie Cool.

Phoebe Not really. The music's shit. But she used to do séances. And she's got tons of books about it.

Jarjar Was she a Satanist?

Natasha Did she used to let you join in?

Phoebe Yeah, a couple of times. Anyone got something silver?

Jarjar My cock-ring.

Natasha Seriously?

Jarjar D'you want to see?

Natasha Don't be rank.

Andy punches him in the arm.

Jarjar Ow!

Phoebe Stop messing about. Just a coin or something; something silver.

Sophie puts a bracelet down on the table.

Sophie What about this?

Natasha That's lovely. Who gave you that?

Sophie It was my gran's.
Phoebe Put it down on the table.
Mark Is that protection as well?

Phoebe nods.

Sophie It's not going to get all sort of evil-ghosty, is it?
Phoebe Not possible. Did you polish the table?

She pushes the glass back and forwards. It slides across the wood with reasonable ease.

Alright.

She sits down, in a commanding position.

Okay, so I've got to tell you some stuff first, before we do this. Can we turn off the main lights?

Mark gets up to do it. Phoebe lights the candles in the centre of the table.

Jarjar Yoiks!
Sophie Why do we have to do that?
Mark Cos it's creepier.
Phoebe They don't like electric lights, it hurts them.

Mark returns to his place.

Andy What's that smell?
Phoebe The candles are scented with sage.
Natasha Sage?
Phoebe They're old ones my mum had. They're what you're supposed to use.
Andy It fucking honks.
Jarjar It's making me want chicken.
Phoebe Right, listen . . .
Mark Yeah, some KFC, man . . .
Jarjar Mmm – hot wings.
Phoebe You've got to listen to this, seriously.
Natasha Listen to Phoebe.

Andy Yeah. shhh.

Pause.

Phoebe Alright. So what we're about to do, it's not a game, yeah?

Jarjar You mean we don't need dice?

Phoebe stares at him.

Oooh – scary.

Ryan Just listen.

Phoebe Alright, so when we start . . . we're all going to rest one finger each on the glass. If anybody tries to push the glass, I'll see it and I'll end the session.

Ryan Yeah, nobody should push it, seriously.

Mark Yeah, there's no point in doing it if we push it. I want to see if it works.

Phoebe Second thing – let me do the talking.

Jarjar Aww, that's not fair – we don't get to talk to them?

Phoebe If I say you can, yeah. But you've got to be careful how you talk to spirits. You have to be respectful. You can't ask them to do tricks and stuff. Alright?

General consent.

Okay, now this is important. We need to make contact with a spirit guide. A spirit guide is a good spirit, and it'll help to find people we want to talk to, and it'll introduce us and stuff. But . . . and it's a big but –

Jarjar (*sings*) 'I like big butts and I cannot lie, you other brothers can't deny . . .'

Phoebe Are you going to keep saying stupid things?

Pause.

Jarjar Probably, yeah.

Phoebe Right, well, then we shouldn't do this because it's too dangerous to have idiots doing it.

Jarjar Yeah, because it's, like, a really serious thing.

Pause.

Come on – does anyone really believe you can sit here
and talk to dead people?

Phoebe If you don't believe, it won't work.

Jarjar Yeah, because it's shit.

Ryan Come on, man –

Mark Yeah, have an open mind.

Jarjar No, listen – the TV works, whether I believe in it
or not. The fucking . . . kettle works.

Natasha Yeah, but you believe in them.

Jarjar I believe in them because they work.

Andy Right, well then, it goes in a circle, doesn't it?

Jarjar No, because if I'd, like, never seen a TV before – if
I was like, a stone-age man –

Mark Instead of a stoner.

Jarjar And you said, 'Ug-ug, this box has pictures of
people talking on it' – why would I believe you? I mean,
until you switched it on?

Sophie Where would you get the electricity from?

Jarjar What?

Pause.

Natasha I think you should have an open mind. I mean,
you'd need to let the person switch on the TV. You
couldn't just smash it up or, like, walk out of the cave,
could you?

Pause.

Jarjar Yeah, whatever. There is no spoon and shit. I'm
cool with it.

Sophie Does anyone know what the fuck he's talking
about?

Natasha Go on, Phoebe.

Phoebe Alright – spirit guides. The thing is, sometimes a
demon will pretend to be a spirit guide, just to fuck
you up. So this is important. If the glass starts moving

in figures of eight, it's a demon and we end the session. If the glass starts to spell out the alphabet – like *a-b-c-d*, in order – that's a demon and we end the session. And the most important thing – if the glass starts to spell out the word 'hell' or 'demon' or 'devil', or anything bad like that, we have to end the session before they can spell out the whole word.

Sophie Why?

Phoebe If they manage to spell out the whole word, they'll gain entrance into this world and they might even possess one of us. So if that starts to happen, we end the session and we burn all these letters and we smash the glass.

Ryan Whoa – what? We have to smash the glass?

Phoebe We have to smash the glass anyway.

Ryan Why?

Phoebe You just have to. If you don't smash the glass, the spirit stays in the house.

Ryan That's a crystal glass. That's one of a set.

Phoebe nods.

Right, well – if my parents come back and find out I've smashed a crystal glass, it'll be me you're trying to contact in the spirit world.

Phoebe I'm sure they'd rather have a smashed glass than a vengeance demon in the house.

Jarjar You've obviously not met his parents.

Andy So just use a cheap glass. Can we smash a cheap one?

Phoebe Crystal is the best kind.

Mark Can I go and get a beer if this is going to take ages?

Ryan You can smash a cheap glass but not one of the crystal ones.

Andy Can we use a normal glass?

Phoebe I can't guarantee it'll work.

Andy Fine, just get a normal glass.

Ryan takes the crystal glass and exits.

Jarjar He wouldn't let us do hot-knives either.
Sophie I don't know if we should be doing this. It sounds
  dangerous.
Phoebe It's alright as long as we're careful.
Jarjar As long as we do exactly what you tell us?

Phoebe shrugs.

Mark Yeah, but I thought this was all about getting in
  touch with whats-'er-name?
Sophie Jenny.
Mark She's not going to be a demon, is she?
Phoebe You can't guarantee who you'll speak to. We can
  ask the spirit guide to fetch someone, but you don't
  know for a fact it's them. Who was her best friend?

Pause.

Natasha Probably Sophie.

Sophie nods.

Mark I thought you said she was a stuck-up bitch.
Sophie I never said that!
Natasha It doesn't really matter what she was, does it?
  She didn't deserve to die.
Jarjar Yeah, but why would she want to talk to us?
Mark Well, to be fair – she probably doesn't get many
  visits.
Phoebe And why did this girl pass over?
Natasha Diabetes.
Sophie They didn't know she had it.

Pause.

Jarjar Are there any crisps or anything?

Ryan enters with a new, cheaper glass.

Ryan – any munchies?

Ryan What?

Jarjar Crisps or biscuits or shit. I've totally got the munchies, dude.

Phoebe You can't eat during a séance.

Ryan Just have something later.

Mark There's biscuits in the kitchen. HobNobs.

Jarjar 'Knob-Hobs'? Excellent.

He gets up.

Natasha Jarjar . . .

Ryan Yeah, man, come on – we just got everyone in here –

Jarjar I'll be, like – one second.

Mark Get me some.

Ryan Oh no – go with him. I don't want fucking biscuits all over the floor getting all fucking . . . walked into the carpet.

Jarjar Alright, Grandad.

Ryan We can go to *your* parents' house if you want. See how you like it.

Mark gets up to go with him.

Mark I'm telling you, man, it's like fucking Auschwitz round here.

Ryan Hurry up though. Get this thing started.

Andy Anyone want a beer, then?

Ryan Is there any left?

Andy There should be. 'Less some bastard's drunk them.

Sophie Where did you get them?

Andy Offy on the corner.

Sophie Did they serve you?

Andy Yeah, course. (*To Natasha.*) Do you want anything?

Natasha No, I'm alright.

Andy leaves.

Sorry, Phoebe.

Phoebe It takes quite a while to have a séance. It takes a bit of time to get warmed up.

Ryan Is this glass alright?

Phoebe pushes it around the table. She shrugs.

Sophie Seeing as we seem to be having a break . . .

She leaves.

Natasha So did your mum ever have any bad stuff happen with, like, demons and stuff?

Phoebe Oh yeah, totally.

Natasha Really?

Phoebe She was possessed by an imp for about . . . four years?

Ryan Nasty.

Natasha So what –?

Phoebe Just bad stuff.

Ryan Like what?

Phoebe Just, like – made her drink lots, get into fights outside in the street, bring lots of men back. They thought she was mental.

Natasha Who did?

Phoebe The police and stuff. They even put her in hospital and gave her lots of drugs and stuff but it didn't work. Then she went to see a spiritual healer and they saw she was possessed and performed an exorcism.

Natasha And then she was alright?

Phoebe Yeah. Then she was totally fine. This glass is dirty.

Ryan Is it?

Pause.

You want me to wash it?

Phoebe It needs to be done properly.

Phoebe exits, leaving Ryan and Natasha.

Ryan Fucking hell.

They sit in silence for a moment.
Then Ryan's hand reaches out to hers. She takes it.

Are you alright?

Phoebe nods.

What?

Ryan leans across the table to kiss her.

Natasha Don't.
Ryan Why not?

She gives him a look.

Ryan At least it'd be out in the open.
Natasha Don't even say that.
Ryan Why not? He's going to find out one day. Isn't he?

Pause.

Natasha Yes, but not today.

Their hands lock tighter together.

Ryan We've done nothing wrong. I love you.

Pause.

Natasha I love you too.

He leans over and kisses her.

Jarjar Shit, fucking biscuits, man, I thought you had –

Ryan and Natasha disengage, as if electrocuted. Jarjar has seen this.
An awkward pause. Jarjar sits down.

Ryan Is there no HobNobs?
Jarjar No, man. Just Rich Teas and Bourbons. Total dad biscuits. And all the crisps are ready salted. What happens to people when they get past thirty?

Pause.

Natasha I'll just . . .

Pause. She exits.
   Jarjar and Ryan sit there in silence for a time. It's very awkward.
   The following exchange about video games can be updated in consultation with the actors.

Jarjar What's that *World at War* like?
Ryan Which?
Jarjar *The Call of Duty* one. Is it any good?
Ryan Yeah, it's pretty good.
Jarjar Is it crazy-hard?
Ryan If you play it on Veteran, yeah. There's a level when you have to storm the Reichstag. Took me about a week, honest to God.
Jarjar See, I'd never finish that.
Ryan They just keep chucking grenades at you. It's mental.
Jarjar Did you try *Fable II*?
Ryan No, but in *World at War* when you finish it, it unlocks a level where all the Nazis become zombies.
Jarjar Yeah, I heard that was wicked.
Ryan It is. It's called *Nacht der Undertoten* or something.
Jarjar *Nacht der Underpanten*?
Ryan Night of the underpants, yeah.
Jarjar Cool.

Pause.

Everyone likes a zombie.

Phoebe, Sophie and Natasha enter.

Natasha Yeah, but has your mum got big boobs?

Phoebe Not massive but that's what I'm worried about –
if they keep growing. But my sister's like, twenty-five,
and she's not too bad.

Sophie Isn't there any ballet dancers with big boobs?

Natasha No, they're all like ironing boards.

Sophie You could do pole-dancing instead.

Phoebe It's not really the same.

Jarjar Am I hearing things or are you talking about
breasts?

Sophie Why, are you getting excited?

Phoebe sits down.

Phoebe Are we ready to start then?

Ryan I'm ready. Where's Mark and Andy?

Natasha Take a guess.

Jarjar I'll go and get them.

Ryan Don't bother.

Jarjar What?

Ryan Cos you'll just end up having another spliff and
then it'll be another half an hour.

Jarjar No, I'll just tell them to come through.

Ryan Yeah, right. Just sit down.

Jarjar Such a fascist.

Natasha So Phoebe – can we contact anyone we like?

Phoebe As long as they're dead.

Jarjar Yeah, cos the living ones we can just phone.

Natasha But I mean, can we contact, like – historical
figures?

Phoebe Like who?

Ryan Napoleon.

Phoebe Well, he was French so he wouldn't understand
you, but yeah.

Natasha What about, like – Emily Pankhurst.

Jarjar Who?

Sophie The suffragettes, you penis.

Jarjar Like you knew before about a month ago.

Ryan The suffragettes? Weren't they on Motown?

Natasha slaps him playfully.

Jarjar Yeah, I mean who wants to talk to some old, dead lezzie?

Sophie Are you being serious?

Mark and Andy enter.

Mark What's happening, man? Have we started?

Jarjar Sophie's pretending she wants to contact Emily Pankhurst.

Mark Who?

Sophie Why would I not want to contact Emily Pankhurst?

Jarjar Umm – cos she's not in *Hello!* that often?

Phoebe We can try to contact anyone. But it's better if you choose someone you know cos then it's more difficult for demons to deceive us.

Mark Yeah – someone who knows stuff only you know.

Jarjar So – family members maybe?

Phoebe Yeah, they're the best. Anyone got any dead family members?

Pause.

Mark My grandad's dead.

Natasha Yeah, so's one of mine.

Jarjar Got a dead granny here.

Sophie nods.

Ryan I'll see your granny and raise you.

Natasha With what?

Ryan Another granny.

Pause.

Phoebe Right, so we could contact grandparents?

A long pause. No one seems keen.

Okay . . .

Natasha I'd maybe talk to my grandad, if everyone promises not to swear.

Jarjar Yeah – Andy can't shout 'I shagged your grand-daughter'.

Natasha blushes.

Andy I've got a better idea. How about we tell your granny that you got caught wanking over your *Star Wars* fucking action figures?

Some general derision directed towards Jarjar.

Jarjar I wasn't wanking . . .

Andy No, that's right, you were 'checking yourself' –

Jarjar Yes. I was. Don't you ever check yourself?

Mark All the bleeding time, mate.

Ryan I'm constantly checking myself.

Jarjar You can think what you like –

Andy I don't like thinking about it –

Jarjar Obviously you do.

Sophie Oh for fuck's sake . . .

Andy Obviously I don't.

Jarjar Oh, *touché* – you really know your comebacks.

Andy I know a wanker when I see one.

Jarjar Yeah, you know quite a lot, don't you?

Andy I know you're an arsehole.

Jarjar Yeah, well, maybe you don't know everything.

Pause.

Andy What's that supposed to mean?

Natasha Andy, leave him alone.

Andy Leave *him* alone?

Natasha Yes, just – leave it alone.

Pause.

Mark Ooops. Domestic . . .
Andy What's that supposed to mean? 'I don't know everything'?
Jarjar Just what it means.

Pause. Phoebe gets up.

Phoebe Right – you obviously aren't serious about this. I wish you'd told me before I bothered bringing all this stuff round.
Ryan Where are you going?
Phoebe I'm going home.

The desired chorus of objections.

Ryan We're going to do it, Phoebe, come on. I'm into it.
Mark Totally.
Natasha Yeah, Phoebe, don't go. They're just being their usual idiot selves.

Pause.

Phoebe This is a serious thing. You have to have respect.
Ryan We will.
Mark I'm totally respectful.
Phoebe Everyone, though.

Pause.

Jarjar Why are you looking at me?
Phoebe Because you already said you don't believe in it.
Jarjar I'm not saying I'm right. I hope I'm wrong. I hope there is an afterlife, that'd be brilliant. UFOs would be brilliant too. I just don't think there are any.
Sophie I saw a UFO in Chepstow.
Mark Where's Chepstow?
Jarjar Yeah, what you mean is you saw something you couldn't identify. That doesn't make it a UFO.
Sophie My dad saw it too.

Jarjar Yeah, but when they say 'unidentified', I don't think they mean unidentified by you and your dad. An Unidentified-by-Sophie-and-her-dad Flying Object.

Natasha So what, you just think there's nothing? After you die?

Jarjar Well, there's not nothing – there's everything else still going on. It's just you don't know anything about it.

Sophie That's horrible, though. Imagine being nothing.

Andy Yeah, but you don't know you're nothing . . .

Jarjar Yeah, you're not sitting there thinking, 'This is shit being nothing.' That would be something. You've already been nothing, before you were born. You weren't thinking. 'God, this is shit not being born,' were you?

Pause.

Sophie Have you ever thought, right, that it's definitely going to happen? That one day you're going to wake up and that's going to be, like – the last day of your life?

Pause.

I mean, that's *definitely* going to happen. No matter what else happens, we're definitely going to die one day. We're all going to die.

They contemplate this. She rubs her chest.

I'm getting a funny feeling just thinking about it.

Jarjar Don't think about it then.

Pause.

Ryan So – shall we do this . . . séance thing?

Pause.

Phoebe?

Phoebe I don't really see the point in it.

Natasha No, Sophie's not saying she thinks we'll all be nothing – are you?

Sophie No, I'm just saying – that we're all going to die.

Pause.

Phoebe Alright – so the first thing we need to do . . .
Natasha Oh!

They all jump.

Oh, I'm sorry – Phoebe – just one second, I'm so sorry – this'll just take one second. (*To Ryan.*) Go and get the camera.

Ryan What?
Natasha Get the camera. Take a picture of us.

Pause.

Sorry – I know it's stupid, but I realised the other day I don't have a photo of us all together. It'll only take a second, do you mind?

Andy Take one with a phone.
Natasha No, they're rubbish – I want a proper one. Get the camera – please. It'll be really quick. And then we can all have a copy.

Ryan goes to get the camera.

Sophie I look a right state.
Mark No you don't. You look fine.
Sophie My hair's a mess.
Mark No, your hair's really nice. Look at me – I've put on about two stone over the holidays.
Sophie No you haven't.
Mark I have, honestly. I've just been stuffing my face.
Jarjar Yeah, with dick.
Mark Yeah, well – your dad didn't seem to mind.

Natasha Honestly, it really doesn't matter – it's just it's nearly the end of the holidays and I just wanted a picture of us all in the one place.

Mark Yeah, no – I'm with you. It's a good idea.

Jarjar I agree. It's a stroke of genius. A photograph! Who'd have thought of such a thing?!

Andy I didn't know Ryan had a camera.

Natasha Hmm?

Andy I've never seen him with a camera.

Natasha Everyone's got a camera.

Andy Not everyone.

Pause.

Sophie Did anyone see there's adverts for school uniforms on already?

Mark Yeah, in all the windows in town, man. It's a bummer.

Jarjar Do we have to talk about it?

Phoebe I don't know. I'm quite bored of the holidays. They seem to have just dragged on this year.

Sophie I'm bored of the holidays but I'm not so bored I want to go back to school.

Ryan enters, carrying a camera.

Ryan It's not the best camera ever . . .

Natasha How are we going to do this?

Mark We can all sit round the ouijy-mabob.

Natasha No, but – how does Ryan get to be in it?

Mark Have you got, like, a tripod thing?

Jarjar Didn't you know – all the girls call him Tripod.

Mark All the boys maybe.

Natasha Has it got a timer thing?

Ryan checks his camera.

Phoebe I'll take it.

Natasha No, Phoebe . . .

Phoebe It's fine. Give it to me.

She takes the camera from Ryan.

Ryan You just press the thing.
Phoebe Yes, I do know how to take a picture, thanks.

They all gather around the table.
Andy's arm slides around Natasha, though he tries to disguise it by doing the same to Mark, on his other side.

Jarjar Alright – everyone say 'headcheese'.
All HEADCHEESE!

Phoebe takes the shot, looks at it. They start to separate.

Phoebe No, wait – one more.

Pause.

Ryan Three, two, one –
All HEADCHEESE!

She takes the shot, looks at it. She looks puzzled.

Ryan What is it?
Phoebe I think you're moving too much.

Ryan comes to look.

Phoebe It's all blurry.
Ryan Oh yeah . . . that's funny.
Mark Turn the big light on.
Ryan Yeah – turn the light on. It might be the exposure.

Natasha turns on the light and they gather round the table. Now Ryan is beside her, with Andy squeezed into the margins.

Sophie Third time lucky.

Ryan Right but everyone has to stay really still, okay?
Don't say anything this time.

Phoebe One, two, three –

She takes the shot, looks at it. Again she's puzzled.

Sophie What?

Phoebe It's still blurred. Are you sure you're not all
moving?

Mark I didn't move.

Jarjar Solid as a rock, I was.

Ryan looks at the camera.

Ryan It's a piece-of-shit camera, that's the problem.

Natasha Oh no . . . seriously?

*Mark's mobile phone rings. He answers it. The others
disperse.*

Andy Just use a camera phone.

Natasha Yeah, but they look so crap . . .

Andy Mine doesn't.

Phoebe Nobody's died in here, have they?

Ryan Died?

Phoebe A murder, a suicide, anything like that?

Ryan Don't think so.

Phoebe Are you sure?

Ryan It's not that old a house.

Natasha Why, Phoebe?

Sophie Yeah, why?

Phoebe Could be a spirit. They sometimes interfere with
electrical stuff.

Ryan Honestly, it's really not that good a camera.

Mark finishes his call.

Mark Hey, man – that's my brother coming over. He's
got the bike.

Ryan The bike?

Mark Bought it today.

Jarjar *The* bike? The famed Bike of Legend?

Mark Yeah, man. *Yamaha XJR 130.* Twelve-fifty-one cc, ninety-six-point-five horsepower.

Jarjar Electric fuel injection?

Mark Course.

Ryan You've got no idea what that means, have you?

Jarjar Not a clue. Who's got the skins?

Natasha is at the window.

Natasha Hey, look – the sky's amazing.

Ryan So is it backies all round?

Mark For me it is. I'm going home in style.

Andy joins Natasha at the window.

Ryan When's he coming?

Mark He's on his way now.

Natasha I'm going outside.

Sophie Yeah, I'll come out. I could do with some air. Phoebe – coming out?

Phoebe sighs.

Natasha Yeah, come on, Phoebe. It' still warm. We can sit on the hill. Just till the sun comes down.

Mark Can you hear that?

Sophie, Natasha and Andy leave. This is not lost on Ryan.

I think I can hear it from here.

Ryan Let's go and see.

Jarjar Is that it with the séance, then?

Ryan No, man, we'll be back. We've got to go and greet the Bike of Legend.

Ryan and Mark leave.
Jarjar is rolling his joint.

Phoebe Can I get a draw of that when you're done?
Jarjar Do you smoke?
Phoebe Yeah, sure.
Jarjar Cool. I didn't know whether to offer you any or not.
Phoebe Yeah. I smoke with my mum sometimes.
Jarjar Oh, wow. That must be so weird.
Phoebe Not really.

He finishes rolling it. He looks at it.

Jarjar Everyone's gone.

Pause.

It is quite a freaky sky.

She shrugs.

I know. So what? But it might make for some nice visuals.

Again, she shrugs. They start to drift towards the door.

Are you pissed off about the séance?
Phoebe Well, I just brought all the stuff over.
Jarjar Yeah, I know. But it's okay. It'll be there when we get back.

They exit.
     The abandoned séance table sits there empty, and we watch it for some time. The light on it changes as a cloud passes over the late summer sun.

The End.

Production Notes

The Séance is concerned with the first glimmers of understanding that life is finite. The play is necessarily vague and unruly and should be seen as an opportunity to examine subtext. Relationships between the characters are often only hinted at, and it is encouraged that the actors extrapolate what they can from the text and invent when there is no clear direction.

The words in themselves are not paramount, and place names, colloquialisms and banter can be adapted to suit the individual productions. However, this should only be attempted after an in-depth examination of the text and with certainty that the meaning of the play remains unaltered. There may, in some circumstances, be a desire to change the sex of the characters, but this should be discouraged as the balance of sexes is important.

The language is often raw, as it is with most children, and it is understood that this may be off-putting to some groups. If the swearing is completely inadmissable, the author would rather it was removed altogether than unrealistically neutered. Be aware, though, that this will upset the rhythm of certain lines and – however lamentably – be a less realistic depiction of most young people's speech patterns.

Anthony Neilson

SIX PARTIES

William Boyd

William Boyd's novels include *Good Man in Africa* (Whitbread Award and Somerset Maugham Prize), *An Ice-Cream War* (shortlisted for 1982 Booker Prize; won John Llewellyn Rhys Prize), *Stars and Bars*, *The New Confessions*, *Brazzaville Beach* (McVitie Prize and James Tait Black Memorial Prize), *The Blue Afternoon* (Sunday Express Book of the Year Award, Los Angeles Times Award for Fiction), *Armadillo*, *Any Human Heart* (Prix Jean Monnet), and *Restless* (Costa Book Award, Novel of the Year). His novels and stories have been published around the world and translated into over thirty languages. He has also published a collection of screenplays; a memoir of his schooldays, *School Ties*; three collections of short stories – *On the Yankee Station*, *The Destiny of Nathalie 'X'* and *Fascination* – a speculative memoir, *Nat Tate: an American Artist*, and *Bamboo*, a collection of his non-fiction writings. His screenwriting credits include *Stars and Bars*, *Mr Johnson*, *Aunt Julia and the Scriptwriter*, *Chaplin*, *A Good Man in Africa*, *The Trench* and *Man to Man*. He adapted for TV Evelyn Waugh's *Scoop* and his *Sword of Honour* trilogy, and his own novel *Armadillo*. His film about Shakespeare and his sonnets – *A Waste of Shame* – was made for BBC 4. He has written two original TV films about boarding-school life in England, *Good and Bad at Games* and *Dutch Girls*. In 2005 he was awarded the CBE.

Characters

Femi
eighteen, a poor local African boy
with high ambitions and powerful dreams;
streetwise, energetic, likeable

Edward
eighteen, English; a good-looking guy, cool,
but a bit morally lazy. Things have come
a bit too easily for him.

Ben
eighteen to nineteen, a rich African boy going
places, with inherited wealth; fairly arrogant
and sure of himself: the world's his oyster

Amy
seventeen to eighteen, Ben's sister: pretty,
clever and theatrical, wants to be an actress

Cathy
eighteen, American, pretty, perhaps a little
worthy and earnest. Not quite the free spirit
an art student should be

Peter
nineteen, an Oxford undergraduate,
self-assured and complacent

Security Guards

PARTY NUMBER ONE

The stage is dark. The music begins. Very loud: 'Can't Buy Me' by Femi Kuti.

The lights come up to reveal an empty stage. Music fades.

A white boy, Edward, eighteen, comes onstage. He's wearing jeans, flip-flops, a T-shirt.

It's hot. We hear the sound of crickets, night birds, frogs croaking. This is Africa.

Edward peers out into the darkness of the garden.

Edward Femi! . . . Femi! . . . Are you there?

Silence.
Edward looks back at the party. Mutters oaths to himself.

FEMI . . !

Silence. A young black guy comes out from the party. This is Ben, eighteen. His clothes look more expensive than Edward's. He has a middle-class London accent, like Edward.

Ben Is he here?
Edward Not yet.
Ben They're getting thirsty in there, Ed.
Edward He'll be here – he never lets me down.
Ben It's your party, mate – but beer and Coca-Cola isn't what they're really after . . .
Edward It'll be sorted.

Ben exits.

Edward peers into the darkness of the garden.

Femi! Where the fuck are you?

From the darkness:

Femi I'm here, Ed. Keep your cool.

Femi steps onto the stage. A young black guy, eighteen. He is wearing a singlet, his jeans look worn almost to rags. He has two clear glass bottles stopped with corks in his hands. His accent is African.
   He puts a bottle on the ground and they do a kind of soul-handshake.

Edward You said you'd be here at eight. Jesus –
Femi They go have road blocks everywhere. The army is on the streets, man. Na very difficult to get here from town.
Edward Okay, okay . . . Sorry. How much?

Femi hands over the two bottles. Ed looks at them dubiously. Takes the cork off one – smells it, recoils.

Femi He dey best. Ten each.
Edward Ten?
Femi One hundred people go get drunk with this, man. One hundred . . .
Edward But will we go blind?
Femi That he go cost you more.

They laugh.

Edward I'll get the money. Don't go away . . .

A white girl comes out of the party, Cathy, eighteen or nineteen. She's American.

Cathy Ed – there you are. What're you doing out here? It's your party –

She sees Femi. Edward doesn't introduce her. He holds up the bottles.

Edward It's for the punch . . . (*Nods at Femi.*) Special delivery.

Femi smiles at Cathy.

Hi. I'm Femi –

Cathy opens a bottle, sniffs it. Recoils.

Cathy What is it? Wow . . .

Edward It's gin. Illicit gin.

Femi They make it in the creeks. I know the people who can make it like the old way. Very strong –

Edward (*to Cathy*) It makes you go blind.

Cathy Great. So that's what all that punch is for.

Edward Yeeeeh . . . Let's go. (*to Femi.*) Thanks, Femi, I'll be one minute.

Ben comes out, beer bottle in hand. Clocks Femi.

Ben Right. The man with the plan –

Edward We got it. I'll put it in the punch. It's the real deal.

He and Cathy go back to the party. Ben and Femi look at each other.

Ben You get the real thing? From the stills in the creeks?

Femi Of course.

Femi is aware of the wealth difference between him and Ben but it doesn't affect his attitude: unperturbed, unafraid.
Ben swigs his beer.

Ben How much did you pay?

Femi Ten a bottle.

Ben Ten? You must be joking –

Femi If you want I can get you shit stuff for less.

Ben (*interested*) Yeah? What else can you get?

Femi I can get everything, man. I'm the fixer. You ask Ed.

Ben Can you get me some baraka?

Femi I go get you weed, I get you dope, I get you baraka.

Ben You get me some baraka, I pay you well. (*Looks round.*) Give it to Ed. He'll bring it to me.

Femi Okay. No problem. I get good baraka, the best.

He offers his hand. Ben affects not to notice.

Ben I'm Ben, by the way.

Femi I know who you are. I know your father. Your family. I know who you are . . .

Ben Then you know if you make me happy –

Drops into African accent.

Den you go be happy too.

Femi Na true-oh.

They laugh.
 Ed comes out, followed by a black girl, Amy, eighteen, Ben's sister. She has a middle-class London accent, like Ben and Edward.

Amy What's going on out here? Who's he?

Femi Hi. I go be Femi.

Ben Femi the fixer.

Ed hands over notes to Femi.

Are we sorted?

Edward I recommend the punch, sir.

Laughter.

Amy Ah-hah. (*Spooky voice.*) My head clears and I begin to understand . . .

Edward See you, Femi. And thanks.

Ben And don't forget –

Femi – I never forget.

*He smiles, waves and is gone. Edward clocks this
exchange.*

Edward (*to Ben*) Forget what?
Ben Nothing. How do you know him, Femi?
Edward He came to fix my dad's car one day. We got
talking. He's a nice guy . . .
Ben Useful guy –
Amy (*affected posh accent*) I have this strange craving
for punch all of a sudden.

They laugh.
    The three of them go back into the party.
    *Femi discreetly steps back onstage, watches them
go. The music swells. Extremely loud: 'Bamba Sunu
Goorgui' by Cheikh Lo.*
    Lights fade to black.

PARTY NUMBER TWO

The music continues. The lights go up. Music fades.
    *Leaf shadows, crickets trill, night birds call. We are in
a tropical garden.*
    *Edward and Femi scale a high wall and drop down
into this garden.*
    They crouch, hiding themselves.
    To one side are a couple of chairs (or a bench).

Femi For why are we doing this, Ed?
Edward Because I wasn't invited.
Femi Whose party is it?
Edward Peter's.
Femi And he never invite you?
Edward Worse: he deliberately didn't invite me . . . (*He
sees something.*) Now you'll see why . . .

363

They crouch down.
    Cathy comes onstage with Peter, nineteen, English,
a student at Oxford University. His accent is slightly
posher.
    Peter clearly fancies Cathy. Cathy's not so sure.
    They linger at the edge of the stage, out of earshot
of Edward and Femi.
    Peter tries to kiss Cathy. She pushes him away,
affectionately. They banter.

Femi Now I go see . . .
Edward I got to get her out of here, Femi. Ben's having a
    party tonight in Bodija – I've got to get her away from
    that guy . . .

    Femi looks at Edward – sees he's in something of a
    state. Femi thinks.

Femi Give me two minutes.

    He scurries off.
        Cathy and Peter move closer.

Peter So when did you hear?
Cathy I got the letter this morning.
Peter Art school. Wow – cool . . . Where is it?
Cathy St Martin's. St Martin's School of Art –

    Peter looks blank.

It's in London.
Peter London? Brilliant. We can see each other. Come
    down to Oxford at the weekend. Next year I move out
    of college – I'll have a flat. Brilliant. Congratulations –
    you're the first art student I've met.
Cathy Maybe it would be better if you came to London –
    few more things to do . . .
Peter I'll come to London to see you any day of the week.

    Tries to kiss her again.

Cathy No! Peter, please –
Peter But I really like you, Cathy . . .
Cathy I'm seeing Edward –
Peter He's a schoolboy. He's doing his A levels . . .

The contempt is obvious.

Cathy I like Ed, he's cool –
Peter Ed Scully – cool? Oxymoron, I'm afraid –

Shout from party.

Voice (*off*) Pete? Pete? Are you there?
Peter Yeah? What is it?
Voice (*off*) Some guy here, says he's got your delivery.

Peter looks baffled.

Peter My 'delivery' . . . (*To Cathy.*) Be back in a sec –

He darts off.
      *Cathy stands there alone, wanders around, turns.
She has her back to the hiding Edward.*
      Edward stands, approaches.

Edward   Hey, Cathy –

She starts, turns.

Cathy Ed, my God. What are you doing here?
Edward I came early. Thought you'd be here. Went for a
    walk in the garden for some stimulation. So fucking
    boring – all those students. God . . .
Cathy Pete was just here –
Edward Yeah, I heard him: 'Come to Oxford, come to
    my college' . . . Why would anyone want to go to
    Oxford? It's a small provincial town in the middle of
    England –
Cathy It was just because I'm going to London . . .
Edward Yeah, I heard that too. St Martin's School of
    Art. Thanks for telling me.

Cathy I haven't told anyone – my parents don't want me to go. 'Why can't you go to art school in New York?' It's all I hear . . . We argued a lot – *(Smiles.)* But I won't. So I'm going . . .

Edward It's my gap year. I can come to London. I've a cousin, he's got a flat in –

Cathy Let's just take it one step at a time, Ed. It's all going too fast for me –

Edward Listen, Cath, Ben's having a small party – tonight, at his parents' house, in Bodija – they're out of town. He's got a band. It'll be great. Let's get out of here.

He takes her hand. She's tempted. Looks back at the party.

Cathy I should say goodbye to Pete –

Edward No, no. I don't think Ben and Peter get on that well. Let's just clear out –

Suddenly, shouts from the party. A crash of breaking glass.

Cathy Jesus!

Angry voices. Sounds of a scuffle, chairs going over.

Edward A fight. Students, see? What do you expect?

Cathy I should check –

Edward No, let's go now –

Cathy *(deciding spontaneously)* Yeah. Okay –

They run off into the darkness. A beat.
Then Femi runs out of the party. His T-shirt is ripped. He's panting, high on adrenaline.
Peter follows him out, blood streaming from his nose.

Peter Where are you, you bastard? Fucking bastard!

Femi *(shouting)* You no catch me, white boy! You nevah nevah go catch me!

He laughs and runs off.
Peter stumbles out into the garden, peering around him. Realises Femi has gone. Calms down somewhat. Looks around.

Peter Cathy? Cathy, are you there . . .? Cathy . . .?

Music swells. Loud: 'Ako' by Fela Kuti.
Lights fade to black. Music continues.

PARTY NUMBER THREE

Music continues. Lights fade up.
Edward and Cathy run on stage. They've just arrived.
Excited. They look around them.
Music fades.

Edward What the hell was going on at that road block? Those guys were so aggressive –

Cathy God, Look at this house! It's a palace . . . Look, there's the pool . . .

Edward (*shouts*) Hey, Ben, where are you? The celebs have arrived. You said no paparazzi!

He looks at Cathy, takes her in his arms.

Glad you came with me?
Cathy Maybe . . .

They kiss.
Amy comes on stage, sees them.

Amy (*sings*) Hello, young lovers, wherever you are . . .

Ed and Cathy break apart, smiling, a little embarrassed.

I thought you were never coming . . .
Edward Cathy was 'otherwise engaged'. Then she saw the light . . .

Amy Very wise. The band have arrived. Wait till you hear them –

Cathy I have to go to the bathroom first.

Amy Up the stairs, take a right on the landing.

Cathy heads off.

Amy (*dowager Duchess's voice*) 'Such a shweet young child . . .' (*Pause.*) You've obviously got a thing for American girls –

Edward For a particular American girl. . .

Amy draws near – she fancies Ed.

Amy You really like her? . . .

Edward Yeah . . . She's nice. She's going to art school in London, though.

Amy Ah-ha. Absent cat – mouse opportunity . . .

Edward What do you mean? –

Amy Face it, Ed. You'll be back in England, at boarding school doing your A levels. Do I need to say more? And she'll be at art college. In London –

Edward So what?

Amy So get real, Ed. It's going to end.

Edward (*suspecting she's right*) I don't see why it –

Amy I really like you, Ed . . . (*She takes his arm.*) *Really* like you, you know? . . .

Edward (*awkward, glancing behind him*) Yeah. Right. And I like you, Amy.

Amy Good. Well let's have a dance on that, then . . .

They go off stage.
    Ben and Femi come on stage. Ben spots Femi's ripped T-shirt.

Ben What happened to you?

Femi Some wahallah with a white boy. Friend of Ed's . . .

Ben Oh, yeah?

Femi I was helping Ed out.

Ben Femi the fixer . . . You know Ed long?

Femi Since his last holiday when he come here for Christmas. His father had problem with car, I fix it – I talk to Ed, I say: 'If you ever want something, first you come to Femi.' And so, like that, I came to know him . . .

Ben Did you 'fix' my deal?

Femi fishes in his pocket, takes out a small bag of white powder.
  Ben opens it, takes a tiny pinch and snorts it, licks his fingers, rubs them on his gums.

Ben How much?

Femi Two hundred.

Ben looks at him. Decides it's a fair price. Takes a big wad of notes out of his pocket and peels off a few, hands them to Femi. Hands him another one.

Ben Buy yourself a new shirt. If this is good I'll come back to you.

Femi Is good stuff, Ben. I never shit you, I promise. If Femi say he can get you good stuff he get you. I nevah lie-oh.

Ben Okay – I get the message –

Femi (*insistently*) And if, perhaps, one day I can help your father –

Ben (*guarded, suddenly*) How could you help my father?

Femi When you are Minister for Defence, every day you must have problem. Every day – big problem, small problem. So maybe one day you say: 'I have small-small problem but he bother me. He trouble me too much. So – I go ask Femi to solve this small-small problem for me.' Femi can do it, very secret, very quiet. Some day, maybe . . . maybe he will have a need for a Femi.

Ben (*laughing*) You think my father would need a
Lokomeji boy like you? You're dreaming, man –

Femi I can dream. We are allowed to dream. No
government, no army, no police can stop us from
dreaming . . .

Ben looks at him. Smiles.

Ben Yeah . . . Tell you what, you come upstairs with me
and we'll find you a proper shirt.

Femi (*cautious, amazed*) I can come for party . . . You go
let me stay?

Ben As long as you behave yourself.

*Femi accedes, gladly. They go offstage, passing Ed
and Cathy.*

Edward Hey, Femi – you alright?

Femi Everything is good tonight, my friend. Everything.

Edward (*meaningfully*) By the way, thanks, Femi –

Femi I see you later.

He and Ben leave.

Cathy Who is that guy? What's he doing here, with Ben?
I don't get it –

Edward He's just a nice guy. Helpful, you know. Lots of
contacts . . .

Cathy Seems weird to me –

Edward I don't want to talk about Femi. I want to talk
about you. And me. Are you coming back out here in
the summer holidays?

Cathy I don't know . . . Depends. I've got to find an
apartment in London. I should be here, in theory. My
parents want me to come, before I start –

Edward Because I'll be finished then, you see. I decided
I'm not going to university – waste of three years. So
I'll be coming out here this summer – it'd be fantastic

if you were as well. We could travel: go to the coast,
take the train north –
Cathy I can't make any plans tonight, Ed. I don't know
where I'll be living. I don't know London, I have to
figure out my course –
Edward But if you come we could travel a bit. Yeah?
What d'you say, Cath? Think about it. I'll be free as a
bird.
Cathy Ah. But what kind of bird?
Edward The all-devouring American eagle . . .

They kiss gently.
  *Music swells. Very loud: 'Greetings' by Joni
Haastrup.*
  Lights fade to black.

PARTY NUMBER FOUR

Lights fade up.
  *Edward comes onstage, a beer bottle in his hand. He
looks terminally bored.*
  The music fades.
  *We hear the metallic trill of crickets, the calls of night
birds. Ed takes a swig from his beer.*
  Amy wanders on stage.

Amy (*American accent*) Well howdy, stranger. (*Pause.*)
Taking the air?

Ed looks at her.

Edward I had to get out of there.
Amy I think I'm slightly more bored than you are . . .
Edward No, you're not. I had to get out because I was
about to die from boredom . . . When are you going
back to England?

371

Amy Next week. Monday . . .

Edward I'm staying on a bit longer. What about Ben?

Amy Going back with me. He's got an interview. (*Awestruck voice.*) With a merchant bank in the City . . .

Pause. They mooch around.

Amy Not the same out here in the summer holidays, is it?

Edward Not enough people. Not like Christmas or Easter.

Amy You had your results?

Edward Next week.

Amy Do okay?

Edward Okay-ish.

Amy What did you do?

Edward Geography, Biology and Religious Studies.

Amy Interesting career path . . . But as you're not going to university it doesn't matter.

Edward Ah . . . slight change of plan there.

Amy 'The parental hand came down firmly on his behind.' What're you going to do?

Edward One-year course in Media Studies.

Amy That's unusual. Where?

Edward Westminster.

Amy Ah. London. The 'big smoke'. (*Pause.*) Thought you might be going to art school . . . In London, you know, St Martin's . . .

Edward Yeah. Right . . .

Amy You seen Cathy?

Edward No.

Amy I thought she was coming out this holidays.

Edward So did I. She may come out. I called her house, asked her mother. All the plans are a bit up in the air . . .

Amy And how is Cathy getting on?

Edward Haven't a clue.

Amy Ah . . .

Edward You were right. I think she's dumped me . . .
I think . . .

Amy It doesn't make me feel any better . . . if that makes
you feel any better.

Edward mooches around. He's pissed off.

Want to play tennis tomorrow?

Edward Not particularly.

Amy Chess?

Edward Ha-ha.

Amy Want to come to my house?

Edward I'm at your house.

Amy But I'll be all alone tomorrow afternoon . . .

Edward gets the message.

Edward Amy, please –

Amy You can't be thinking of that American girl –

Edward Cathy –

Amy (*American accent*) Oh, gee, sarry, Caaaathy . . .
She's history, mate . . . Or should that be: you're
history, mate?

Edward But when I go to Westminster –

Amy 'Hope lives eternal in the human heart' . . . I like
you, Ed, got it? Do you want me to go around
carrying a sign? 'AMY FANCIES EDWARD SOMETHING
ROTTEN'?

Edward Leave it out. I like you – I just need some time.

Amy (*in Cockney*) I need some time. I need some time . . .
Me 'eart is broken . . .

Edward Bruised . . .

Pause.

Amy You like me . . .

Edward Yes . . . I do . . . Genuinely . . .

Amy But not enough.

*Edward gestures – 'Whatever.' Whatever 'enough'
means . . .*

Is it because I'm black?
Edward Don't be stupid. My head's just a bit fucked-up
over Cathy –
Amy It *is* because I'm black.
Edward Paranoid –
Amy Then kiss me.

She comes over to him.

Amy Your girlfriend's dumped you. You're bored, you're
feeling very sorry for yourself and this beautiful black
girl has just come up to you and said, 'Give us a kiss.'
What do you do? What does a red-blooded Englishman
do in these circumstances?

*Edward puts his arms around her. Not exactly
enthusiastically.*

Edward I don't mind kissing you –
Amy Thanks a lot –
Edward – just to prove that it's nothing to do with you
being –
Amy Point taken –
Edward But it doesn't change anything.
Amy Why don't we give it a go and see?

*Their heads move slowly together. Amy closes her
eyes. Their lips nearly touch.*
Suddenly –
*Low whoops as sirens start up – revving, gunning
of car motors. Sirens scream off into the night.*

Edward (*shocked*) Jesus Christ! What was that?

Amy is angry, the moment gone, the mood broken.

Amy Our police cars.

Edward 'Your' police cars?

Amy We have two police cars outside the house, twenty-four-seven.

Edward Why?

Amy Because of the situation in the country. Because of who my father is.

Edward looks blank. Amy explains things to him as simply as possibly.

Amy The government thinks there's going to be a civil war. There are rebel militias in the river delta, guerrillas. Don't you read the newspapers . . .? Why do you think there're all these soldiers on the streets, the road blocks? They're mobilising the reserves, drafting new recruits – I don't know. I can't go shopping without a bodyguard these days – an armed bodyguard.

Edward Why?

Amy Why what?

Edward Why can't you go shopping without a bodyguard?

Amy (*exasperated*) Edward! . . . Because we're like . . . My family, my father, his father – my mother, her father, Ben, and me – sort of – we're like . . . Like the royal family in this country. We have to be protected . . .

Edward Oh, I see . . .

Edward gives a deep bow.
Amy's irritated. She listens to the sirens coming back again.

Amy Something must have spooked them . . .

Edward Yeah . . .

Amy (*approaching*) Now, where were we? . . .

Edward I've got to go . . . (*Gives her a peck on the cheek.*) Let's have that game of chess tomorrow. I'll give you a call . . .

He goes, with a wave.

Amy stands there, reflecting. Music swells. Very
loud: 'Swing Yela' by Baaba Maal.
Fade to black.

PARTY NUMBER FIVE

Fade up lights, music continuing.
Edward and Cathy come onstage. Cathy looks
different, older somehow, more sure of herself.

Edward I'll be there in September. Maybe even before.
We'll be in London together – at college. I've got to
find a flat. Maybe I could share with you –

Cathy It's not like that, Ed. It's not like being here –
everything's different. We'll have different circles of
friends, it's all –

Edward Fantastic. I hate my friends –

Cathy Ed, you have to –

Voice (*off*) Cathy? Where's the ice? –

Cathy I got to go –

Edward They'll find the ice. Ice – refrigerator. How
difficult can it be?

Cathy Look. It's my party –

Edward – and you can cry if you want to . . .

They look at each other.
Cathy has to laugh. Edward takes her in his arms.
Kisses her gently.

Cathy Bastard . . .

Edward See, I told you everything would be fine . . .

Femi Hey, Ed!

They both look round.
Femi is there. But Femi changed, in a silk shirt and
a gold chain around his neck. Cocky, nervy, full of
himself.

Edward Femi . . . How are you, man? Haven't seen you for ages.

They do their little soul-handshake.

Femi I'm okay. For the moment.

Edward You know Cathy –

Femi (*glancing at her*) Yeah. Hi, Cathy. Ed, I have to talk to you –

Cathy (*cold*) I don't remember inviting you to my party.

Femi (*unfazed*) No problem, Ed go tell me to come.

This is clearly news to Edward.

Cathy (*to Ed*) You did?

Femi Sure. Of course you did, Ed . . .

Edward Yeah, ah, I said if he was around he should drop by –

Cathy (*pissed off*) Great. I'm gonna find some ice . . .

She walks off.
 Edward and Femi watch her go.

Femi Ow!

Edward (*bitterly*) Thanks, Femi –

Femi (*urgently*) Ben, he dey here?

Edward Yeah, I just saw him.

Femi Can you fetch him for me?

Edward He's inside. Just go and see him. You're a 'guest', remember –

Femi Ed, I want for you to bring Ben here. Ask him – say Femi he dey for outside – in garden. He go come.

The new Femi has a strange authority. Ed takes this in.

Edward Okay – I'll go and tell him.

He wanders off, leaving Femi – who despite his apparent assurance is clearly in some kind of a state. Femi mooches around, then Ben comes out.

Ben Hey, Femi. I called you today. No answer . . .

Femi Oh yeah?

Ben No worries – I've got the money.

He takes the wad of notes out of his pocket and begins to peel off a few.

I might need some more stuff for the weekend, right? Couple of hundred – best you've got . . .

He hands over the notes.

Femi Keep it.

Ben What?

Femi You can keep it.

Ben (*cautious*) But I owe you. You've been very patient . . .

Femi You can pay me in another way . . .

Ben Oh, right, I get it –

Femi No you don't get nothing, my friend.

He takes some papers out of his pocket.

You know what he dey be?

Ben No.

Femi (*with some passion*) This paper call me for army. He say: Femi you go to Alokuju Barracks, Monday morning. You go for army. You go fight rebel soldier in river delta. We give you rifle – we give you bullet – we give you uniform. Femi, you soldier-boy now –

Ben I don't see what I can do . . .

Femi (*getting riled*) Hey, Ben, please, don't treat me like madman fool from the bush. Your father he dey be Minister for Defence. *Minister for Defence.* In the gov'ment for our country. He go control the army. Your father he say – we don't want this Femi for soldier. We don't need him for army. He no be good for army. (*Pause, spreads arms.*) Problem he done go away . . .

Ben says nothing, running through the implications.

Ben Take the money, Femi –

Femi I no take money. You pay me this way.

Ben I can't do it. He won't do it for *me* . . .

Femi Then we have plenty wahallah for you, my friend. The son of the Minister for Defence in big, big trouble. Maybe I write him letter – 'Your son, him like baraka too too much . . .'

Ben (*quickly – suddenly worried*) Okay. Okay. I'll ask him. I'm sure something can be done, you know? Pull some strings. We can do it – don't worry, Femi.

Femi And I go bring you your weekend party petrol – a special gift from me. Femi go be your friend, Ben – don't forget.

Ben Yeah, sure. Thanks . . .

Femi hands him his call-up papers. Ben takes them. Femi leaves with a swagger in his step.
    Ben watches him go. Smiles.
    Then he tears up his call-up papers. Lets them drop on the ground.
    Music swells, very loud: 'Beng Beng Beng' by Femi Kuti.
    Ben wanders off, back to the party. Fade to black. Music continues.

PARTY NUMBER SIX

Lights fade up. Music fades.
    Leaf shadow. Crickets trill. Night birds call. People mill around – go in and out of the party. Femi comes onstage.
    He's in camouflage uniform. He has a bloody bandage round his head.
    He crouches, hides in the undergrowth.

He watches as Ben, Amy, Cathy and Edward come out into the garden. They talk and laugh among themselves. He can't hear what they're saying.

Two Security Guards, in black uniforms with Uzi sub-machine guns slung round their shoulders, come by on their patrol round the house.

Femi hugs the ground.

They go by.

Ben gives them a wave. They acknowledge him with a salute. Femi relaxes, marginally.

Ben, Amy and Cathy go back in to the party. Edward wanders out into the garden.

Unzips his fly for a pee.

Femi Ed!

Edward Jesus! What? Who is it? –

Edward composes himself, zips up fly.

Femi? . . .

Femi emerges from his hiding place.

Christ, Femi – what's happening, man?

They do their soul-handshake, a little half-heartedly.

What're you doing in that get-up? What happened to you?

Femi They call me for army. They come take me for barracks. I no go be good soldier so they beat me. I run away . . .

Edward You ran away?

Femi I run away from barracks – they shoot at me but they no hit me –

Edward Jesus, Femi, you're in big trouble. You'd better get out of here –

Femi No. Ben he say he go help me, he go talk to his father. His father be Minister for Defence. He tell them – leave Femi, we no want him for army . . .

Edward It's not going to happen, Femi. You'd better just run.

Femi Where I go run? They find me anywhere. I go stay with you, Ed. You shelter me, you hide me in you house –

Edward No way, sorry, Femi –

Femi (*in some desperation*) Why? I go need you help, Ed. You my friend. I beg you to help me. I go beg you. Let me hide for your house. They never look for me in white man house –

Edward (*panicking somewhat*) No, no. That's impossible. Impossible . . . Look, I'll go and get Ben. Stay here. And watch out, they've got guards –

He runs off into the house. Femi takes cover.
The Security Guards do another circuit.
Edward and Ben come out, followed by Amy and Cathy. Ben is furious, confronts Femi.

Ben What the fuck are you doing here? Get out before I call the guards.

Femi (*angered*) Hey. Hey – you no talk to me like that. You done promise me – you say you talk to your father –

Ben My father doesn't deal with a piece of shit like you. Don't you know who he is? My father doesn't know people like you are alive. You're dreaming, you stupid Lokomeji idiot. Now get out of here – that's the biggest favour I'll do you –

Femi I no go, my friend . . .

He reaches into his pocket. Draws out an automatic pistol.
The girls scream. Edward recoils in shock.

Edward Femi! Don't –

Femi has the gun pointed in Ben's face.
  Ben is terrified. Femi is acting crazed, almost ranting in his desperation.

Femi Why you no go help me? I give you everything you want. I give you white friend everything. You say you my friend. No! No! You never my friend – you English man like him. (*Points at Ed.*) You no like me – you have hate for your heart. Hate for Femi . . . Why you call yourself 'Ben'? You want to be like white boy? You black man. You name Kwabena Ogomo. You nevah *Ben* . . . And you also –

He wheels on Amy, pointing the gun at her. She screams, recoils. Cathy grabs her, hugs her.
  Femi's seized with a kind of pure rage and resentment.

(*Shouting at Amy.*) You go be Amoka Ogomo. Amoka Ogomo . . . Who dey be this 'Amy'? (*Turns back to Ben.*) Who go be this 'Ben'? You go lie for your country, you go lie for your soul. You try to destroy me. Me, Femi – you make me suffer – I feel my suffer in my bone – me, Femi, black man for this country, black man for like your brother. You take from me, then you kill me –

The gun is now inches from Ben's face. He's terrified.

Ben Please, Femi, I'll do anything for you. I'll get you out of the army –

Femi No. I go kill you before – Kwabena Ogomo –

He levels gun.
  Suddenly –
  Edward shoulder-charges him. The gun goes off, harmlessly into the air. Femi goes flying.
  Edward and Ben leap on Femi, grapple with him.

*The sound of the shot brings the Security Guards
rushing through the garden.*
*Femi is hauled to his feet, his arms twisted brutally
behind him. He yells in pain.*
*Cathy has moved beside Edward. They are all
shaken, frightened.*
Ben dusts himself down. Seething, ashamed.

Ben Take him away.
Femi Ed! Ed – I go beg you. Help me! They go kill me, Ed!

He struggles against the Guards.

Cathy Ed – do something!
Edward What can I do?

*She looks at him with contempt. Turns, advances on
the Guards.*

Cathy Where are you taking him! He has the right to a
lawyer –

Ben steps in front of her, bars her way.

Ben Back off, Cathy. He's a gangster and a deserter. He
was going to kill me –
Cathy He's frightened – he's desperate. He wouldn't kill
you, for God's sake – he's your friend. And Ed's –

She looks at Edward.

Ben He was using us – we were all taken in. Leave it,
Cath – you don't understand. You don't understand
him – and what he's capable of – this is nothing to do
with you any more . . .

Cathy looks around. At Edward and Amy.

Cathy Are you just going to stand there?

*They don't move. Ben takes Cathy's arm. She tries to
shake him off but he won't let her.*

383

He begins to usher her away.

Ben You should go home, Cathy – best thing . . .

She shrugs his arm off in disgust, walks off.
Ben, Edward, Amy confront Femi, now limp,
exhausted, pinioned by the arms of the Security
Guards.
Ben talks to the Security Guards with a new
assurance and natural authority. He's back in control
again. His accent is suddenly African

You go take him to the garage. You go understand? Give
him some *kiri-kiri* – yeah . . . ? Then take him back to
the barracks . . . Throw him to the soldiers . . .

Security Guard Yes, sar. We give him some small *kiri-
kiri.*

Ben laughs. The Guards laugh.
They drag Femi away.

Femi Ed – I go beg you – help me! Help me, Ben! They
go kill me . . .

Edward stands there – torn, helpless, aware of his
utter weakness.
Ben walks off some way, picks up Femi's gun,
checks the clip. Amy goes up to Edward. She's moved.

Amy You saved his life, Ed –
Edward No, I was just trying –
Amy Okay. Not the right time. But you'll be rewarded, I
promise you. We won't forget this . . .

She kisses him on the cheek.
Ben comes over. The gun in his hand. He throws it
away. He puts his arms around them both. His 'normal'
accent is back again.

Ben Hey. I thought we were meant to be having a party, here . . .

They turn and walk back into the party, Ben's arms around the shoulders of Amy and Edward . . .

Music swells. Very loud: 'Can't Buy Me' by Femi Kuti.

Hold on the empty stage.

We begin to hear Femi's screams offstage as the guards go to work on him in the garage.

The relentless pounding beat of the music can't quite drown them out.

Fade to black.

Music continues.

The End.

Production Notes

Each of the six parties takes place on the verandah or the garden of a house in Africa. Depending on the size of the cast available, we can if we want be aware of other partygoers, semi-offstage, perhaps seen through a semi-transparent screen or doors: people dancing, drinking, chatting, generally milling about. They can spill onto the stage if required – but the key scenes featuring the main characters all take place some distance from the general revelry, on verandahs or further in the gardens. The action covers a few months in one year – two school holidays, Easter and Summer.

I suggest everyone wears jeans and changes tops for each party/scene – T-shirts, blouses, shirts, whatever. The clothes will tell us a certain amount about each character. Ben and Amy are rich, so what they wear will be expensive, designery, cool. In the case of Femi, it's even more important: his costume changes will reflect his rising fortunes – singlet, T-shirt, shirt, silk shirt, etc., until his last scene. The basic instruction is that each character wears a different top for each party.

I have noted suggestions for the music to introduce and end each party. I can provide a CD of all the tracks if required. All the music I've chosen is West African in origin and of differing periods from the 1970s to today. But any music will do as long as it is loud and percussive – music that makes you want to get up and dance.

I suggest a minimal number of props. Maybe a table, a couple of chairs. You could perform this play with no stage scenery or furniture. Lighting and sound effects can suggest everything each scene requires.

In this play I do not specify any particular country or any specific historical period. However, in my mind I'm thinking West Africa – if only because I was born in Ghana and brought up there and in Nigeria. But this play could theoretically take place anywhere in Africa – in South Africa, Kenya, Nigeria, Ivory Coast, Egypt, Gambia, Zambia – you name it. It could also take place in Latin America or the Far East with minimal changes. Its issues and dynamics are both timeless and completely contemporary.

FROM THE WORKSHOP

William Boyd is a successful and prizewinning novelist and screenwriter. He was awarded a CBE for his work in 2005. William was born in Accra, Ghana, in 1952 and grew up there and in Nigeria. His mother was a teacher and his father a doctor working in the then colonies of West Africa. His imagination is coloured by his African childhood, which he experienced till the age of nine, when he was sent to Scotland to boarding school, returning to what he called home in the school holidays.

A term he uses to describe the experience of being sent to Scotland is of being deracinated (to be uprooted from one's native or accustomed environment), which informs some of the themes explored in *Six Parties*. Scotland consisted of school and relatives, but Ghana and Nigeria were his home. Nigeria was the world he knew, understood and felt most comfortable in.

The West Africa that William grew up in had no white settler class. People came to work there to escape the hardship of post-war rationing and then went away. This resulted in there being little or no racial tension as in other African countries. The Nigeria William experienced was very racially mixed and completely multicultural and egalitarian, as is represented within the play. This proved to be a very exotic way of life but completely the norm.

Six Parties is the closest of his works to fictionally reflecting his memories of being a seventeen- or eighteen-year-old growing up in Nigeria. He would go back there for the school holidays, and there would be parties every night, with the parties in the summer holidays feeling flatter than others as they were longer and many families used to go home. There was a melting pot of nationalities, Dutch, French, American, Nigerian, at the parties and among his friends.

William has become interested in and is writing more and more about the concept of identity, what makes us who we are. Is it our parents, our home, our friends, where we went to school? He describes himself as being an Afro-Scot, and his African upbringing is very important to his own identity. He has become aware in developing countries like the one he grew up in of an alienated middle class developing. Children of wealthy parents are sent to English schools, creating a privileged elite in their native lands. These people are being alienated from the country they were born in and have different accents, expectations and wealth from the society around them.

This will affect future generations and impact on the whole society. It creates a cultural schism which provides some of the tension and dynamic in the play, especially between the characters of Ben, Amy and Femi. The play could be set in any developing country where this is happening – such as Argentina, China, the Ukraine – by simply changing the names.

The character of Femi feels very culturally centred. Having been born in Nigeria and living there, he is in touch with the world around him. Ben and Amy are caught between two cultures – the middle-class English of their education and the Nigerian of their birth. This informs much of the way they associate with and react to Femi. They are not at all associated with the Nigeria Femi represents. Their worlds are very different – the world of Ben and Amy being very privileged and middle class, the world of Femi being progressively more violent and aggressive.

One of the challenges of the play is to realise these two separate worlds and show the difference in wealth, social status, class and power which are the other themes visited in the play. The parties mentioned are very isolated from the world around them, taking place within virtually a gated community. As the play progresses the increasing instability of the outside world encroaches, becoming ever more present with the increased security checks, the sound of police sirens, and Femi being drafted into the army – suggesting that civil war is imminent or taking place by the end of the play.

It is important to create a sense of the violence of this outside world creeping in, as Femi becomes more and more desperate to escape it. There are several ways to do this, through some of the music mentioned in the play, which is very political and associated strongly with Femi, and other sound effects such as the police sirens. There is a choice to be made as to the advance of this world into the isolated community of the parties. There is room to play with the idea of the audience as the outside world.

The play also tackles the ideas of power, class and social status. What is your place within a group of friends, what are your values, and how are they formed? Although the play is based on William's experiences of growing up, the dilemmas faced by the characters in the play are entirely contemporary.

Ben and Amy seem more reluctant than other characters to engage with Femi. They are the children of wealthy parents who are being educated outside the country they were born in, returning only during the holidays. Femi is from the streets, trying to haul himself up. There is a sense that the culture that Femi represents is one Ben and Amy are not connected to and one they do not associate with. It is a side of Nigeria that they almost ignore and don't acknowledge. They will use Femi when he is of use to them but only on this basis. Ben especially seems to assume that money can buy you anything.

There is a clash of class rather than race between Ben, Amy and Femi. Femi's world is less of a threat to Edward and Cathy, and it is interesting to see how differently they react in the face of pressure from their peers. This is especially evident in the way the more independent and mature Cathy approaches the final scene, in contrast with the more insecure Ed, who seems more concerned with trying to impress Ben.

Nothing mentioned in the play locates it in terms of time. There are elements that could be added, such as mobile phones, which would make it contemporary, but it is the apparent minimalism of the props and sets that helps focus the relationships of the characters. The dialogue and setting are naturalistic and allow the director and actors to make exciting choices regarding how the characters really feel and behave. How much do they show about what they are really feeling and how much is this a mask to achieve what they want? The characters can seem manipulative and arrogant at times, but what fuels this? Where do their insecurities lie? They are smart and clever but very young and often naive about the world and the people around them.

The music mentioned can be changed to suit the location and the only prerequisites are that it should be loud and addictive. The beat of the music to suggest the parties in the background is more important than the lyrics. Another challenge of the play is to differentiate the parties and give a sense of their timescale. The music and costumes are a good way of defining them as different parties. The costumes will help to inform the difference in wealth and class of the characters.

There are several resources that William suggests would be useful when directing the play – the films *A Good Man in Africa* and *Mr Johnson*, and the novels on which they are based.

From a workshop led by Roxana Silbert,
with notes by Alex Sims

SUCCESS

Nick Drake

Nick Drake's *To Reach the Clouds*, an account of Philippe Petit's high-wire walk between the Twin Towers, was staged at Nottingham Playhouse in 2006. His first poetry collection, *The Man in the White Suit*, was winner of Waterstone/Forward Prize for Best First Collection 1999, and a Poetry Book Society Recommendation. His second collection, *From The Word Go*, was published in 2007. He was one of the Next Generation Poets selected by the Poetry Book Society in 2004. He wrote the screenplay for *Romulus My Father*, which won four Australian Film Awards, including Best Film, in 2007. His *Nefertiti: The Book of the Dead* (Bantam, 2006) was the first of a historical crime trilogy. It was short-listed for the Crime Writers' Association Historical Mystery Dagger award. *Tutankhamun: The Book of Shadows* was published in 2009. He has adapted Anna Funder's *Stasiland* for the National Theatre Studio.

Characters

Nick Shadow

Tom Rakewell

Richy

Feelgood

Lucy

Flower Sellers

Busker

Ping

Pong

Hoodie

Kid

Eva

Cool

Singer

Mirror Girls One, Two and Three

Figure

Bag Lady

Waitress

Street Kids One and Two

SCENE ONE

Friday night. Happy hour.
   A crowd run on, cheering and bearing a young man,
Tom, on their shoulders. He carries a stylish case of some
kind, e.g., an attaché case or briefcase. They are all City
types. Affluent and with the arrogance of their affluence.

Nick Shadow Three cheers for young Tom. Today is his
   lucky day! And what do we say?
Crowd (*repeating*) Yachts! Property! Cars! Yachts!
   Property! Cars!
Tom Rakewell Now then – drink! Bucketloads. What
   shall we have?
Richy *Bollinger!*
Feelgood *Cristal!*
Nick Shadow *Dom Pérignon!*
Tom Rakewell A magnum of each –!

   Tom holds up his case. The crowd roar their approval.
   Richy snatches the attaché case.

Richy So what now, baby? A designer wardrobe, a
   custom sports car, an off-plan penthouse –

   Feelgood grabs the case off him, holding Tom off.

Feelgood You can have it all, young Tom. Art, mansions,
   football teams . . .

   He throws the case to Nick Shadow.

Nick Shadow Gentlemen, before we get into the Big
   Spend, tell us something, Tom, you butter-curled,
   silver-spooned prodigy. How did you do it? How did

you make the money? Did the market drop out of something? Did you buy low and sell high? And what we all want to know is:

All (*chanting*) *How much? How much? How much?*

Nick is about to open the case.

Tom Rakewell Stop, Nick Shadow. That's my secret. I can't be giving that away. Otherwise, everyone would be making their first million or ten before they're twenty-one. All I can say is this: I spotted a chance, took the risk, and *bang*, it paid out! Big time.

Nick Shadow Did it, Tom? Simple as that?

He clicks his fingers. Tom nods.

Tom Rakewell I got lucky beyond my wildest dreams.

Slowly Nick grins. He hands back the case to Tom.

Nick Shadow And now: as King of the Hill, Head Honcho, Leading Light and Supremo of the City, I induct you now into the Club of Success. All members must worship only the Lady Luck, in all her glittery must-have manifestations. And what's our secret sign?

All (*chanting*) *Number One! Number One! Number One!*

Nick grabs Tom in a neckhold, aggressive-playful.

Nick Shadow Aren't you lucky, Nick Shadow's here to look after you? I can guide you through the pitfalls of superwealth; I know who the conmen are, in their off-the-peg suits and cheap shoes, and the High Street girls with their eyes the colour of maxed-out credit cards. I can open up my secret book for you. *And everyone will want you.* You'll be the man of the night, the flavour of the month – but stick with me, and you can be the success of the century.

He lets Tom go.

Tom Rakewell And what's in it for you, Nick Shadow? A percentage?

Nick Shadow Nothing so crude, my super-rich friend. One good turn will deserve another, and you'll be the judge of that. Just enjoy the ride. So what will it be, champagne baby?

Tom Rakewell (*sings*) Simply the best! Better than all the rest!

Nick raises his finger.

Nick Shadow Celebrate good times, come on!

Richy Sex and drugs and rock and roll!

Feelgood (*mock sincere*) I'd like to teach the world to sing, in perfect harmony!

All SHUT IT!

Laughter. A waitress approaches.

Lucy What can I get you, sir?

Tom Rakewell (*smug*) I'd like – a penthouse shag-pad with a TV the size of a soccer pitch, a mirrored boudoir with a circular bed – and you, waiting for me on top of it like the cherry on the icing on the cake!

A roar of approval.

Lucy This is a quality establishment. It's not All Bar One. It's not Walkabout. It's not Lock, Stock – and two halves of cherryade. So I don't pull pints, or anything else.

Nick Shadow Oh come now, darling, don't be so dull. It's Friday evening, we're celebrating our *luck*. Would you care to celebrate our *luck* with us? You look like a girl who'd just love to share a bit of our lovely, juicy *luck*.

Pause.

Lucy I'll take your order now.

Feelgood I'd like a Hot Kiss on Ice!

Richy And for me an Atomic Dog on the Rocks!

Lucy Certainly, sir, one Domestos and soda, and one lime and vinegar. And for you, sir?

Nick Shadow Oh, just holy water, blessed by your pure hands. But perhaps you could add some sweet fizzzz by stirring it with your finger.

Lucy Tap water, certainly, sir.

Tom Rakewell I'm sorry, we're foolish with luck tonight. Please bring us a magnum of your finest champagne.

*He smiles. She goes. They snort with laughter –
schoolboys. Tom watches her go.
    Young Flower Sellers enter, weaving through the
crowd, offering their cheap blooms.*

Nick Shadow Don't worry, young Tom. Plenty more starfish in the sea, nightingales in the hand, cats to skin, crows to stone, and bridges to burn. The world is yours. Now let's set fire to it and watch!

A Flower Child offers Tom a rose.

Flower Child A rose, sir? For your love?

Nick Shadow A rose is a rose is a waste of time. Get lost, kid.

Flower Child This rose is forever –

She insists Tom take it.

Tom Rakewell Thank you. Here's money.

*The Flower Child nods and goes. Tom keeps the rose.
    A Busker approaches the table. He stares at the
crowd. Gradually the group go silent.*

Nick Shadow Who let you in?

The Busker says nothing.

A silent singer! Very droll . . .

Feelgood Sing, man, sing!
Richy Sing a song of luck.
Busker (*sings*)
  Today is your lucky day;
  Everything will turn to gold;
  Love will not grow old;
  Time won't run away;
  Fortune dances to your tune;
  All your dreams will come true;
  That which was lost, will be won;
  But remember this: I was once you.
Feelgood I liked the song well –
Richy But the ending was dismal!

  But Tom gives the Busker a big note.

Tom Rakewell May some of my luck shine on you.
Busker
  Your generosity will pay you back
  Everything that you will lack.
Richy Boo!
Feelgood Hiss!
Nick Shadow Scram!
Busker You get what you give, sirs. You get what you give . . .

  *He bows and exits. Tom turns to the front and falls to
  his knees, making a toast with his glass.*

Tom Rakewell To Lady Luck! I'll make an offering at
  your shrine. By making more money! Millions and
  millions more. Gentlemen, I propose a toast to the love
  of my life: to that which makes the world, and the sun,
  and all the stars, go round and round: to money!

  They toast.

INTERLUDE ONE

The city at night. Establish the parade of a metropolis of luxury and vice, of glamour and disaster. Poverty and wealth walking the same streets. Rich kids in designer gear and poor kids in high-street fashion; mobiles, iPods, accessories. Here fashion reigns supreme.

Two pizza-delivery boys – Ping and Pong – enter, sit and watch, enjoying the scene. Perhaps they sit on deckchairs, as if on the beach.

Kids on bikes and skateboards doing elegant moves. Girls in gangs staggering about, laughing and screaming. Wandering girls with shopping bags. Execs with suitcases on wheels talking on their mobiles. Street vendors and palm readers and one madman shouting lines from the holy book in his head.

The thud of club music. Taxi horns, slot machines, sirens. A late edition newspaper-seller calls out weird hoarding headlines such as GIRL-GANG BLEW UP MY DAUGHTER *and* TIME TRAVEL – CLOSER THAN EVER? *(Invent your own.)*

But then, like magicians, Ping and Pong click their fingers. The characters leave the stage and the scene changes, the lights fade or go out, and now we see:

Beggars, sorting through rubbish bags, choosing anything of any value, and putting it in black bags to sell. And a Hoodie coming past, pushing a rusty old shopping cart containing a Kid, standing as if he were at the prow of a ship. He holds a bunch of out-of-date flowers, like an angel in an Annunciation. He looks about at everything, nods respectfully at Ping and Pong, then positions the cart, so the Kid can watch the following scene . . .

SCENE TWO

*Lucy, a girl in the white working clothes of a restaurant
kitchen, comes out, exhausted. She is joined by Eva,
eating a very green apple.*

Eva (*accented*) That was a long, hard night.

Lucy Why does the world go crazy on Friday nights?

Eva Because everyone's bored and angry all week.

Lucy And isn't it like that where you come from, Eva?

Eva Where I come from people get drunk, talk shit, cut
off their hands, kill their friends. Then they wake up
sober, remember nothing, then remember everything,
and then have another drink.

Lucy It sounds lovely, your country!

Eva Ha. It's a shithole. There's a ghost-Eva, who never
left. I think about her sometimes. She's got a boring
job in an office, and she's married, and soon she'll have
her first screaming kid. But *this* Eva escaped! *Da-da!*
Still, you know what I think?

Lucy What do you think, Eva?

Eva I think there's too much of everything here. Have
you seen what a fashion magazine looks like if you
leave it in the rain? That's what this city has become.
Gorgeous, impossible things all crinkled and stuck
together.

Lucy I think you're right. But I like money. Don't you?

Eva Are you kidding, I *love* it! It's the only thing makes
me really happy these days.

Lucy But then it's gone the moment it appears. And
you're back where you started.

Eva Wow, you've really cheered me up, Lucy! I'm too
hyper to sleep. I'm thinking I'll go dancing. Want to
come?

Lucy No!

Eva So like a good girl, you're going home?

Lucy I think I'll walk. The night bus is a zoo on Fridays.
  And it's a nice enough night. The moon's full. See?

They look up at the moon.

Eva My God, she's looking terrible. She needs a facelift.
  The moon needs a facelift, Lucy!

Lucy laughs.

Lucy Night, Eva. Take care.

Eva Yeah, yeah, yeah. And don't walk too near the
  shadows. Sometimes you act like you think you've got
  fairy dust sprinkled all over you.

*She goes, and Lucy starts to walk. She passes the Kid,
and he offers her the flowers.*

Kid Hello, Lucy!

Lucy How do you know my name?

Kid I just do. It's obvious. Lucy, from the Latin: *luce*,
  light. A light in the darkness . . .

She offers a coin.

Lucy Very funny. Keep the change.

The Hoodie accepts it, on behalf of the Kid.

Kid I am the keeper of change. Everything is change.
  Small change. Big change. Change is coming. Change
  of heart.

Lucy Change of clothes for me! Goodnight, boys!

Kid Bye, Lucy! See you soon.

*She walks on. And then a figure approaches her from
the shadows.*

Lucy What do you want?

Tom holds out the rose.

Tom Rakewell I want to apologise. For how we behaved.
My friend Nick – well, he's an arsehole with a heart of
gold.

Lucy A heart of bullion maybe. You're all the same,
waltzing into the place like fairground ponies,
admiring yourselves in the mirrors as you whirl
around the carousel of your success.

Tom Rakewell Woh! Then you don't know me very well.
Listen: it's really late, can I walk you home?

Lucy I live far away. And I'm fine on my own. I've done
it a thousand times. I could do it in my sleep. In fact, I
have done it in my sleep.

She makes to walk on.

Tom Rakewell Hey, don't go. You'll make me feel like an
old post box. Empty and useless but still grinning.

She laughs.

Lucy What are you like?

Tom Rakewell I'm – like – excited. I feel lucky. Tonight's
the night . . .

*He executes a little dance and presents the rose again.
She smiles, at last, and takes it.*

Lucy Luck is fickle.

Tom Rakewell Yeah. I heard. I'd like to prove that wrong.

*He offers her his arm, chivalrously. She is charmed,
despite herself.*

I hear the High Street by moonlight is one of the seventy-
six billion wonders of the world. The shopfronts are
magical. The dummies come to life. The pavements are
strewn with stars. Join me?

Lucy If you can show me these wonders – yes.

*She smells the rose deeply, then takes his arm and they
go off.*

INTERLUDE TWO

As they go, the two pizza-delivery boys Ping and Pong appear from the shadows. They are jazzed up with energy. Super cool with shades, trainers, etc. Perhaps they speak on their mobiles to each other as they approach, during the following.

Pong Did you see what I just saw, Ping?

Ping With my own eyes, Pong. Otherwise I'd not have credited it.

Pong Just when it seemed nothing true and beautiful could ever bloom from this waste land of concrete and barbed wire, this vast dump of broken, busted, ruined –

Ping Shattered, wonky, destroyed –

Pong And *pointless* things.

Ping This world which we call home is indeed harsh, my friend. It is an STD clinic of infections and mishaps and miseries.

Pong And yet beauty survives, in the cracks –

Ping Nurtured by the falling rain –

Pong The filthy falling rain.

They both look up.

Ah, but look up, Ping! A cloudless night. A full moon. She looks like my gran – once beautiful, now deranged.

Ping Show some respect, Pong. Still she shines so bright.

More.

And soon she will be new again. Shall we moon-bathe, Pong? Shall we partake of her cool sparkle, her wild neutrinos, her naughty quarks?

They put on shades and settle back, hands behind their heads, like moon-bathers. After a moment:

Pong Do you know what, Ping?

Ping What, Pong?

Pong I feel a little chaos coming on!

Ping Oh, I love a little chaos, Pong. You and me, we're the twins of chaos and the night.

Pong Well then – let's get to work.

SCENE THREE

Tom is getting dressed up in front of a mirror. None of the clothes really suits him. He has his attaché case with him.

Tom Rakewell I've never had a party. But Nick Shadow says it's the right time. He says it has to be the best party in history. He says it's my chance to get ahead. To capitalise on my success. It's cost a fortune. Literally. I've given it almost all I've got. But I'm keeping that a secret. Thank God for credit. To the max! Here's to success!

He kisses the case and puts it behind the mirror.

I'm from the suburbs. Dirty word, I know. I hated the place. Careful lawns and careful hedges, careful cars and careful savings. My mates all ran away; they went backpacking for a year and a day. Not me. I got a job. I went to work. They sent me e-cards from temples in jungles, and hidden beaches, and the highest waterfalls. And they'd say: *Cool! Awesome! Wow!* And I'd just delete the lot. And now I've found what they were seeking: the lost treasure.

Enter Lucy during this speech. She looks amazing.

Lucy I'd like to travel.

Tom Rakewell I'll take you! All around the world. We could do it in a week.

Lucy I'd rather take my time.

Tom Rakewell As the Devil said to God.

Lucy What?

Tom Rakewell Just something my father used to say.

Lucy Tell me more about your family.

Tom Rakewell Oh, they're all dead.

Lucy Tom. That's terrible! I'm so sorry.

Tom Rakewell Yeah. My dad was bored all his life. His eyes would bleed with boredom. He was trapped like a tiger in the sitting room. But I've made my escape, without any help. And here we are! In the jungle – grrr!

He roars like a lion, then kisses her.

Lucy How do I look?

Tom Rakewell Like a woman dressed in Beauty and Truth.

Lucy You make it sound like a designer label.

Tom Rakewell And how do I look?

Lucy Umm –

Suddenly the doors fly open, and the party crowd, with Nick Shadow at the centre, flow in. They are all dressed in crazy fashions, high colours, big wigs, everything, anything, to make a mark. Establish a huge party.

Nick Shadow (*ignoring Lucy*) Oh Tom, you look like –

Feelgood A Japanese rock star!

Richy I think he looks – *amazing*.

Nick Shadow And what do you say, Cool?

Enter Cool, a very cool dude who only ever says 'Cool'.

Cool Cool.

Nick Shadow What Cool says, goes.

Tom Rakewell Thanks guys, help yourselves. No expense has been spared. Only the best on the guest list: the rich, the famous, the important, the influential, the good, the bad –

All – and the ugly, only if they are also one of the above!

Nick takes Tom to one side.

Nick Shadow So where did you disappear to last night?

He stares at Lucy who is now mingling. She catches Nick's look.

Tom Rakewell Oh, you know.

Nick Shadow Yes. And I don't approve. She's not the girl for you, Tom.

Tom Rakewell I like her. She's special.

Lucy joins them.

Nick Shadow She's –

Lucy What?

Nick Shadow Here. Hello, darling.

Lucy It's Mr Tap Water himself. And don't call me darling. You don't know me.

Nick Shadow No need to go sulky.

Lucy No need to go whiny. What were you talking about before I so rudely interrupted?

Nick Shadow Just saying Tom is a man with the power to realise all his desires. He has the *wherewithal* . . .

Lucy And what exactly is this *wherewithal*?

Nick Shadow The means to the end, darling. Do you know what I mean?

She walks around him, assessing him.

Lucy If by 'mean' you mean selfish, avaricious, grasping and petty-minded, sure I know what you *mean* . . .

Tom Rakewell Lucy's joking. Say you're joking, Lucy.

Nick Shadow We're all joking, darling. Me, I'm famous for it.

Lucy Perhaps you should go into stand-up!

Sudden silence in the room, aghast at her audacity.

Nick Shadow Listen, darling; I hear you sing a little. So go make small talk, meet some people and improve your career prospects. Do you mind?

She is about to respond when Eva approaches.

Well, greetings, hail, and well met by moonlight.

Eva gives him a long, curious look.

Lucy This is my friend Eva. Eva, this is Nick Shadow.

Nick Shadow Eva. The first lady. The one who listened to the snake and ate that little apple.

Eva Old Nick, the diamond snake himself, bringing his own shadow to the party. Interesting . . .

Lucy Come on, Eva, let's leave these two boys to play with their *wherewithals* . . .

They walk away. Eva glances back at Nick, who can't take his eyes off her.

Tom Rakewell I don't like it when you're rude to Lucy.

Nick Shadow Your Lucy? Your bird, your sparrow, your little songster?

Tom Rakewell Yes.

Nick Shadow Nick Shadow's Second Rule of Love: the ruder you are, the more they want you.

Tom Rakewell And what's the First Rule?

Nick Shadow Never mean a word you say!

Tom Rakewell Is that your motto?

Nick Shadow I'm joking, Tom!

Tom Rakewell Listen, Nick. I've done what you said. Laid on the best. Hummingbird sashimi. Deep-fried baby sea horse. Crushed ice from the Arctic. Crisps

made from the wings of endangered blue butterflies.
I just hope –

Nick Shadow Is this fear I hear, young Tom? I'm
disappointed. '*Spend to seem who you would wish to
be*.' That's my first advice!

Tom Rakewell Don't worry on that score, Nick. I've
spent a fortune tonight, but I've still many fortunes left
to spend.

Nick Shadow And fortunes more to make, Tom. And
this is the start. These guests are the top rungs of the
slippery, slimy food-chain of success. Through them
lie your dreams. True, I've seen better gargoyles on a
crypt. I've seen happier faces after a car crash. I've met
snakes I'd rather kiss. And look more closely and what
do I see?

Tom Rakewell I don't know.

Nick Shadow I see fear and appetite. Even though the
rich have everything, the truth is they are terrified it
will never be enough.

*Enter Ping and Pong in their pizza-delivery outfits,
carrying a pile of pizza boxes which they pass out
among the guests.*

Tom Rakewell Who are those boys? I didn't invite them.

Nick Shadow Nobody open the boxes until I say! Stop
the music!

*He holds up his hand, consulting his watch as we hear
the chimes of midnight start to ring.*

Feelgood I hate waiting!
Richy It's killing me!
Cool Cool.

Lucy stands apart, holding her box, watching everything.

Nick Shadow Five, four, three, two, one –

Everyone waits for it. We hear the bells chime midnight.

It is exactly midnight. Ladies and gentlemen, you may now open your boxes!

Everyone opens their box. Inside they all find the same thing: an unmarked CD. They hold them up to the light, examining them curiously.

Mind your dirty, greasy fingers please. Prints of existence will spoil everything. For each of you holds in your hot little hands a very special gift. A recording. Just like this one. Please listen carefully. (*Like a pantomime villain.*) Shhhh!

But all we hear is absolute silence. Everyone is confused, disconcerted; then suddenly they get it. They're enchanted.

Feelgood Oh, that is totally awesome.
Richy It's just so –
Cool Cool.
Feelgood Yeah, it really so is cool!
Crowd Bravo! Bravo!

Nick silences them all with another click of his fingers.

Nick Shadow Boo! *Who's there?* No one. They say silence is golden. But I say silence is worth nothing!

He clicks his fingers. Ping and Pong bring on a strange object.

This is the oracle. It is a dream machine. Inside you may insert your silver disc, like a coin upon the tongue of the dead. And then you must confess and record your deepest wish. After, you will give the disc to me, for safe keeping. And let me tell you now: no matter how strange and dark, no matter how violent and ugly, you must be truthful. And in a year and a day, I will play

each one back to you. And then we will see who has
had success, and who has had *nothing*.

Silence.

Young Tom, go first. This is your party.
Tom Rakewell I will, then.

Applause.

Lucy Tom! Be careful.
Tom Rakewell Why, Lucy? What is there to fear?

*Tom enters the booth. Absolute silence reigns for the
time he is inside. It does not take long. Tom emerges
and hands his disc to Nick.*

This is my true and secret wish.
Nick Shadow Live according to the confession of your
dream, young Tom. And now: music!

*Enter a Singer. She is stunning. She takes centre stage
and a spotlight encircles her. A glitter ball begins to
revolve, scattering stars. She sings her own version of
'Who Wants to be a Millionaire'. She sings seductively
to Tom, who is mesmerised by her. The Crowd joins in
with the responses, but it is Tom who does so with the
most excitement.*

*During this, Ping and Pong steal from the pockets of
the guests.*

Singer
Who wants to be a millionaire?
Crowd
I do!
Singer
Who longs for servants everywhere?
Crowd
I do!

Singer
  Who wants to own a country estate?
Crowd
  A country estate? Oh yeah, that sounds great!
Singer
  Who wants to shower in champagne?
Crowd
  I do!
Singer
  Who wants to own a private plane?
Crowd
  I do!
Singer
  Who wants a supermodel girl?
Tom Rakewell
  I do!
Singer
  Then kiss me on the lips!

  Tom does so, to the whoops of the Crowd.

Cool Cool.

  Nick sees Lucy watching.

Nick Shadow Isn't that the most beautiful thing you've
  ever seen?

  *Lucy stares at him, then suddenly turns and leaves,
  very upset. Tom does not notice, because everyone
  from the party is now encircling him, holding up their
  CDs, which glitter in the light.
  Tom looks into the glittering lights, dazzled.*

INTERLUDE THREE

Ping and Pong, running down the street.

Ping I'm Bubble –
Pong I'm Squeak –
Ping I'm Trouble –
Pong I'm Strife –
Ping I'm Pick –
Pong I'm Mix –
Ping I'm Tooth –
Pong I'm Nail –
Ping I'm Shady –
Pong I'm Dodgy –
Ping I'm Traffic –
Pong I'm Jam –
Ping I'm Naughty –
Pong I'm Nice –
Ping I'm Profit –
Pong I'm Loss –
Ping I'm Yin –
Pong I'm Yang –
Ping I'm Itch –
Pong I'm Scratch –
Ping I'm Car –
Pong I'm Crash –
Ping I'm Hip –
Pong I'm Hop –
Ping I'm Hee –
Pong I'm Haw –
Ping I'm Ding –
Pong I'm Dong –
Ping I'm Ping –
Pong I'm Pong –
Ping I'm Here –

Pong I'm Gone!
  They grin and vanish.

SCENE FOUR

Sounds of the party continuing offstage. Lucy is in the powder room. Several other girls from the party are in there.

Lucy Have any of you girls got a mirror?

  Everyone plucks one out of their bags, and they hold them up to her face, to create a mirror made of many parts. The girls look like a many-handed goddess of the mirror.

No. I don't like that one. I want a different mirror.
Mirror Girl One You want a mirror made of flattery.
Mirror Girl Two Or a mirror made of bliss.
Mirror Girl Three Or a mirror made of dreams.
Mirror Girl One Strange thing about a mirror –
Mirror Girl Two Even if you smash it –
Mirror Girl Three It's always full.
Mirror Girls So tell us, Lucy, what do you see?

  Lucy stares into the mirrors, as they now move about her in a strange dance.

Lucy I see a fool. I believed –
Mirror Girls She believed! Oh, the fool. Love is –
Mirror Girl One An ice cream left in the sun.
Mirror Girl Two Rain on the window pane.
Mirror Girl Three A lonely walk back up a dark lane.
Lucy It must have been the moon.
Mirror Girls Now she blames the moon!
Lucy It was such a beautiful night . . . and I woke up feeling so happy.

Mirror Girls And now it's all dark again. Ah . . .

*Enter Eva. She flicks her hands at the Mirror Girls,
and they all back off, holding their mirrors away. She
sees Lucy's sad face.*

Eva Ah, girl, you got it bad.
Lucy I know.

*She holds the CD in her hand, turning it so the light
catches its surface.*

Eva Record your dream now.
Lucy But I don't have the machine.
Eva Just sing. We'll remember. Won't we, girls?

*They all chorus their agreement and turn their mirrors
round Lucy in a new arrangement, more like a crown
of mirrors now.*

Lucy I'm embarrassed.
All Don't be!

Pause.

Lucy (*sings beautifully*)
I want a man with an open heart;
I want a man with an open face;
I want a man who will make me laugh;
I want a man who will act with grace.
And most of all I want a man
Who'll want me simply as I am.

The Mirror Girls look a little doubtful.

Mirror Girl One It sounds nice –
Mirror Girl Two But perhaps a little –
Mirror Girl Three Boring?
Lucy I know! I'm sorry . . .

Mirror Girl Two But you've got a good voice, girl. Men fall in love with a voice like that.

Lucy Thank you. What about you, Eva? What's your confession?

Eva Mine? Oh, that's easy. (*She sings.*)
I want the toy boys and sugar dads,
The biker lads and romantic cads.
I want low baddies and high-flyers,
I want brilliant poetic liars,
I want romantic getaways,
And room service in paradise;
I want the best the world can give –
And then I'll take another look at love.

Lucy Neither of us is asking for much!

They laugh.

You liked Nick Shadow. Didn't you?

Eva You know me, Lucy. I always fall for the bad guy. It's my tragedy! And you always fall for the good guy, and that's yours! Come on, let's have some fun. The night is young, and so are we.

Lucy No, thanks. You dance with your snake. I'm going to find Tom.

Eva and the Mirror Girls go, leaving Lucy searching for Tom. Nick finds Eva and they dance together. The Mirror Girls dance with Feelgood, Richy and Cool. Gradually they dance their way offstage.
  But Lucy, alone now, can't find Tom anywhere. Finally she gets out her mobile, and calls him.
  Now, on another part of the stage, a phone rings in response, from within a big pile of discarded party clothes. From out of this pile a figure rises, weirdly dressed, partly awake. This Figure finds the phone.

Hello?
Figure Hello?

Lucy Who's this?
Figure Who's this?
Lucy Is Tom there, please? I'd like to speak with him.
Figure Is Tom there, please? I'd like –

Nick Shadow enters and grabs the phone.

Nick Shadow Lucy? How lovely of you to call. Tom's
busy right now. Can I take a message?

*Lucy cuts off the call. She throws her CD like a frisbee
away. She leaves, miserable. Nick Shadow smiles, picks
up her CD, and goes back into the noise of the party.*

INTERLUDE FOUR

*The City scene again. The panorama of the night. Tom
stands, waiting for Lucy. He's been waiting a long time,
    The Hoodie, pushing the shopping trolley containing
the Kid, crosses the stage. They approach Tom and stare
at him.*

Tom Rakewell Can I help you?
Kid No.
Tom Rakewell I'm sorry?
Kid You will be.
Tom Rakewell Listen, I don't know who you think you
are –
Kid My knowledge is not for you. Not yet. But that day
will come. I see it clearly.
Tom Rakewell What day? You're talking rubbish!
Kid I say what I see in my mind's eye. I see you in a
graveyard, wearing a crown of old cans; your soul will
be a broken radio. Your heart will be an empty wine
bottle. The label will read: LOVE.

Tom is astonished.

Tom Rakewell That's ridiculous. Look at me!
Kid I am.

He stares at Tom, then signs to the Hoodie who obediently pushes the trolley forward.

Tom Rakewell Where are you going?
Kid To meet you, of course. Later!

They go off, leaving Tom alone.

SCENE FIVE

Outside the restaurant. Tom is waiting. Enter Lucy and Eva.

Eva Well, look what's come crawling back.

Tom approaches.

Tom Rakewell Hello, Eva.
Eva Bye-bye, Tom-Tom! Lucy – take care.

She goes.

Tom Rakewell I miss you. I miss talking to you.
Lucy Love's a big decision, Tom. You made other choices.
Tom Rakewell I made mistakes.
Lucy I'll say.
Tom Rakewell Worse than you know. I spent all my
fortune on that party. Everyone ate the butterfly wings
and drank the champagne and in the morning they all
left. They didn't even say thank you. And now –

He shrugs.

Lucy Your crown of success has slipped. So what?
Tom Rakewell I'm just not feeling so lucky these days.

He looks away. Pause.

Lucy Why have you've come to find me, Tom? Do you need money?

Tom Rakewell No! I don't want your money.

Lucy Yes, you do. I can see it in your eyes.

Tom Rakewell Thanks. But I can't take your money, Lucy.

She takes out her purse and gives him a banknote. He refuses it. She insists, and folds it and places it in his pocket.

Lucy Pay me back when you can.

Tom Rakewell I will. You're my lucky star.

Lucy Am I?

Tom Rakewell I love you.

Lucy That's so easy to say –

Tom Rakewell Look into my eyes. You know my words are true. Maybe the question is: do you love me?

Lucy I thought I did.

Tom Rakewell True love never alters. So they say.

Lucy That's in songs and poems, Tom.

Tom Rakewell What's wrong with songs? Some songs are true. You should know. You like to sing.

Lucy I've never sung for you.

Tom Rakewell Perhaps one day you will.

Lucy I've got to go, Tom. Goodnight.

Tom Rakewell Lucy! My ace of hearts. I will win you back as well. Trust me.

Lucy looks at him.

Lucy I'm not a pile of cash, Tom. I'm not a sports car. I'm not an acquisition.

She goes.
Ping and Pong have entered and watched this exchange.

INTERLUDE FIVE

Ping Oh dear oh dear oh dear.
Pong I think Tom's in trouble!
Ping Asking his ex for money.
Pong I think that's sad.
Ping I think that's bad.
Pong I think that's mad . . .
Ping It's bitter –
Pong It's sweet –
Together It's absolutely perfect!

They saunter into the following.

SCENE SIX

*A gambling den. Tom is seated at a table with Nick Shadow, Feelgood, Richy and other seasoned gamblers.
Ping and Pong stand to one side, observing.*

Ping I love a game of chance, Pong.
Pong The wheel of fortune is our favourite wheel.
Ping Win some –
Pong Lose some!
Together *Love it!*

They pretend to hide behind their newspapers – The
Sun *and* The Mirror.

Tom Rakewell I'm going to win, Nick Shadow! Tonight
I feel lucky again.
Nick Shadow Of course you're going to win, Tom!
Chance is the greatest of the gods. He has his attendants,
Risk and Strategy. And he has his many beautiful
forms –
Feelgood Liar's poker, blackjack, baccarat –

Richy Pachinko, mahjong, roulette –
Feelgood The Razzle. Hazard. Hanky Panky –
Nick Shadow You see, Tom; you have the most money.
Therefore you will win. It's one-hundred-per-cent
certain.
Feelgood It's a win-win –
Richy No-lose situation. It's –
Cool Cool.
Tom But I'll start cautiously.

Tom puts down a low stake. The men are not impressed.
A round takes place in tense silence. Tom wins, and
euphorically rakes in the small pile of chips.

I won!

Nick Shadow gives Tom a pat on the back.

Nick Shadow Just as I said!
Tom Rakewell And I'll win again!

Nick playfully punches his arm.

Nick Shadow Attaboy!
Feelgood Go on, my son!
Richy Oh, splendid fellow! Bigger stakes.

They play again. Tom wins again, a bigger pile.

Tom I'm a winner! Number one! Number one! Sorry,
Richy-Rich! Sorry, Feelgood! No hard feelings, eh?
Another round, gentlemen?

The other men smile, and look sideways to Nick, who
discreetly nods. They smile.

Both Of course!
Tom Rakewell And now I'm going to risk everything.
The penthouse suite, the cars, the yacht. Even the suit
I stand up in.

Nick Shadow This, Tom, is why I respect you. I'm
behind you all the way. But are you going all the way?

Tom Rakewell Yes! And to prove myself true to the god
of chance, I'll even gamble my case, and everything in it.

He puts the case on the table. Nick is mesmerised.

Nick Shadow Oh, that is heroic, gentlemen. Let's PLAY
THE GAME!

The last round.
 Great tension. A result: and then absolute silence.

Tom Rakewell So tell me. What happens now?

Nick Shadow Well, Tom. It seems perfectly clear to me.
You wagered everything. And you lost everything. Ergo,
everything you have is mine. Your life is mine.

*Nick clicks his fingers. Tom takes off his designer
jacket, and trousers. Richy and Feelgood can hardly
hide their amusement.*

Tom Rakewell But Nick –

Nick Shadow Oh, Tom. Don't ask me to feel sorry for
you. Surely you don't expect me to just – give it back?

Tom Rakewell You encouraged me. I did what you said.

Nick Shadow Poor Tom. You forgot the First Law of
Everything. What was the very first thing I told you?

Tom Rakewell I don't remember!

All *Never believe a word I say!*

Nick smiles, heaps up his winnings, picks up Tom's case.

Nick Shadow I've always wondered just how much
money was in here!

Tom Rakewell Now you'll find out.

*Nick clicks his fingers again, and the other men
confront Tom, forcing him out of the room:*

424

All (*chanting, a chorus, in no order*) Yachts, property, cars! Yachts, property, cars! Number one! Number one! Bollinger, Cristal, Dom Pérignon!

INTERLUDE SIX

Tom is alone in the street. People walk by, laughing at him in his pants and T-shirt and socks. He cannot believe that everything he had he has lost. He falls to his knees.

Tom Rakewell Lady Luck, Queen of Fortune, why have you forsaken me? Now, in the hour of my need, send me some sign –

Enter Ping and Pong.

(*To the heavens.*) Thank you, sweet Lady Luck!
Ping Nick Shadow sends you greetings.
Pong He thought you might be hungry.

He produces a pizza box.

Tom Rakewell That is so kind of him. I find losing everything I possess makes me strangely ravenous.
Ping That will be the fear –
Pong I thought I could smell something. Here –

Tom takes and opens the box enthusiastically. But he is horrified.

Tom Rakewell He sends me a box of crusts?
Ping He's a real joker, eh!
Pong No hard feelings, eh?
Ping Win some!
Pong Lose some!
Ping Over –
Pong And out!

They go, leaving Tom alone with his crusts, in despair.
He starts to eat, but starts to weep again, then suddenly
throws them away in fury. Slowly he looks up at the
night sky.

Tom Rakewell I want the world to crash and burn.
I want all the lights to go out. I want the dancers to
turn to dust. I want everyone's dreams to die. But it's
strange – I'm starting to feel – *lighter*. Suddenly,
anything seems possible. The world's a wheel of fire
but I want to laugh and laugh. Am I going mad?

During this speech a strange and wonderful figure has
appeared. Her hair is wild as a Medusa, her clothes as
crazy as can be. She holds tatty old plastic bags and
pulls a battered, old lady's trolley.

Bag Lady Tell me about it! And before you catch cold,
try these robes upon you.

She pulls a random selection of ninth-hand clothes
from the bags, and Tom dresses.

Look at you now. A king!

SCENE SEVEN

A twenty-four-hour fast-food diner.
A Waitress takes their order.

Bag Lady Two teas, please, Denise.
Waitress My name's Lily Lotus Flower.
Bag Lady Peaches and cream! The names people give
their children these days!
Waitress I chose it myself.

She goes.

Bag Lady I'm five hundred and seventeen years old. I've had more names that you've had hot dinners!

Tom Rakewell I'm starving!

Bag Lady You'll get used to it. You'll dream of food. Dream roasts. Dream desserts. I'm a fan of sweet things. *Crème brûlée.* Apply intense heat for just exactly the right number of seconds, and the sugar swims, and runs, and then turns golden like the summer sun . . . *Ah* . . .

Tom Rakewell We'll have two of those then.

The Waitress returns with two mugs of tea.

Your finest *crème brûlée* for the lady and me, please!

Bag Lady And two silver spoons.

Waitress This is the modern world. Everything is plastic. Cheap and disposable. And I'm not just talking about the spoons. Music's lost the muse, and left the *ick* behind. Where have all the flowers gone? And the honey bees? I look at the world, and I despair, sometimes.

She gives them a plastic spoon each and goes. Tom holds his up, stares at it.

Tom Rakewell I'm on a night bus to Hell. It's very dark and very late, I'm very, very tired, and now I've reached the end of the line. The café at the end of the world.

Bag Lady So tell me, my king with a plastic spoon, what's your story?

Tom Rakewell I had money. I had good clothes. And I had a girl. I had success.

Bag Lady And you lost those things? That was very careless.

Tom Rakewell Everything was taken from me. By a former friend.

Bag Lady That which is taken from us is not ours.

Tom Rakewell That sounds far too saintly for me.

Bag Lady I know, darling. But there's a question we all
have to ask ourselves, we who have fallen through the
net, we who drink tea in chipped mugs with plastic
spoons. It's this: if you didn't wake up tomorrow, who
would care?

Tom is silent.

Exactly. No one. So here we are, standing alone on the
spinning earth, with the cold stars above our heads,
and the dead beneath our feet. Alive!

Tom Rakewell Is this it, then? The end of the road? The
bottom of the ladder? The junk yard of the world?

Bag Lady Yes, darling. But I have to warn you. The truth
is: soon you will start to smell. You'll be hungry
always. The rain will fall, and the park bench will lose
its minimalist appeal. You'll start to look like a polluted
pigeon. No one will talk to you any more. You'll talk
to yourself. You'll find yourself interesting, and then
boring. Soon you'll be telling yourself to shut up . . .

Tom can't take this. He raises the plastic spoon.

Tom Rakewell The bill, please!

Bag Lady Oh, but it gets worse. There is nothing beyond
the gauze of this world. If you took down the thin
walls of this restaurant, which are all that separate us
from everything we strive to transcend, you would see
chefs and under-chefs and assistants sweating and
toiling in the heat of the kitchen. You would see racks
of dead meat, and piles of vegetables, and poor people
washing the dirt away. Beyond that you would see the
animals being led to slaughter, and the plastic curtains
they pass through slicked with blood. You would see
the fields of stuck mud where peasants and workers
toil in the relentless rain, picking and picking and
picking and earning nothing. You would see the worms

and the ants and the spiders, fighting for the fruit on the trees. You would see the fallen fruit, rotting back into the earth, to feed the grinning skulls of the dead. Now do you see?

Tom is in despair.

Oh hello, lovely little Lily Lotus Blossom.

The Waitress delivers the bill to Tom. Tom looks at the bill. He smiles and produces a stone from his pocket. He offers it in payment.

Waitress What's that?

Tom Rakewell It's all I possess. So what's the worst that can happen to me now?

Bag Lady That's right! Good lad. Now you get it.

She laughs. Tom joins in.

Waitress I have to call the police now. Sorry, I know it's a bore.

Tom smiles, grins at all the diners.

Tom Rakewell You all think you're so lucky, with your hot dinners, and new clothes for the evening, and credit cards in your pockets. I was like you. I had it all. I had air miles and a gold card and an overdraft. And then, in a moment, it was gone . . .

He stands to leave, but Ping and Pong appear at the door.

Ping Oh dear.

Pong Oh dear.

Ping *and* **Pong** Oh dear.

Tom grins at them and makes a dash for the back exit, but he is bundled away by Ping and Pong.

INTERLUDE SEVEN

Tom tries to escape, running down the labyrinth of streets and alleyways, followed always by Ping and Pong, who are soon joined in the chase by Richie, Feelgood and Cool.

Nick Shadow watches. He is very angry and very aggressive.

Finally Tom runs directly into Nick. Nick Shadow goes to whack Tom. Darkness.

SCENE EIGHT

A multi-storey car park, or a pub toilet, or any insalubrious locale.

Tom is tied up before Nick.

Nick Shadow Tom, Tom, Tom. What am I going to do with you?

Tom Rakewell Why, Nick? Has something made you angry?

Nick Shadow Well, Tom, I'm very successful, so I don't get angry. But I have to say, I'm – aggravated. I'm provoked. I'm displeased, piqued, pissed off, offended, affronted, miffed, irritable, irascible, splenetic, choleric and generally speaking – *on the warpath*.

Tom Rakewell Oh! *Gosh* – and why's that, Nick?

Nick Shadow Well, Tom, I went to open your famous case – and –

Tom Rakewell Tell me, Nick Shadow. What did you find?

Nick Shadow I found: nought, nowt, nil, zero, zilch, sod-all. I found, in short, a void, an emptiness, a nullity, non-existence. I found *nothing*.

Cool Cool!

Nick Shadow No, it's not cool, you monosyllabic cretin!

Silence.

Now listen, Tom. I don't like people very much. They're a little bit irritating when they don't do what they're told. So tell me. *What's the story?*

Ping Morning glory!

Nick Shadow SILENCE!

Tom Rakewell Well, Nick. I told you the story. I spied with my little eye a business opportunity. I created a plan, I built a gilt-edged deal, a future-proof cert, I bought thousands of almost worthless shares for next to nothing, and one came up gold. So I closed it out. And I made a fortune in a day.

Feelgood But he didn't, did he?

Richy Because the case was empty.

Both Oh, I see . . .

Nick Shadow So?

Tom Rakewell But let me tell you another story. My dad was mean as old toast, but when he and the old girl were killed instantly in a head-on collision, I, the grieving only son, inherited everything. In his meanness, he had accumulated a fortune. And it was all mine. So I sold the house, with the lawn and the three-piece suite and the incontinent family cat, and I invested the money. Brilliantly.

Ping Poor Tom.

Pong A sad story.

Nick Shadow But it isn't true.

Tom Rakewell No. The incontinent cat remains by the hearth. The TV plays on. My father's eyes still bleed with boredom.

Richy So blimey, I'm confused now.

Feelgood Yes, Tom, I'm feeling confounded. What am I supposed to believe?

Tom Rakewell Believe what you will.

Nick Shadow Come, Tom. Tell the beautiful truth.

Tom Rakewell The beautiful truth is this: the case was always empty.

Silence.

I never had any cash. I never made a million. I just said I did. And everyone believed me. The man who gave me credit for the party believed me. *You* believed me, Nick.

Nick stares at him. It could go any way.

Nick Shadow Oh, that's rather good.

Suddenly laughs like a dog. The others join in.

Richie That's excellent!
Feelgood It's terrific!
Ping I think it stinks.
Pong I think it pongs. (Get it?)
Cool It's cool.
Feelgood It is, it's terrifically cool.
Tom Rakewell Is it cool, Nick?

Nick considers.

Nick Shadow You've had us on. You've had a laugh. You've taken the Michael, the piss, the pot. But now we're going to pull the other one!

He produces Tom's CD.

Remember this?

Tom nods.

Shall I tell everyone what you said? Your deepest wish?
Tom Rakewell I don't care. I'm over it.

Nick approaches Tom.

Nick Shadow 'I want success. I want the best of the world, no matter what the cost. Wise men say: we are

nothing without love. Those wise men were fools.
Love is nothing without money. Money is power, it's
talent, it makes me feel alive. And I want more.'
Feelgood But now look at you.
Richy The epitome of failure.
Feelgood It's a very pretty picture, to my eye.

Tom smiles.

Tom Rakewell So what? You can't harm me now.
Nick Shadow No?

Nick holds up another CD.

Guess who this belongs to? Your little friend. Little Lucy.
The girl you loved and lost. Shall I tell you what *she*
said?
Tom Rakewell No, no, no, that's private, you can't –
Nick Shadow (*singing/reciting sarcastically*)
I want a man with an open heart;
I want a man with an open face;
I want a man who will make me laugh;
I want a man who will act with grace;
All these things I find in Tom,
Who loves me truly as I am.

*The others send this up cruelly by singing it as a cynical
four-part harmony. But Tom is aghast at what he has lost.*

Tom Rakewell Lucy . . . I'm sorry . . .
Nick Shadow Oh, wonderful. 'I'm sorry.' As if that solves
everything. But there is no forgiveness, no redemption,
no making amends. The real truth is the cruel truth:
money makes the world go around. It is the governing
law of the universe. Everything you see is made of it.
Time itself is money. Wherever fear and disaster tread,
money follows. A little war in the third world? Guns
and ammo? *Ker-ching*, I make money. Turn the page
of the cheap newspaper: a humanitarian disaster?

Ker-ching. The world is a money-go-round. And it's driven by fear.

Tom is furious and focused now.

Tom Rakewell I see you, Nick Shadow, in your fine tailored suit, with that costly haircut, and that gold watch that whispers on your wrist. Underneath it all, you are the same as me. You are a poor scrap of flesh and blood, vulnerable to the cold wind, and to time, and to misfortune. And somewhere, you know this, and *you* are afraid.

Nick Shadow Oh, Tom. How affecting. How poignant. And by God how pathetic. You're out of the club and onto the streets. May you fade and rot like yesterday's newspaper. Good luck!

He clicks his fingers, and Feelgood and Richy follow obediently. Ping and Pong pass by Tom.

Ping You're here –
Pong You're gone.
Ping *and* **Pong** You're no one.

Cool follows. He looks at Tom and smiles, sadly.

Tom Cool?

He shakes his head, unties Tom, and goes.

INTERLUDE EIGHT

Lucy and Eva outside the restaurant.

Eva So have you seen him again?
Lucy No.
Eva And did he pay you back?
Lucy No.

Eva So much for the good guy.

Lucy And the bad guy?

Eva Oh, you know bad guys. They're so predictable. They always do the wrong thing.

She looks sad. Enter the Kid, pushed in the trolley by the Hoodie.

Kid Lucy. Eva.

Eva How does he know my name?

Kid I know everything. And now I need you to come with me.

Lucy No, Kid. I'm going home. I'm weary.

Kid It's important. It's Tom.

Lucy Tom knows where to find me if he needs me.

Kid You're wrong, Lucy. Please come.

He turns to go. Lucy hesitates.

What have you got to lose?

Lucy I don't know. I feel I've lost what matters.

Kid Come then.

Lucy Eva?

Eva This I have to see! Can I ride in that thing too?
She sidles up to the Hoodie. They go off.

SCENE NINE

Tom sits on a park bench in a graveyard, with two Street Kids, one on either side. Both have cans. Also a broken radio and an empty bottle. One offers a can to Tom.

Street Kid One Cheers!

Street Kid Two Cheers!

Tom Rakewell Cheers!

Street Kid One Here, mate. Do you want a pet of my bird?

Tom Rakewell What bird?

Street Kid One Why, the place is full of birds! Can't you hear them? Here's mine. He's a toucan. He's got red wings and a green beak, but he's shy, like.

He pets the imaginary bird.

Street Kid Two And mine's a swallow. He's just alighted on my shoulder. Be very quiet, and he might stay a little while. What's yours?

Tom Rakewell Oh. A crow. Black wings. Sharp beak. Can't sing.

Street Kid Two Here, mate, I made this. You might as well have it.

He crowns Tom with a crown of old cans.

Tom Rakewell Thank you.

Enter the Kid in his rusty trolley, pushed as always by the Hoodie. They approach Tom.

Street Kid One *and* **Two** Morning!
Kid Good morning. All hail. Greetings. Hi!

He looks at Tom.

So here we are. About time.
Tom Rakewell What do you want me to say?
Kid Anything or nothing. It's fine. I'm just passing through. But I've brought someone to see you.

Enter Lucy and Eva.

Lucy Hello, Tom. How are you?

Tom is overwhelmed.

Tom Rakewell I'm – It's good to see you. It's so good.
Kid He speaks the truth.
Lucy At last . . .

The Street Kids politely make room for Lucy and Eva.

Lucy Thank you. So what were you all talking about?
Street Kid One Birds!
Eva Why birds?
Street Kid Two What else is there to talk about? Listen –

Birdsong around.

Eva Yes. It's very nice. But I prefer CDs! And a good
  strong beat . . .!
Kid Perhaps Lucy would sing for us?
Lucy I've never sung for Tom.
Tom Rakewell Please, Lucy. I'd love to hear you sing.
Lucy (*sings*)
  'When I was just a little girl
  I asked my mother, what will I be
  Will I be pretty, will I be rich
  Here's what she said to me.

  Que sera, sera,
  Whatever will be, will be
  The future's not ours to see.
  Que sera, sera
  What will be, will be.

  When I was young, I fell in love
  I asked my sweetheart what lies ahead.
  Will we have rainbows, day after day?
  Here's what my sweetheart said.

  Que sera, sera,
  Whatever will be, will be
  The future's not ours to see
  Que sera, sera
  What will be, will be . . .'

*She stops, unable to continue . . . the birds have stopped
singing to listen to her. A long pause.*

Tom Rakewell Thank you, Lucy. That was really –

She lets him kiss her.

Street Kid One Hey, even my toucan listened to you!
Street Kid Two And my swallow!
Tom Rakewell What happens now?
Lucy I don't know. First of all, let's take that off you.

She removes the crown of cans.
  The sound of more dawn birds rises slowly around.

Tom Rakewell Listen. Can you hear –?
Street Kid One I told you.
Street Kid Two We told him.
Lucy Yes. I hear it. It's getting light. Tom, will you walk
me home? I hear the park is beautiful at dawn.
Tom Rakewell With pleasure. We could take a turn on
the roundabout. We could watch the moon in the
pond. We could take two deckchairs and watch the sky
turn blue.

He offers her his arm, and she takes it.

Street Kid One That's very touching.
Street Kid Two It's moving, it really is.
Kid It's cool. Isn't it?

He turns to the Hoodie, who removes his/her hood
and speaks for the first and last time.

Hoodie It's love.

The End.

Production Notes

Success is a fast-paced, epic yet intimate play about truth, love, greed and excess, loosely inspired by Hogarth's allegorical sequence of paintings *The Rake's Progress*, eight panels that chart the decline and fall of Thomas Rakewell. *Success* strongly differentiates itself from this chilling depiction of greed and offers us a new and contemporary story that inhabits its own world and that is above all active, three-dimensional and human.

NICK DRAKE 'Originally the play was made up of eight panels like the Hogarth paintings but the play changed as I wrote it.'

TELLING THE STORY

Success is a love story between Tom and Lucy, and it is important to give their story centre stage as they collide, are driven apart and then finally find each other at the end of the play. Their story is the heart of the play – an intimate 'chamber drama' that it is surrounded but not engulfed by the epic and Rabelaisian elements of Nick Shadow's world.

Each scene is written like a piece of music with a series of narrative beats and events. It is important not to throw away any elements of the story, while at the same time maintaining pace. There is some scope for the use of physical movement, visual spectacle and lighting effects, particularly in the interlude sections; but deal with the narrative detail first and decide on what is happening in each scene. For example:

SCENE ONE – Narrative Beats or 'Events'

- *All enter the bar celebrating Tom's wealth.*
- *Nick makes a claim on Tom.*
- *Tom buys into it.*
- *They try to recruit Lucy.*
- *Lucy deflates their bubble.*
- *Tom and Lucy make a connection.*
- *A flower seller wants to sell a flower to Tom.*
- *Tom buys a flower.*
- *A busker wants to warn Tom.*
- *Tom commits himself to the pursuit of money.*

Make decisions about the timescale in the play – for example, in Scene Five, when Tom tells Lucy he has spent all his money after his party and that he wants to win her back, how much time has passed since the previous scene?

Think about the structure and pace of the story. Use the scenes to focus, tell the story, then move on. Keep the ball in the air during the scenes and keep the interludes swift and fluid – one to two minutes max. At the same time make it clear what's happening – for example in Interlude Four it is essential that the audience see that Tom receives a warning.

The interludes were written as pathways in time or passages for the characters to pass through to tell the story. While they are part of the world of the play, they were written to have a life of their own, and are not the same as scenes.

NICK DRAKE 'I wanted to distinguish moments between the scenes, so I created interludes to give the feeling of passing time and transitory moments.'

KEEPING THE CHARACTERS ACTIVE

The characters are three-dimensional and contemporary. Avoid using symbolism to portray them – for example, Nick Shadow as the Devil. Instead look for his 'playable', real situation and his psychological story in the play – Nick Shadow as the market trader who manipulates Tom.

Make choices in each scene about what each character wants and how they go about getting it. Find out what's at stake in each scene for the protagonists. Keep it simple and find active words instead of 'actions' and 'intentions'. For example, in Scene One:

- What do the characters want and how do they get it?
- What does Nick want?
- Nick wants to recruit Tom to own him / to consume him / to ruin him.
- How does he get him? (He befriends him / he blinds him / he builds him up / he bullies him / he dazzles him.)

NICK DRAKE 'Tom is presented with a series of illusions that he must strip away to get closer to what is real.'

Tom Rakewell is the protagonist and it is essential that we follow his journey as he celebrates his winnings, speculates, loses all, then finally finds what he is looking for. His speech at the close of Scene Eight (p. 434) is a crucial moment of reckoning and a psychological climax for his character; circle this speech and make sure your Tom knows this is where he's heading to in his journey.

It's also important to work out what's at stake for him at different points in the story – for example in Scene Six, when he decides to gamble all his possessions away.

441

Differentiate between Tom Rakewell's passive and loyal lover in Hogarth's *Rake's Progress* and Lucy. Lucy is Tom's counterpart and is active to the story. Her unswerving quest to find truth and her perseverance in spite of the obstacles that are presented to her prove her to be a beacon of authenticity and a key protagonist. Explore all her decisions in the play and her resistance to temptation.

Sum up what happens to each of the protagonists at the end of each scene. For example:

- *End of Scene One:* Tom pledges his allegiance to money.
- *End of Scene Two:* Lucy accepts Tom.

Some of the other characters, such as Ping and Pong and the Kid, although playing a supporting role to Tom and Lucy's story, are are also vital to the whole story. Avoid turning them into stereotypes and find ways to give these characters concrete 'playable' roles: for example; the Kid knows everything and can travel in time.

KEEPING THE LANGUAGE TRUTHFUL

NICK DRAKE 'The language in the play is the language of the characters' world.'

The language is poetic, persuasive and real. It is the language of excess, and it is important to give it some shoulder while keeping it truthful and keeping it rhythmic. Every word counts – don't change the words at all.

The dialogue is pacy and fast; push through the lines and let each word land, as well as deciding where to breathe. The punctuation helps, so try to obey all full stops, commas and pauses.

Observe the way the language changes for each character and the length of sentences. For example, the Bag Lady speaks in long sentences and there are lots of ideas in her lines; and the Crowd in Scene One say their lines in unison until indicated in the play. This helps to keep the rhythm of the language moving.

SETTING THE PLAY

The play was written for the present tense, as the iPods in Interlude One suggest. Make sure your world reflects the audience you are performing for. The play belongs to an urban, contemporary world.

Success moves effortlessly from scene to scene, with scene changes that can quickly unravel and sweep across the stage. It is not naturalistic and it is important to keep your set as minimal and fluid as possible.

Avoid bringing on too much furniture – it is more important to keep the action fluid, so interrogate the need for extraneous props and settings or the use of projections. Ask yourselves if you really need them: can you not create the world of the play through a simple concept or by relying on the language and characters in the play?

Keep it cheap! Use only the props indicated in the play: CDs, pizza boxes, shopping trolleys, the suitcase, the rose. Remember the significance of these key props and follow their journey through the play.

In some places the action of the story and the psychological events take precedence over the set. For example, in Scene Three it is less important that Tom hides his suitcase behind a mirror than that he conceals it *somewhere* before the guests arrive; and in Interlude Three it's more important that Ping and Pong create mischief, less significant that they are seen to be running down a street.

CASTING THE PLAY

NICK DRAKE 'It is a play about reflections, and it is important to keep sight of the reflections in the play which serve the story. For example Ping and Pong are reflections of each other and act as polarities.'

Each company will have different casting requirements and challenges, but it is important that your casting serves the play. Thus, it's vital that Ping and Pong work as polar opposites and that there are only two people playing these parts; and while it is also crucial that there is only one Bag Lady, it is possible to have lots of Flower Sellers.

Think about the casting of Eva and where she is from. She is written to be East European, but this can be changed to suit culture/gender/age and the requirements of your company.

The Hoodie/Cart/Kid act as one unit. It is important for you to make choices about why the Hoodie is pushing the Kid.

STAGING

Think about how you are going to stage your crowd scenes. In Scene One watch how the suitcase travels as a way to focus the crowd. Its up to you how you do this, but the important element to this scene is that it is a celebration.

In Interlude Seven find a way to stage running through a labyrinth – for example, running on the spot, 'cat and mouse' games. The key aspect to this interlude is that it ends with tension and that the arrival of Nick must be dangerous.

Make strong entrances and be precise about their timing. Thus, in Scene Three it's important to decide when Lucy enters in Tom's speech.

The stage directions reveal the architecture of the scenes – make sure you don't miss them as you work through the play. Explore the ambiguity of some of the moments. For example, in Scene Two the Kid offers Lucy a bunch of dead flowers, but does she accept them? If so, is she holding them when Tom gives her a rose? Some of the stage directions are left open for you: in Scene Six it's up to you to choose what gambling game you want to play.

Apart from 'Que Sera, Sera', which is an old familiar tune which can be found on the internet, it's up to you to compose or decide on your music for Lucy's song in Scene Four. Further music can be integrated into the interludes, but avoid the use of underscoring in the scenes themselves.

From a workshop led by Angus Jackson,
with notes by Charlotte Gwinner

THE THINGS SHE SEES

Ben Power
adapted from the novel by Charles Boyle

Ben Power is Associate Director of Headlong. He was Literary Associate on *A Disappearing Number* for Complicite (Evening Standard, Critics' Circle and Olivier awards for Best New Play). Work for theatre includes *Six Characters in Search of an Author*, *Faustus*, *Paradise Lost*, *The Tempest*, *Much Ado About Nothing* and *Tamburlaine the Great*. Radio includes *A Disappearing Number*. Forthcoming work includes *A Tender Thing* for the RSC.

Charles Boyle has written the unpublished novella *The Things She Sees*, and six poetry collections, most recently *The Age of Cardboard and String* (shortlisted for the T. S. Eliot Prize and Whitbread Award), and a novel under the pen-name Jennie Walker, *24 for 3* (McKitterick Prize). In 2007 he founded the small press CB editions.

Characters

Dizzy
aged thirteen

Tad
aged thirteen

Older Tad
aged seventeen

Mrs Kennedy

Girl in Art Class

Boy in Art Class

Waitress in Ladbroke Grove Café

Tad's Mum

Sayyid
Tad's Cousin

Marek

Frank

Waitress in Hammersmith Café

Sayyid

Dawoud
Dizzy's Grandad

Dizzy's Gran

Matoub
Dizzy's Great-Grandad

Waiter in the Arif Café

Woman in East London

Young Mohammed
Dizzy's dad, aged eighteen

Young Ahmed
Sayyid's dad, aged eighteen

Young Kathy
Dizzy's mum, aged eighteen

Trader
in Portobello Road market

Janice

Mohammed
Dizzy's dad, aged fifty

Older Dizzy
aged seventeen

*Music. A thirteen-year-old girl (Dizzy) sits in near-darkness.
She has a large sketchbook on her lap and is drawing.
Her attention is fierce, a reverie. From the darkness
beyond, shapes begin to emerge: a boy on a bike holding
a bunch of flowers; a chubby man in an armchair. Then
horses, with Moorish riders, rearing up in the shadows.
After several moments, the shapes fade. A boy (Tad), also
thirteen, appears. At first he too is spectral, then he steps
out of the gloom and looks at Dizzy. Then another, older
boy steps out from behind Tad. It is obviously the same
boy, three or four years on. He looks at his young self.*

Older Tad This is a story about memories and prophecies.
It's the story of a girl, a girl who drew the future. This
is the story of a girl called Djanira. Dizzy.

*Music, and we see that Dizzy is sitting in a classroom,
in the middle of several rows of pupils the same age.*

It's not hard to guess why we called her Dizzy. The first
time it happened was three weeks into Year Seven, a
bright September afternoon. We were sat in an art
class, working on pencil drawings . . .

*Suddenly we're in an art classroom. Large sheets of
sugar paper everywhere. Tad sits on a table full of
other boys, laughing and doodling on one another's
paper. Mrs Kennedy, a young teacher, doesn't quite
have control of the class. Dizzy, to one side, works
furiously, alone.*

Mrs Kennedy Take care not to overwork the image . . .

Dizzy suddenly begins to convulse. Her paper and pencils fall to the floor.

Girl Miss . . . Miss . . . something's up with Djanira . . . she's being weird . . . MISS!

Dizzy holds her hands to her head and begins to shake and shiver. The rest of the class stare, some of them shouting 'Ugh!' or muttering 'Freak!' as her body starts to spasm.

Mrs Kennedy (*loudly*) Djanira!

A long pause. Dizzy stops shaking, takes a deep breath.

Djanira? Toby, go and get a cup of water. (*Beat.*) Do you want to go to the nurse?

Dizzy looks around the classroom.

Dizzy No . . . really, Miss. I'm okay.

Pause. Everyone is staring at her.

It's okay, Miss. I'm just feeling dizzy, that's all.

Beat.

Boy It's art, Miss. Makes you feel ill.

The class erupts in laughter, pointing at Dizzy. Some make vomiting noises, others mimic her fit. They go quiet when she starts twitching again. Her papers and pencils fall to the floor. Mrs Kennedy runs over to Dizzy. She holds her as the fit gets worse and worse. The class are silent now.

Mrs Kennedy Djanira! Djanira, can you hear me? Erm . . . Adam, go and get Mr Hughes . . . Djanira?!

The young teacher is panicking. Eventually Dizzy's seizure comes to an end. She coughs, settles, opens her eyes. Mrs Kennedy, slightly embarrassed, lets go of her.

Right. Back to work, everyone. Tadeusz, help Djanira
pick up her things and take her down to the nurse's
office. I mean it, everyone. Back to work.

*Tad goes over to Dizzy, who is quickly and furtively
picking up pencils. He picks up her pieces of paper.
Everything freezes as he stares at them.*

Older Tad There were two pictures. They'd been drawn
quickly but they were incredibly detailed. In the first,
an African man sat in an armchair watching television.
He was overweight, sweaty and wore thick glasses. He
looked . . . afraid or anxious, I couldn't tell. The
second picture also showed a man, but this one was
stranger. The man was close, bulky, and around him
blackness. I couldn't see his face but his hands were
clear. And in his hands was a knife. He was coming
out of the darkness, coming towards me. (*Beat.*) It was
amazing and awful all at once. I felt afraid.

*Dizzy grabs her bag and runs from the classroom,
leaving Tad holding the picture.*

Mrs Kennedy Djanira?
Tad (*looking after Dizzy*) Should I . . . ?
Mrs Kennedy Oh, never mind, Tadeusz. Just get on with
your work.

*The art class resumes. Dizzy runs out of the school
and stands, panting. The space around her darkens
and there, from the black, shapes emerge. Repeatedly,
men with knives, coming toward her. Music. Dizzy
holds her head and sinks to her knees.*

SCENE TWO

*The pavement outside Ladbroke Grove tube. Dizzy is
sitting on the kerb.*

Older Tad Dizzy didn't come back to class for the rest of
the day. But that evening, as I stepped out of the tube
on my way home, out into the grime of Ladbroke
Grove, I saw her sitting on the kerb, almost as if she
was waiting for me. I'd never spoken to her before,
before the art class, I don't think she even knew I
existed. But there she was, outside the station.

Tad goes to Dizzy and sits down next to her.

Tad Hey.

Dizzy just looks at him. Then she touches her head.

Dizzy Ow.
Tad You okay?
Dizzy I'll be fine. I've just got a headache.

Pause. Dizzy's face is screwed up in a frown.

Tad Where do you live?
Dizzy Over there. Just off Golborne Road.
Tad Not far then. (*Beat.*) Are you okay to get there?
(*Beat.*) I could go with you, if you want.

Dizzy shakes her head but shows no sign of moving.

You know that drawing you did in Art, that man
watching TV? It was really good.
Dizzy That's my dad.
Tad Oh. He didn't look like you. How come he's so big
and you're so small?

Dizzy shrugs.

I've got some money left from lunch, do you want to go
somewhere? I'll buy you a Coke.

Beat. Dizzy looks at Tad.

Dizzy My dad's gone. He's gone.

*Music and we move with Dizzy and Tad into a busy
café on Ladbroke Grove. People bustle around them*

and a Waitress brings them two Diet Cokes and a piece of cake for Dizzy, who eats hungrily as she speaks. Tad watches her.

It was last Wednesday. I got up for school and he wasn't in the flat. Gone. And he hasn't been back since.

Tad So where's he gone to?

Dizzy looks at him and after a moment she shrugs.

What about your mum?

Dizzy My mum left ages ago. I live with my grandad now. And my gran.

Tad So maybe he's gone off with a woman? I mean, maybe he's found someone he likes.

Dizzy laughs.

Dizzy He's not like that.

Tad Does he go off like this often?

Dizzy No, he doesn't. He's my dad.

Tad Maybe he had an accident, maybe he's in hospital. Have you called the police?

Dizzy There's no point. He's okay, he's not hurt. I just don't know where he is.

Tad But he must be somewhere. Don't your grandparents have any idea?

Dizzy shakes her head.

And anyway . . . I mean . . . how do you know he isn't hurt?

Beat.

Dizzy Have you got my picture?

Tad hands her a folded piece of paper. Dizzy opens it and lays it over the table – the man in the armchair. We see the figure in the darkness.

There. Do you know where that is? Have you seen that place?

Tad Er . . . no. It's just a room. It could be anywhere.

Dizzy pulls out her large sketchbook, places the picture inside. She's about to put the book back in her bag when she stops.

Dizzy What happened to your face?
Tad (*touching the plaster over his eye*) Rode my bike into a lamp post.

Dizzy flicks through the sketchbook before finding a particular page and turning it to Tad. She shows him the picture. Everything freezes as he looks at it.

Older Tad It was me, in the drawing. My hair that needed cutting, my sticking-out ears – all me. And more than that, it was me *here*, in this café. My bag on the chair, the empty Coke can on the table. (*Beat.*) The thing was, I'd never been in that café before. Up to that day I hadn't even known it existed.

We see him there in the distance. Tad is amazed. He looks at Dizzy.

Tad How did you . . .
Dizzy Not now. Later, maybe.

They sit at the table, looking at each other. The café disappears into darkness.

SCENE THREE

Older Tad I'm Tad, short for Tadeusz.

Tad's Mum appears.

That's my mum. She's Polish. When she was eighteen, she came to England for a holiday. This was in the 1980s, when there were big political problems in Poland, and while she was here the army took control of the government. So she decided not to go back, and started making a new life for herself in London.

Mum I want you to be English, Tad! You must read the books of Charles Dickens, you must understand the rules of cricket, you must learn the words to 'God Save the Queen'. All three verses!

Older Tad I tell her that those are just ideas she's got from watching old films. Most people in this country aren't English in that way any more. But it doesn't put her off.

We see Tad's Mum polishing plates with pictures of the Queen on. Stephan appears.

That's my cousin Stephan. He was born in England too, but with him it's different. He speaks Polish at home and a lot of his friends are Polish. He's nineteen, and he shares a flat in Hammersmith with another Polish guy, Marek.

Marek appears. He and Stephan light cigarettes.

At this point, he hasn't got a regular job or a steady girlfriend and shows no sign of getting either. My mum can't understand why he doesn't have any ambition . . .

Mum Everything I've achieved, I've earned by years of hard work. Stephan, you're a waste of space! You don't know what you want to do with your life, you think the world owes you a living! Get out of bed! Bloody scrounger!

Tad's Mum disappears.

Older Tad Stephan works on building sites. There's a street he goes to in Hammersmith where, if he's early enough and he's brought his tools, he can pick up work any day he wants. Vans pull up, someone wants a couple of plasterers and an electrician, someone else wants a carpenter.

Stephan I work hard when I need to. I pay the rent, then I stay up late and sleep till lunchtime. That's how I like it, and no nagging from my auntie is going to change me.

Marek Look, the pay's crap but . . . there's always more work.

Older Tad West London's like the United Nations – half the children in my school speak another language as well as English, and some hardly speak English at all. There are council estates where you take your bike indoors rather than leave it outside and other streets where the houses are owned by film stars. People are always on the move – arriving or leaving, moving up in the world or down – and the buildings need fixing up or changing around.

Stephan And that's where we come in.

Outside a row of large Notting Hill villas, Stephan and Marek begin to mix cement and pile bricks. Tad and Dizzy are walking to school.

Older Tad The morning after we'd talked in the café, I saw Dizzy on the way to school. We were early, so I suggested we go and see Stephan, who was working on a house nearby. Seeing Stephan with sweat on his face at eight-thirty in the morning always made me feel that school wasn't so bad after all.

Dizzy God, Tad, look at these houses.

Tad I know. I told Stephan that when I grew up I was going to live in one of these houses. He said no way. One, you've got to be rich; two, you have to be *really* English. Like, a British passport isn't enough, your whole family have to be English for at least two hundred years. There he is.

Stephan has seen them and is waving.

458

Stephan Tad . . . *Tad*! Why so shy? (*Nodding at Dizzy.*)
Aren't you going to introduce me?

Tad (*embarrassed*) Yeah, Stephan, this is Dizzy . . . er,
Djanira. She's in my class.

Stephan Very pleased to meet you. (*Grins.*) I can see why
Tad's been keeping you a secret. What are you doing
tomorrow night?

Dizzy blushes and looks away. Marek sniggers.

Tad How come you're taking a break so early? Isn't
Frank around?

Marek Gone to get some wood or something. So we're
taking a well-earned rest.

Stephan Either that or he's gone to get reinforcements.
He had an argument yesterday with the woman who
owns the house. Money, I reckon. Money, Frank likes.
Women, he doesn't. Some men just don't know how to
handle women. (*Winks at Dizzy.*)

Tad Stephan, about those trainers you said you'd get
me . . .

*Suddenly a transit van turns noisily into the yard and
screeches to a halt. Stephan and Marek stub out their
cigarettes and trot back to work. A large man with a
comb-over and tattoos on his forearms jumps out of
the van and marches towards them. He pushes past
Tad and Dizzy, past Stephan and Marek, and on into
the house. They watch him go and we hear shouting
from inside. Dizzy grabs Tad's arm and is shaking,
unable to speak.*

Dizzy? What's up? Are you . . . ?

*Frank comes back out of the house, shaking his head
and spluttering with rage. Dizzy runs off. Stephan and
Marek jump back to work. Frank lifts a chunk of sawn-*

off wood. He smashes it across his thigh, breaking it in two. He turns on Tad.

Frank What are you staring at?!

Tad grabs his satchel.

Tad Dizzy . . . wait! Bye, Stephan, see you later! Bye, Marek!

Frank Yeah, get lost! Bloody hoodlums.

The pavement scene fades into darkness.

SCENE FOUR

Older Tad I've always reckoned that there are two ways to find someone. Either you walk down every street in London, looking at everyone you see; or you stay still in one place, hoping that the person you've lost will pass by. They're both useless, of course, because if you're walking around, the person could be a few paces behind you and you'd never see him . . . and if you stay in one place, the person might simply never go there. You could wait a hundred years. After we'd been to see Stephan, I ran to school, but Dizzy wasn't there. She wasn't in all day. But no one seemed worried, no one noticed.

Dizzy appears, sitting at the same table in the same café, gazing out. She is wearing a large grey jumper, far too big for her. It is the jumper worn by the man watching television in her picture.

When I thought of her, I saw her sitting at the table in the café where we'd talked, looking out of the window at all the people passing, waiting for one of them to be her dad. After school, I got off the bus early and went to the café.

Tad joins her at the table.

Tad Has your dad turned up yet?
Dizzy No.
Tad Is that his jumper?
Dizzy I'm glad you're here.
Tad Were you waiting for me?
Dizzy I knew you'd come. Tad, could you ask your cousin if he knows anything about my dad?
Tad How would he know anything? He's only met you once.
Dizzy But that man who came when we were there, the one who was shouting . . .
Tad That's Frank, his boss . . .
Dizzy I've seen him before, Tad, he came to our flat. He said my dad hadn't turned up for work and he wanted to know where he was. He gave us a number and said to call if my dad came home.
Tad What did you tell him?
Dizzy We said we didn't know where he was. I don't think he believed us, he got really annoyed.
Tad He's always annoyed.
Dizzy He's a bully, Tad. And he smells. He tried to push past my gran and come into the flat. But I think my dad worked for this man. Like your cousin.
Tad So Stephan might know your dad?
Dizzy That's what I'm saying.
Tad What did your dad do? I mean what *does* he do? What's his job?
Dizzy He's an electrician.

Tad goes quiet.

Tad?
Tad I've seen him. Your dad. About three weeks ago. At the big house. Stephan and Marek knocked down a wall and they needed an electrician . . . I didn't see him

461

up close but . . . that drawing of your dad? That was him. Him exactly. The electrician. (*Beat.*) When you showed it me, you said he was okay, there was no need to tell the police or anyone.

Dizzy Yes.

Tad But how can you be sure?

Dizzy He *is* okay. I mean, he's not hurt. I know that. But I think he's in some kind of trouble, and I want to help him.

Tad Okay . . . that other drawing, the one of me. Here in the café. What was that about?

Pause.

Dizzy Haven't you worked it out for yourself?

Tad No, I haven't. I've thought about it, but . . . it doesn't make any sense.

Dizzy What have you come up with?

Tad You did that drawing of me before it happened. I'd never been here before, in this café, I didn't even know it existed. So that means you drew something that hadn't happened yet but did happen later. (*Beat.*) You saw the future.

Dizzy grins.

Dizzy That's right, Tad. I can see the future. *I can see the future.*

Tad But . . . that's impossible.

Dizzy I know. But it happens. And I can explain it.

Tad Dizzy, you can't explain it, it doesn't happen. It's like seeing round corners or something, it goes against all the laws of science . . .

Dizzy Do you know what *déjà vu* means?

Tad A *déjà vu* is when you see something, like someone coming into a room, and you have this weird feeling that you've seen it before, exactly as you're seeing it now.

Dizzy Have you ever had a *déjà vu*?

462

Tad I think so.

Dizzy Well, it's like that, only with me it happens the other way round. I get this strange feeling in my head sometimes – that's when I go all dizzy – and what I'm seeing is like a photograph of something that hasn't happened yet, but I know, I just know, it *will* happen. Understand?

Pause.

Tad Who's going to win the FA Cup?

Dizzy shakes her head.

What I am going to get for Christmas? How many GCSEs will I get? Are my mum and dad going to get divorced?

Dizzy It doesn't work like that. I can't choose which bits of the future I see, and mostly they're very ordinary. They don't *mean* anything, even to me.

Tad So you can't tell me which horse will win the Grand National?

Dizzy Think, Tad. If I could tell you that, I'd be rich.

Pause.

Tad Can I see your sketchbook? I want to see the pictures.

Dizzy No, not now. It wouldn't help you understand. Maybe later. (*Beat.*) Look, I can't choose what I see. And the things I do see, I know they're going to happen, but I don't know *when*. And of course, there are trillions and trillions of things I *don't* see, so it's not like I can really *see the future* because I just see tiny random bits of it and they don't join up. It's pretty useless, really, the whole thing.

Beat.

Tad I'm confused. Is this to do with your family?

Dizzy How do you mean?

Tad Well, you're Moroccan . . . Is it something to do with that?

Dizzy You think it's because I'm different, because I come from some strange faraway place?

Tad Dizzy, I'm just asking –

Dizzy I'm British, Tad. As British as you are. My father was born in Morocco, yes, but my mum's Scottish.

Tad Can your dad see the future too?

Dizzy No, he can't. And nor can my gran. But my grandad, I think he sees things, so maybe it *is* to do with my family. (*Dizzy looks suddenly close to tears.*) I can't tell you anything more, I don't know myself.

Tad Dizzy, it's okay. I'll talk to Stephan.

Dizzy Thanks, Tad. I've got to find out if he knows anything.

Tad Okay.

Dizzy And Tad? You should get the brakes fixed on your bike.

Tad touches the scar on his head. Dizzy smiles. One café turns into another. Dizzy disappears and is replaced by Stephan.

Older Tad The next day I found Stephan in a Polish café in Hammersmith. He fancied one of the waitresses. He wouldn't tell me which, but it was obvious.

A Waitress passes. Stephan waves at her. She ignores him. Tad sips a Diet Coke. Stephan drinks a coffee and searches for his cigarette lighter. He continues throughout the scene.

Tad Steph, about the trainers you said you'd get . . .

Stephan Sorry, mate, no can do. Frank hasn't paid us yet.

Tad Why not?

Stephan The woman in the house won't pay *him*. Something's gone missing and till she gets it back, no

pay for Frank, no pay for me and no trainers for you.
It's that bloody electrician.

Tad What?

Stephan Well, work it out. He disappears and something
gets stolen. Must have took it. And now I can hardly
afford a pack of fags. Have you seen my lighter?

Tad No. What was he like?

Stephan Who?

Tad The electrician.

Stephan He was okay. Big bloke. Moroccan or something.
It's weird, him nicking stuff, cos I quite liked him. He
was friendly but he got on with it. He's got big clumsy
hands, but put a screwdriver in them . . . wow, like a
precision tool, all the tiny wires. Impressive.

Tad Did he ever say anything about his family?

Stephan Nah.

Tad And where do you think he's gone?

Stephan How should I know? Why do you care?

Tad You know that girl who came by with me yesterday?

Stephan Too serious for you, Tad. She's pretty, though.
Do you like her?

Tad I think the electrician's her dad.

Stephan Really? Well, you tell her to send him back, with
whatever he's nicked and I can get bloody well paid.

Tad What did he take, Stephan? What's gone missing?

Stephan Haven't a clue. There was plenty in the house.

Tad What kind of stuff?

Stephan A piano. But I doubt he's nicked that. Pictures.
Books, carpets, loads of little African statues. All the
stuff that people have, you know? It's probably worth
a lot, or some of it is, if you know where to take it. If
I knew that, I'd probably be in there myself. After
all . . . (*He produces a key.*) Frank gave me this, so
we could start early, as soon as we got there. Back
door key.

465

Tad Steph— you wouldn't nick . . .

Stephan Course not! I wouldn't know what to do with that stuff. But Frank doesn't get this key back until I get my money. Are you sure you haven't seen it? My lighter?

Tad No! Anyway, that's probably useless now. Soon as the woman found her spare key was missing she'll have changed the lock. Anyone would.

Stephan So it's useless?

Tad Yup.

Pause.

Stephan Swap.

Tad What?

Stephan You know what I mean.

Tad produces Stephan's lighter from his pocket.
Stephan hands Tad the key and lights his cigarette.
He waves at the Waitress again. She ignores him again.
Tad looks at the key. The café disappears.

SCENE FIVE

Tad stands under a street light. Night.

Older Tad I showed Dizzy the key on the bus to school. Why did I do it? I didn't want to get any deeper into this. Or did I? The moment she saw it her eyes lit up. I knew there was no going back.

Dizzy approaches. All in black, with a flashlight.

Dizzy (*alert, professional*) Ready? Let's go.

They start to walk towards the big house. Music. Tad gestures and they move around the back. Tad begins to fumble with the key and the lock of the back door.

Come on.
Tad I'm trying.

Suddenly Tad drops the key loudly. They look at each other and up to the window of the house. Dizzy begins to giggle.

Sshhh!

Tad continues with the key and suddenly the door swings open. They look at each other, serious. Dizzy walks past Tad and into the house. They move through into the kitchen silently. Tad flicks through a pile of magazines. He doesn't know what they're looking for. Dizzy is efficient, moving around the room with her flashlight. She suddenly stops.

Dizzy Look.

Tad goes to where Dizzy's torch points. She is looking at a row of African masks on the wall. There is a gap in the middle where one mask has been removed. Dizzy looks at Tad, her eyes shining. Tad nods.

Tad Okay. Let's get out of here.

But Dizzy is off, out of the kitchen. Tad waits, scared. We hear Dizzy's footsteps going upstairs. Then silence. Only the ticking of the kitchen clock.

Older Tad (*whispering*) I stood for what seemed like forever. Just me and the masks on the wall. They were beautiful . . . strange and fantastical but also human. I wanted to touch them. I thought that someone would do a lot to get their hands on those masks.

A car passes outside and Tad jumps. Dizzy reappears and gestures to the door. Quickly she passes Tad and moves back outside. He follows. She runs ahead to the street corner as Tad locks the door. He catches her up.

Tad What did you find upstairs? What took you so long?

Dizzy Nothing there. Just rooms. I've never been in a house like that. But we know what he took, don't we?

Tad The mask? But why would he take that? I mean, it's not really valuable, is it? It's only wood.

Dizzy smiles and walks on. After a moment she turns to face Tad. Suddenly she leans forward and kisses him on the cheek.

Dizzy Tad, you've got to meet my grandad. He can explain better than me.

And she moves off into the darkness.

SCENE SIX

Dizzy and Tad walk towards the door of a council flat.

Dizzy Listen, he's old and he's ill. And he speaks no English. If he gets tired you'll have to leave.

Tad How am I going to understand what he's telling me? I don't actually know much Arabic . . .

Dizzy He won't be talking in Arabic. We're not Arabs, we're Berbers. He speaks in the Berber language.

Tad Oh, that's fine then.

Dizzy Don't worry. Sayyid will be there too.

Tad Who's Sayyid?

Dizzy My dad's friend. He'll translate.

Tad Is that the language you speak at home, then, barber?

Dizzy It's what my grandparents speak. My dad and I speak English. And my mum spoke English too, of course, when she was here, but she had this funny Scottish accent so none of us could understand her. Come on . . .

Tad Hang on!

Dizzy What?

Tad Well, first of all you have to tell me who the barbers
are . . .

Dizzy Not barbers, you idiot – you're not coming to
have a haircut! It's *Berbers*. Come on.

She pushes the door open and they enter the flat.
A picture of Mecca hangs on the wall next to a TV.
There's a sofa-bed and two armchairs.

Older Tad The room looked normal enough. But the
smell . . . it was like nothing I'd ever known . . .
Foreign . . . Africa.

On the sofa, under a blanket, lies Dizzy's Grandad,
frail, very old, with a straggly beard. In an armchair
sits Sayyid, a Moroccan man aged about nineteen. He
wears a baseball cap too big for his head. In the other
armchair sits Dizzy's Gran. She sleeps. Tad and Dizzy
approach the sofa as Sayyid waves at them. They
kneel. Pause.

Dizzy Grandad? Grandad. This is Tad. I was telling you
about him.

Dizzy's Grandad looks at Tad for a moment then
nods. He coughs violently, then begins to speak rapidly
in a high voice, long Berber sentences pouring from
him.

Sayyid Tad. Dawoud welcomes you to his home. He says
it is very important that you understand him and his
family. If you are to help us all.

Tad looks at Dizzy.

If you are ready, he is going to tell you a long story.
When he's finished, you'll understand. Are you ready?

Tad Er . . . yeah.

Sayyid First, he is saying, you must understand the Berber people. The Berbers were the original inhabitants of North Africa . . .

The scene continues quietly. But all around the tiny room Morocco appears. We see the Atlas Mountains, the Medina of Marrakesh.

Older Tad He spoke for what seemed like hours. I kept looking at Dizzy for support, but she just stared at her grandad. I learned that the Berbers had been in Morocco for over three thousand years. They fought all invaders and only the Arabs were too strong for them. But even though the Berbers accepted Islam, the Arab religion, they kept their own customs and traditions, and married among their own people. In their own language Berbers call themselves *Imazighen* – 'the free people'. Those who live in the mountains of Morocco are especially independent – and it was from here that Dizzy's family came. Their life was hard, and their village in the mountains was often cut off by snow.

Dizzy's Grandad pauses in his Berber oration and starts wheezing,

Dizzy Grandad?
Tad Maybe I should go?
Dizzy No!

She speaks to her Grandad in Berber. He nods.

He's just tired, that's all. He says that Sayyid must finish telling you. Sayyid?

Tad turns to Sayyid.

Sayyid Dawoud's father – Djanira's great-grandfather – he lived in the village, high in the mountains. His name was Matoub. He was – how do you say this? – he was a prophet. Yes, a prophet. Understand?

*Matoub appears in the distance. Dizzy takes Tad's
hand and her Grandad nods vigorously.*

Tad He could see the future?
Sayyid This is right. Many things, things that no one else
can see.
Tad What kind of things?
Sayyid He can see when strangers will come to the village,
when the harvest will be good. So when people need to
know what will happen, they ask him. And for one
thing that he saw especially, he is still famous among
all the Berber villages.

*Matoub moves in the darkness as figures sit with him
and listen.*

Early in the last century Morocco came under the rule of
France and a French army was sent to subdue the Berber
tribesmen. In the year 1924 Matoub saw into the future,
and he told the people of his village that French troops
would approach along a particular route, a narrow
valley. He could tell at what time they would come
because in his vision there were pink flowers on the
cliffs, and this plant only flowered at a particular
season and for a short time. Pink! It was a pink flower!

*Dizzy's Grandad interrupts in Berber. Sayyid replies
and they begin to argue. Dizzy coughs loudly and
Sayyid turns his attention back to Tad.*

Pardon us, Tad. The flower was a sort of reddish-pink.
All the Berber men from the village gathered their
weapons and hid along the cliffs. It was an ambush,
and completely successful. The French troops arrived
exactly as Matoub had foreseen, and the Berbers
opened fire. The French were massacred. Not a single
soldier survived.

Sayyid smiles. He leans towards Tad.

And it was at this time that a mask was made.

Tad A mask?

Sayyid A very special mask. Not a mask of Matoub himself, but a mask which signified his power. His power as a prophet!

Dizzy I told you it was an interesting story.

Pause.

It's late, you'd better go.

Sayyid We'll talk more another day.

Dizzy I'll see you out.

Tad and Dizzy walk out of the door and stand on a balcony outside the flat. He looks at her.

Tad So it does run in the family, this seeing the future?

Dizzy It seems to. But I'm not a prophet, Tad, really I'm not. It sounds like something from an old history book. For me, it's much more . . . personal.

Tad Does your grandad keep a sketchbook like yours?

Dizzy No. He keeps it all in his head. When I got my first pictures, I'd no idea about my family history. My dad didn't tell me anything about this until he realised that I could see things too.

Tad So how come your dad hasn't got this weird gift?

Dizzy (*sadly*) I don't know why, Tad. No one does.

Tad Your family are . . . you should be proud of them.

Dizzy Of course I am. I just wish this 'gift' had stayed where it belonged, back in the village. It's not normal here! I've got *nothing* in common with that Matoub man, the one they call a prophet, and my grandad too, we hardly speak the same language. I love him, but he wasn't even here when I was born – to me he's an old man from far away who happens to be my grandad. He's Moroccan, I'm English. The only person I feel close to, the only family I'm part of, is my dad. And does he have this gift? No. You have to help me find him.

Pause.

Older Tad What could I say?
Tad Of course. Of course I'll help.

The scene disappears.

SCENE SEVEN

Marek appears, on the phone.

Marek Stephan. Now *this* is a tip. A cert. Tangerine Moon: twenty pounds – at odds of seven to one.

Stephan and Tad in Stephan's flat.

Stephan Do you know where it came? Tangerine-bloody-Moon? Last. Three lengths behind. Now I'm completely broke.
Tad You should never listen to Marek! What does *he* know about horses?

Stephan swears and lights a cigarette. Silence.

Older Tad I could see why Stephan had acted on Marek's tip. When someone says they know what's going to happen in the future and it's going to be something good, you *want* to believe them. When they say something *bad* is going to happen, that's different. At school we'd been reading *Julius Caesar*. In the play a man warns Julius Caesar to stay at home on the day called the Ides of March. Caesar ignores him, goes to the Senate and gets murdered. Unfortunately for Julius, unlike Marek, the Roman prophet had got it right.
Stephan We've got work with Frank for another couple of weeks – two derelict flats over a shop in Harlesden –

and he's upped the wages. I think he's trying to make up for not paying us at all for the work on that woman's house. But he's still mad as hell about that. And he's still looking for your girlfriend's dad . . .

Tad She's not my . . . Never mind. How much does the woman owe him?

Stephan About six grand, I guess. I don't know exactly.

Tad Six thousand pounds! No wonder he's angry. You could buy a swimming pool with that. Or a trip round the world. Or – (*He furrows his brow*) – two hundred PlayStation games! Or . . .

Stephan Is your girlfriend looking for her dad too?

Tad Yes, but she knows what he took now. It was one of the African things, a mask.

Stephan How does she know that?

Tad I don't know. She just does. Maybe her grandad told her.

Stephan But that would mean her grandad has seen her dad recently, after he took it . . . He probably knows where he is!

Tad shrugs and looks away. He starts rummaging through a cupboard.

Anyway, what's so great about a mask? I remember them, they were in the kitchen.

Tad Well, that's what they want back. And I swear it, Stephan, we've still no idea where her dad is.

Stephan *We*, eh? So you're in this together?

Tad I'm sort of helping her, yes.

Stephan Helping her? Is that what you were doing when you were out so late the other night? Or were the two of you doing something else?

Tad blushes.

No, you don't have to answer that. There aren't any biscuits, by the way, Marek's eaten them all.

Tad sits down, disappointed.

But I hope you two find her dad before Frank does.
Because if Frank gets to him first, there won't be much
of him left to find.

Tad But Frank only wants the mask, doesn't he? I mean,
as long as he gets that, he'll be happy. He wouldn't do
anything to hurt Dizzy's dad, would he?

Pause.

Stephan If he likes you, Frank's okay. But get on the
wrong side of him, you get done. Frank's a hard man,
and he knows how to hit.

Tad He sounds horrible. He *is* horrible. Why do you
work for him, Stephan?

Stephan Let's just say, it's better to be with him than
against him. It's safer. And I need to pay the rent.

Tad He's been round to Dizzy's house. Looking for her
dad.

Stephan How did he know where he lived? He doesn't
know my address, he's only got my mobile number.
I didn't think he knew where any of us live.

Tad Well. He knew. Somehow. I've got to go. Sorry
about the horse.

Stephan Yeah. See you later.

Tad See you.

As he leaves, Tad steals Stephan's cigarette lighter.

SCENE EIGHT

Older Tad I've always thought that we're trapped in the
present, that's why we can't see the future. There's this
wall around us. But for Dizzy, I suppose, there were
cracks in this wall through which tiny bits of the
future were visible: a boy in a café with a plaster on

his head . . . her father in a chair, worried, alone . . .
a man with a knife raised to strike. The next day was
Sunday the fifteenth of March. The Ides of March. So
I did what Caesar should have done and stayed at home.
But on Monday, after school, I met Dizzy. I decided to
ask her about that picture. The one which had scared
me when I saw it in art class. The man with the knife.

*Tad opens the picture and hands it to Dizzy. She looks
at it for a moment, then quickly folds it and puts it in
her sketchbook.*

Dizzy It's nothing.

Tad But it is yours, isn't it? You drew it in art.

Dizzy Yes, Tad, it's mine. And thanks for saving it. But
not *everything* I draw has to be connected to this thing
about the future, does it?

Tad What happened to the top bit, where it's torn off?

Dizzy Why are you asking me all these questions?

Tad Because I want to know, Dizzy. You can't tell me all
this stuff about seeing the future, ask me to help you
and then expect me not to be interested.

Dizzy looks away.

Okay, we can talk about that later. We're looking for
your dad, and so is Frank. We've got to find your dad
before Frank does, or he's going to be in big trouble.

Dizzy So what do we do?

Tad Well, if Frank found out your address just by asking
around, maybe we could try the same. Nobody just
vanishes without leaving some clues.

Dizzy No one knows where he is. He doesn't talk much,
he lets others do that. I think he's just waiting somewhere, and then he'll come back. When he's ready.

Tad *Someone* must know. He needs food and things.

Dizzy Even if someone does know, they wouldn't tell.

Tad Not even for money? What if Frank starts counting a bundle of cash in front of them?

Dizzy No. I told you. No one.

Tad How do you know? Has he done this before? Surely it's worth trying.

Dizzy Of course he hasn't done this before.

Tad And he hasn't stolen anything before?

Dizzy No. Of course not. He's not like that!

Tad But he's taken something now, we know that. So maybe things are different, maybe he's changed.

Dizzy Look, Tad, I know it looks like he's stolen that mask, but I still don't think he's a thief. He wouldn't. I can't explain this, but I know he hasn't done anything wrong.

Tad Okay, so he's not a thief. But he's still missing, and Frank's still looking for him, and if Frank finds him . . .

Dizzy So what do you want to do? Who do you want to ask?

Tad Well, his friends. People who know him well. Like Sayyid.

Dizzy He has friends. But he wouldn't tell them.

Tad Where does he see them?

Dizzy Either they come to the flat or he sees them in the Arif.

Tad What's the Arif?

Dizzy It's a café he goes to.

Tad Well then, let's go there. Where is it?

Dizzy It's on the Golborne Road. But . . .

Tad What?

Dizzy Think, Tad. How many children of our age have you seen in a Arabic café by themselves?

Tad You don't want to go?

Dizzy It's just . . . well, I don't think there's any point.

Tad You asked me to help, Dizzy. And I can't see what else we can do.

Beat.

What is it?
Dizzy My grandad . . .
Tad What about him?
Dizzy He wouldn't want me there.
Tad It's not a pub, Dizzy, there's no alcohol. And going to a café – it's not a crime, is it? (*Silence.*) Your dad wouldn't stop you, would he?

Pause.

Dizzy Fine.
Tad Fine? So we'll go?
Dizzy Yeah.
Tad Right now?
Dizzy Okay. (*Beat.*) Tad?
Tad Yeah?
Dizzy Thanks.

They walk, and an Arabic café appears.

Older Tad It was a small café in a street off Golborne Road, a couple of tables on the pavement outside and, inside, men drinking mint tea from glasses.

Arabic music plays from a cassette recorder. One man is sitting at a table, smoking a shisha. Tad and Dizzy sit down. A Waiter brings two glasses and two bottles of fruit juice and silently places them on the table in front of them before disappearing again. Pause. The other customer drops some change onto the table and leaves. Pause.

Tad (*whispered*) Do you recognise anyone?

Silence. Dizzy looks uncomfortable.

When the waiter comes back, ask him about your dad.

*Dizzy shakes her head. The Waiter re-enters, wipes the
table with a cloth and leaves. Both Tad and Dizzy keep
their eyes fixed on the ground. Pause.*

Dizzy I don't recognise anyone. No one here can help.
Can we go now?
Tad Fine.

*They stand, push their chairs away and walk off from
the café. They haven't got far when the Waiter comes
running after them. Dizzy sees him first.*

Dizzy Tad . . .
Tad Oh . . . I forgot to pay. Hang on.

*As he scrabbles in his pockets, the Waiter hands Dizzy
a brown envelope and leaves. Puzzled, she opens it and
removes a small piece of paper.*

Dizzy It's an address. Flat 176, 44 Holyhead Close,
Crossways Estate, E3 7TG. That's East London.

Tad's eyes widen.

Tad It's where he is! That's where your dad is! Someone
in the café must have guessed why we were there.

*A car horn sounds and then the sound of a vehicle
driving away. Tad looks off.*

Weird. That was Frank's van.
Dizzy What's he doing here?
Tad never mind. Come on, we're going there now. My
mum's got an *A–Z* we can borrow. Let's go.

Tad moves off but Dizzy stands still, looking at him.

Let's go!

Dizzy smiles and they run off together.

SCENE NINE

*A street in Bow, East London. It's raining. Tad and Dizzy
stand outside a block of flats. Pause. A Woman with
shopping bags approaches. She punches a number into a
security pad. The door clicks and she pulls it open. Dizzy
steps up to her.*

Dizzy Sorry. Forgot my key.

> *The woman looks at her, then enters. Dizzy holds the
> door open and gestures to Tad.*

Come on!

> *They move inside. In the hallway, Dizzy pushes Tad.
> He approaches the Woman as she waits by the lift.*

Tad Excuse me. (*The Woman looks at him.*) We're
looking for Flat 176. Can you help me?

> *The Woman looks confused. She shakes her head.
> Dizzy steps forward and speaks to her in Arabic. The
> Woman again shakes her head. Then she takes the
> piece of paper from Dizzy and looks at it closely. Then
> she looks at them, smiles and holds up ten fingers, then
> seven fingers.*

Dizzy Seventeen. The seventeenth floor. We'll walk.

> *Tad looks at Dizzy.*

Tad The *seventeenth* floor?

> *But Dizzy is already off, running up stairs. The walls
> are dirty, covered in graffiti. They climb and climb.
> Eventually, they reach Flat 176. The door is open.
> Dizzy immediately walks in.*

Dizzy!

Tad follows her in. They enter a small room. It is obviously empty, just a few bits of furniture. Half-light through the closed curtains. A long silence.

Dizzy He's not here.
Tad I'm sorry, Dizzy.

Dizzy sinks down to the floor and curls into a ball. After a moment, Tad turns on the lights.

Dizzy No. Leave it off.
Tad Hang on.

He goes to the table in the corner and picks up a small object. He holds it out in front of him – a pair of reading glasses. Dizzy stands. Looks at him.

Dizzy They're my dad's.

Dizzy takes the glasses and walks to the window. She begins to sob. Tad stands behind her, awkward. Eventually, he picks up a blanket and wraps it around her shoulders. She slowly stops sobbing. They look out of the window at the lights below.

Tad Eight million people live in this city.
Dizzy Yeah.
Tad I mean, it's so easy to disappear, to hide. How can you possibly find one person, if they don't want to be found?

Silence.

Older Tad And as the two of us stood there, in a cold block of flats, I realised that not everything can be solved. Not every mystery has a solution. Sometimes things just happen and we can't explain them and . . . everyone has to live with that. Suddenly I felt sick, I wanted to leave. And I began to worry about Dizzy.

Her grandparents would be waiting for her, angry that she was coming home so late.

The flat dissolves behind him. We see Sayyid, sitting, waiting.

I found out next morning in school that only Sayyid had been at the flat, waiting for Dizzy. Her grandfather was in hospital.

Dizzy walks over to Sayyid and he starts to speak to her.

Earlier that evening, while we'd been in East London, he'd had a heart attack.

They fade into darkness.

SCENE TEN

Older Tad Dizzy wasn't in school the next day or the next. Rather than just sitting around waiting for news, I went to see Stephan in his Hammersmith café.

Stephan (*mid-speech*) . . . Basically, Tad, you've got to decide what you want, then go for it. For me, it's the bike I told you about. My mate's holding it for me till the end of the month, not a day longer. So no beer for me tonight. (*The Waitress passes.*) Hi!

She ignores him.

Tad How's work?

Stephan Better, actually. Frank put me in charge of one of his new sites. So . . . pay rise! Hence . . .

He shows off a shiny new leather jacket. Tad steals his cigarette lighter.

Tad Nice. And how's Frank?

Stephan Still mad. He's still after your mate's dad, the electrician. He won't stop until he gets his money back. Does she know where he is yet?

Tad No. And her grandfather's in hospital.

Stephan There's something odd about that family. They keep disappearing or dying off.

Tad Stephan, it's not funny. Dizzy's really upset.

Stephan Sure she is. But if I were you, Tad, I'd step back a bit. Don't take everything she says at face value. She could be leading you on. I think she knows very well where he is, only she's not telling you. She's making a fool of you.

Tad Why would she do that?

Stephan (*looking at the Waitress*) Women.

Tad She's no idea where he is, I know it. And if she did know, she'd tell me.

Stephan How come you're so sure? Tad, with his long experience of women, has spoken! Nobody tells everyone everything. There's a few things you don't know about me, and let's keep it that way.

Tad But if you trust someone, why keep anything secret?

Stephan You tell me, Tad. I'm not prying, I'm not angry, but there's stuff you keep to yourself, isn't there? That mask, for instance. I bet you know why her dad took it. And you still haven't told me what you were doing out so late that night.

Tad Okay, okay. But this is different, Stephan. We're looking for her dad *together*, she asked me to help her. Why would she keep anything secret?

Stephan Lots of reasons. Adds to the mystery, for starters. Girls know how to play this game, Tad.

Tad She's not like that, really.

Stephan None of them are. Think about it. (*Downs his coffee.*) Right!

Tad Have you got a date, Stephan?

Stephan Like I said, there's other things in my life besides work and buying treats for you. But there's also more money to be made by helping Frank. So if your girlfriend starts talking, tell me about it. (*Stretches out his legs, showing shiny white trainers.*) You want a pair of these for yourself, don't you? I haven't forgotten.

Tad What? Are you saying that if I tell you about Dizzy's dad I can have . . .

Stephan stands.

Stephan Oh, you can keep that lighter you just stole.

Pulls out another lighter from his jacket, lights a cigarette. He grins.

Always be prepared.

SCENE ELEVEN

Older Tad On Friday, Dizzy came back to school. I thought it was a good moment to come back, because we had double Art and she'd be able to open her sketchbook and just draw. But no, she didn't even take her sketchbook out of her bag. She sat all day with her head in her hands. I wondered if she'd ever speak or look at me again. But then, after school, she was waiting for me. I knew when I looked at her what she was going to say and her voice cracked as she told me that her grandfather had died. Then she asked me to go with her, to her flat, to her grandfather's wake.

Dizzy's flat. The wake is in full swing, lots and lots of people, music and Moroccan food everywhere. Tad walks through the mêlée.

I moved through the party and tried to remember how I'd got so involved in all this. It was so far away from anything that had anything to do with me. I couldn't help thinking that Stephan was right about Dizzy, that she knew more than she was telling me. The answer must be here, either in the flat itself, or in the pages of Dizzy's sketchbook.

Tad finds Dizzy on the balcony outside the flat.

Tad Hi.
Dizzy Hi.

Beat.

Tad You know you said you didn't see the mask?
Dizzy Yeah.
Tad So you don't even know what it looks like? Isn't there a picture of it in your sketchbook?
Dizzy Tad. I've had enough of the mask. Just don't talk about it, okay?

Beat.

Tad Aren't we supposed to be looking for it?
Dizzy No, Tad, we're not. We're looking for my *dad*, not the mask. I couldn't care less about the mask. I hate it.
Tad But it's yours – your family's, anyway. For your grandad it was the most important thing in the world.
Dizzy If it wasn't for that stupid mask, my dad would still be here. (*Shakes her head.*) And none of these people here seem to care. My dad's gone and it's like they've forgotten he ever existed.
Tad Okay, I won't mention it. But about your dad, I was thinking. Those pictures in your sketchbook, maybe . . .
Dizzy You think one of them will tell us where he is, don't you? I've been through them all. They don't.

Silence.

Tad It's a good party. I hope when I die, you know . . .

Dizzy looks at him.

The food's great.

Dizzy I know.

Tad Did you help make it?

Dizzy No. I can't cook Moroccan food. My gran tried to teach me, but I couldn't do it. (*Gesturing at the crowd of African women surrounding her grandmother.*) *They* made it.

Sayyid appears.

Sayyid I'm glad to see you, Tadeusz.

Tad Hi.

Sayyid Djanira and I thought it was time you learnt a little more about her father and grandfather. If you are to help us, it would be best if you were fully informed.

Tad Okay.

Sayyid Sit down here and I'll tell you a story.

Tad sits.

Djanira's father is named Mohammed and it was he who came to England first.

Young Mohammed appears.

Mohammed was born among the Berber people, but had always hungered to be elsewhere. Because he wasn't a prophet like his father and his famous grandfather, the village believed that he must have offended the spirits. Aged fourteen he left the mountains and came down to the town of Meknes, where he became an electrician. Four years later, he left Morocco completely.

Young Mohammed meets another young man.

My father met him two weeks after he arrived in London. It was 1973. Dad'd been here six months and showed Mohammed a little of London life. They drank beer, they watched football, they learnt English. And one day Mohammed met a Scottish woman in a bar and he married her. That was Djanira's mother.

We see Young Mohammed meeting Young Kathy.

Then things got tricky. My father died and Mohammed took care of me and my mother. Then his own father, back in Morocco, became ill. He needed special treatment. So Mohammed arranged for his father and mother to come to London. They moved them into this tiny flat.

We see younger versions of Dizzy's grandparents arriving in London.

Little Djanira was only two years old. Mohammed's father was a devout Muslim – he disapproved of his son drinking alcohol, mixing so freely with English people, and he disapproved of his wife. The feeling was mutual and the tension grew.

Dizzy Eventually, my mum met another man in another bar and went back to Scotland.

Young Kathy disappears from the group.

Sayyid Life was easier then. But, as the years passed, Mohammed's father, Dawoud, became homesick. Although he'd been ill and would have died if he had not come to London, he blamed Mohammed for taking him away from the only world he knew, the Berber village. (*To Dizzy.*) But he never blames you. Her grandad loves Djanira very much. He's very proud of her. She has the gift.

Tad She told me.

Sayyid So Mohammed and his father are arguing. There is tension. His father is getting sicker and . . .

Tad And then he found the mask.

We see Mohammed in the kitchen of the house, seeing the mask, lifting it from the wall.

Sayyid Chance, complete chance! But what can he do?
This mask of course is his family's, and he must take it
back. And he thinks to himself, when I give this mask
to my father, all will be well. We will be a good family
again. We will be happy.

Tad And maybe his father will think this is why he came
to England . . . to find the mask?

Sayyid Yes, this too. He'll forgive Mohammed for everything. And perhaps this also: now the mask is found,
his father may believe that Mohammed too will have
the gift, and the chain will not be broken.

Dizzy It happened. My dad brought the mask home, and
he showed it to Grandad, and he was happy.

*We see Mohammed and Dawoud looking at the mask,
embracing.*

I didn't know about any of this . . . not until this week,
until my grandad was in hospital.

Tad You didn't see the mask?

Dizzy No. Grandad would often talk to me about the
mask when I was little, so I knew what it meant to
him, but I didn't see it when my dad brought it home.
I was asleep. And there wasn't time. My dad couldn't
stay in the house, because people would come looking
for him. He had to go.

The scene freezes and dissolves.

Tad What'll happen to the mask now?

Sayyid Who can tell? It is not mine to say. It is
Mohammed's, and then it is Djanira's. Yes. Now her
grandfather has died, most of all it is Djanira's.

Tad But maybe its job is done. I mean, the way it brought
Mohammed and his dad back together. They made
peace.

Dizzy We should send it back to Morocco. To the
mountains.

Sayyid Perhaps this lady whose house it was in, perhaps it is safest with her?

Dizzy My dad must decide. He'll know.

Tad I wonder if he's still got it. Maybe he's given it to someone for safe keeping? A friend?

He looks at Sayyid. Sayyid smiles.

Sayyid Until we find him, we won't know.

Pause.

Tad I did have one idea. About how to find him. When you first showed me your sketchbook, you said I could maybe see it later?

Dizzy Tad, there's nothing there. It's random, like I said. It doesn't tell you anything. There's no meaning to those pictures, I just see them and then – nothing.

Tad So you're not going to show me them?

Dizzy What's the point?

Tad Well, if they're so meaningless, then why do you draw them?

Dizzy Have you ever kept a diary?

Tad Yes. Well, not for long. A few days, really. Then I gave up.

Dizzy How would you feel if I asked to see your diary?

Tad (*sighing*) It would be weird.

Dizzy You see? There's probably nothing important in it, but showing it to someone is like giving yourself away. A bit of yourself, at least.

Tad Does it matter? I can't see that it changes anything. Me seeing your pictures, I mean, it won't change who you are.

Dizzy The point is, once you've let something go, you can never get it back.

Tad Okay. (*Sighs.*) It's private, I get it.

Dizzy It's *me*, Tad. Or I think it is. And I'm just not ready . . . I don't understand it myself.

Sayyid steps forward.

Sayyid Djanira, I think Tad should see your book. I think so.

Dizzy looks at him, then turns and runs into the flat. Pause.

You know, Tad, this seeing of the future, it doesn't make you happy. Of course people wish to know what will happen. This is natural. Better not, I think.

Tad Her dad, Mohammed . . . why can't he see things like his own father? And like Dizzy?

Sayyid I do not know. But he prefers it this way. He is like the rest of us.

Tad You said that maybe now he has the mask, he'll be able to see the future too?

Sayyid Does he want this? I think not.

Tad But surely seeing things like Diz— like Djanira does, it's wonderful?

Sayyid There are things it's not good for her to see, things she cannot understand.

Tad I think she can cope.

In the distance, the man with the knife.

Sayyid But she is so young. This is why I think you should see these pictures too. It is not good for Djanira to keep everything to herself. You must help her. What is it they say? A trouble shared? It is something very heavy, and she needs someone strong to help her carry it.

Tad looks away.

Someone her own age, like you.

Tad Her grandfather was pleased she had the gift.

Sayyid Yes, this is true. This was a comfort to him, that this way of seeing had not died out. That he was not the last. And when he knew that he would die soon, he was ready. All his life he saw things, and then nothing. Nothing to see, eh? Then he knew the time was short.

Tad And what about his own father? The one they called a prophet. Did he know he was going to die too?

Sayyid Oh yes, surely.

Tad What happened?

Sayyid It is not, Tad, a happy story. Some weeks after the Berbers had triumphed over the French in the gully, more troops were sent to punish them, to exact revenge. This time, the prophet did not foresee their coming.

We see the village, Matoub and the French soldiers.

When the French soldiers came in sight, the prophet told the villagers to flee. He and a small number of men occupied some huts on the outskirts of the village and kept the invaders at bay. They fought for long enough, long enough for villagers to escape into the hills, but they were too few to defeat the French. They knew what would happen to them if they were captured, so, rather than surrender, they waited until the last moment, until the French soldiers were almost upon them, and then they set fire to the huts. In the hot dry air the huts burned rapidly. The prophet and the other Berber fighters died in the flames.

Fire and the Moroccan scene disappears.

Some say the prophet escaped from the fire, and one day will return to help the village. I think not. You should see the book. You should understand the gift. Come with me.

Sayyid and Tad walk back into the flat. The last of the visitors are leaving and it suddenly feels very empty. Tad looks at the sofa and at Dizzy's Grandad's blankets.

Sit here.

Tad sits on an armchair as Sayyid walks into Dizzy's room. Dizzy's Gran brings Tad a cup of tea and some sweet cakes. Dizzy and Sayyid emerge.

Tad Djanira and I are going out for walk. We'll be back shortly.

Dizzy looks at Tad. Sayyid ushers her out of the door. Beat. Dizzy's Gran goes into Dizzy's room and returns with the sketchbook. She hands it to Tad and leaves.

Older Tad I had to keep reminding myself that I was looking at pictures not of things that had happened, but of things that were going to happen. I thought of them as messages, as postcards from the future.

Tad opens the sketchbook slowly. The flat disappears and he is surrounded by Dizzy's drawings/prophecies.

A rough timber shack, like a shanty town, with a corrugated iron roof and a sheet of cloth covering the doorway. The background is the silhouette of two cranes high above some distant building site. There is a man next to the shack, but his face is dark.

Dizzy's Gran taking clothes off a washing line hung from a balcony. She has clothes pegs in her mouth.

A cart laden with sacks pulled by a donkey being led round a corner in a narrow street or alley by a man wearing a long cloak and something like a scarf around his head. On one side of the street a child and a woman wearing a veil are pressed into a doorway, so that the cart can pass. This scene is clearly in an Arab country.

A woman with dark hair is sitting with a cello between her legs, staring straight to the front. Her bow is poised: she is about to start playing, or has just finished. On the woman's right and behind her, the case of the cello is leaning against a table. On her right, a man is lying on a sofa, reading a newspaper.

*A group of eight men running, seen from the front.
They are wearing loose, baggy clothes, which could be
military. No background – in a street, in a field, on a
beach? The men's faces have vivid, fierce expressions.
Some of them are clearly shouting. They could be angry,
charging towards someone; they could be running
away from something terrible behind them; they could
be chasing a ball that someone has kicked.*

*A boy is cycling down an empty street with a bunch
of white flowers in the basket on the front of his bike.
The boy's hair is blown back behind him – maybe it's a
windy day. He is cycling past a row of shops, but they
are all closed. It looks like a London street. Tad watches
the boy carefully. He is familiar.*

*The man with the knife. Leering from darkness,
terrifying.*

*The images repeat and repeat, overlapping,
interrupting each other, before exploding into white
light and then darkness.*

SCENE TWELVE

Older Tad When I left the flat, Sayyid was waiting outside.
He said that Dizzy was waiting for me in the café . . .
that we'd have things to talk about. But my mind was
whirring. I wasn't sure I wanted to speak to her. And
when I got there, it didn't seem like she wanted to talk
to me.

*The Ladbroke café appears. Dizzy is sitting at the
usual table, looking very miserable. Tad sits down.
Silence.*

Dizzy How's my gran?
Tad She's okay. I didn't really see her.

Pause.

You were right. There wasn't anything in the book.

Dizzy I told you.

Tad I liked the pictures. You're a really good artist. You should think about art college.

Dizzy Leave it.

Tad No, I won't leave it. Dizzy, you asked me to help. But how can I help you if you don't trust me, if you don't tell me things?

Dizzy What are you talking about?

Tad The pictures in your book, they're what's going to happen, aren't they? And they're going to happen to *you*, no one else.

Dizzy Yeah.

Tad So I need to ask you something. The first picture I saw, the one of your dad in a room – it was the room in East London, wasn't it? The empty flat? You drew it, drew it exactly. So that means that you must have been to that room before we went together. You must have seen your dad there. I'm right, aren't I? Tell me.

Dizzy Tell you what?!

Tad Am I right?

Dizzy Yes. (*Beat.*) You're right. I'm sorry, Tad. I'm really sorry.

Pause.

Tad It makes sense, now. I mean, you seemed to know the way. You didn't need the map at all, did you?

Dizzy Sayyid knew where my dad was, he took me there. My dad made me promise not to tell anyone where he was, no one at all.

Tad So why did you let *me* go there? Running around like an idiot.

Dizzy That was Sayyid too. He saw us in the Arif, and he wrote down the address and sent out the waiter with the envelope. Because he thought that you could help me through all this. But only if we both knew the same things.

Older Tad I felt a surge of anger towards Sayyid. I hated his stupid baseball cap and the way he waved his hands around. It was his meddling that had got us into this. He was so pleased with himself when he told me the story of the mask. And he'd made Dizzy show me her sketchbook. All the time he thought he knew best. And the result was a mess.

Tad Why didn't you tell me?

Dizzy Because afterwards, it wasn't important. I mean, after we went to the flat together and my dad wasn't there. I don't know where he's gone to, and nor does Sayyid. He's gone, Tad, he's *really* gone, and I've no idea where he is or when he's coming back. And that's the only thing that matters.

Tad You could have said, Dizzy. You must have known I'd recognise the room. You could have explained.

Dizzy I didn't think. I'm sorry.

Tad Why did he leave the flat?

Dizzy I don't know, Tad. I'm sure Sayyid thought he was still there, that was why he gave you the address. Maybe my dad thought the flat wasn't safe any more.

Tad Is there anything else you haven't told me?

Dizzy No. I don't know anything and I'm scared. You have to believe me.

Tad I thought you trusted me, Dizzy. But when you don't tell me things . . . it feels like you've used me, like I'm a servant you get to do things for you.

Dizzy is silent.

You know that time we went into the house? What would have happened if we'd been caught? To the police, we'd have been burglars. You could have got me *expelled*, Dizzy.

Dizzy is silent.

And why did you go upstairs? When I was in the room
with the masks and you went upstairs – why?! Did you
take anything?

Dizzy No, I didn't take anything. There's nothing else
I can tell you. Okay?

Tad And what about the pages in your sketchbook that
aren't there? Did you tear them out so I couldn't see
what was on them? Did you? *Dizzy?!*

*Dizzy looks at the floor. Tad stands, drops some
money on the table and leaves the café. Lights slowly
fade on Dizzy.*

SCENE THIRTEEN

Tad is sitting alone on the kerb, in the rain.

Older Tad Later, of course, I realised I'd got nothing to
blame her for: she hadn't told me about visiting her
dad in East London because her dad asked her not to,
and she loved her dad so much she'd do anything he
said – she'd walk off the end of the world if he asked
her to. Two days later, I tried to make up in art class.

*The art classroom. Tad goes over to where Dizzy works
alone in the corner. She is doodling absent-mindedly.*

Tad Dizzy . . . hey. (*Silence.*) Listen. I wanted to say I'm
sorry, I shouldn't have said all that stuff . . . in the café.
I want to be friends again. Can't we go back to how it
was before? (*Silence.*) What are you drawing?

Mrs Kennedy Tadeusz. Leave Djanira alone. If she chooses
not to participate in the lesson, that's her lookout. Go
back to your desk.

Tad slumps away as Dizzy continues to doodle.

Older Tad Even though I couldn't speak to Dizzy, I still
thought about her pictures. They were so deliberate, so
detailed, I knew they must be true. But apart from the
one of her gran, most of them had no connection to
her life now, as a schoolkid in London. Where was, or
rather where *will be*, the men running? Or the woman
with the cello? I began to worry that Dizzy might
disappear like her dad. She'd leave this life in West
London and start a new one. One full of all these
things she'd seen and drawn. One away from me. The
next day she didn't come into school and I was sure
that she'd gone. I began to search for her.

Tad goes to Dizzy's flat. Her Gran answers the door.

Tad Is Djanira here?

*The Gran replies in Berber. She looks worried and
shrugs her shoulders a lot. Tad writes his phone
number on a scrap of paper and hands it to her.*

Tell her to call me if you see her. (*Miming a phone call.*)

*Tad searches for Dizzy through West London. He goes
into the Arif and speaks to the Waiter. He walks
through Portobello market. He stops at a junk stall
and picks up an old family photo album. He leafs
through it. The pictures appear behind him as his older
self speaks.*

Older Tad I turned the pages of an old album of black-
and-white photographs. A group of young men and
women on board a ship, their mouths open as if singing.
Two young girls dressed as fairies with wire wings,
maybe for a school play. I recognised the same children
over and over again – you watched them growing up
as you turned the pages. Those children would be old
people now. I stared at their eager faces. Then I thought
about Dizzy's pictures, and about how time is like

some animal that slowly creeps up on all the things that
will happen in the future, and then it pounces and
chews them up and spits them out, which is when
they become the past.

Trader Are you going to buy that? If not, clear off. It's
not a library.

*Tad carries on down the street. It begins to rain. He
steps into a bus shelter to escape. His mobile rings. We
see Dizzy in her flat on the phone.*

Tad Hello?

Dizzy Tad?

Tad Dizzy?

Dizzy Tad, is that you?

Tad Where've you been?

Dizzy My gran just gave me this number. Have you found
out anything, Tad? About my dad?

Tad Oh. Erm . . . no. No, I haven't.

Silence.

Dizzy?

Dizzy I've been out with Sayyid. He took me to the zoo.
I think he was trying to cheer me up.

Tad I was looking for you, Dizzy. I thought you'd gone.

Dizzy What do you mean, *gone*?

Tad I thought you'd gone looking for your dad.

Dizzy I'm not going anywhere. What if he came back
and I wasn't here?

Tad How was the zoo?

Dizzy I'm like one of those animals in a cage. Trapped.
There's nothing I can do, Tad. I've just got to wait.

Tad Yeah.

Dizzy Pardon?

Tad I said . . . yeah.

*Silence. Light fades on Dizzy. Tad steps out of the
shelter. It's stopped raining.*

SCENE FOURTEEN

Older Tad And suddenly there was nothing more to say. The whole thing might have ended there. Winter turned into spring.

Tad and Stephan appear. Stephan has grown a beard and is wearing a leather jacket.

I knew that Stephan had lost interest in the mask. His life was changing. He'd bought his motorbike and sometimes took me out for rides. He also had a girlfriend.

Janice appears – a small, pretty girl who gazes adoringly up at Stephan.

Stephan Tad. This . . . *this* . . . is Janice. Say hello.
Janice (*in a high Scottish accent*) Hello, Tad. (*And she giggles furiously.*)

Janice disappears and Stephan and Tad climb onto a motorbike.

Older Tad The clocks changed at the end of March and Stephan took me out on the bike in the evenings. One night we were out, half thrilled and half scared that we were riding too fast, because it had been raining earlier and the road was wet. We were going up Scrubs Lane, towards Harlesden, and suddenly I had a tingling feeling at the base of my neck. It was like a *déjà vu*.

Slowly, Tad climbs off the bike. Lights change.

Older Tad / Tad (*together*) On the right two cranes rose high in the sky. There was something about them, about the way they stood – I'd seen them before. The cranes were moving, swinging from one position into another and suddenly, for a single moment, they were in line with each other. And I knew where I'd seen them. Dizzy's sketchbook.

As Tad looks, we see the image from the sketchbook, the hut with the cranes behind. It is real and huge before him. The figure stands next to the hut and then steps out of the darkness. He looks straight at Tad. He is large, with a moustache and sad eyes. Tad approaches.

Tad You're Dizzy's dad. Djanira's dad. You're Mohammed.

Mohammed begins to cry.

Mohammed Tad?

Tad nods. Mohammed holds his arms out and Tad approaches. Music as they talk, Mohammed holding Tad's shoulders. He goes into the hut and returns with something wrapped in a sack. Tad stares at it.

Tad Is that . . .?
Mohammed Yes.

Mohammed opens the sack. The mask falls out between them. It is dark, beautiful. After a moment, Mohammed wraps it again.

Tad Mohammed. What's going to happen to the mask?
Mohammed This is a question I ask myself every day.
Tad But if you don't know, why did you take it? Did you think you'd be able to see the future too?
Mohammed I don't believe in magic, I believe in family. I knew that my father would die soon and that he was not ready to go. I took it for him.

Silence.

But who am I to believe in family? I ran from one, I started another, I couldn't keep that one together. Belief can't change what's happened. What's done is done.

Tad It wasn't too late. You made your father happy.

Mohammed Maybe. He never liked it here. When I gave him the mask, when he held it in his hands, it was like he'd gone back to his village. You can't understand, Tad.

Tad I do understand. The mask's from where you were born. It's home.

Mohammed No, it's not *my* home. I live here, in this city, not in some village up a mountain. And now the mask is left over, it doesn't fit anywhere. For me and for Djanira too, it's not part of our lives.

He shakes his head, like Dizzy.

It should have gone to the grave with my father.

Tad Give it back.

Mohammed I cannot. That's why I left that flat. For my father's sake. To give it back, to people to whom it means nothing? No. If I did this, I would betray my father.

Stephan starts to climb down the slope, looking for Tad.

Stephan *Tad?!*

Tad I have to go.

Mohammed Yes.

Tad I'll be back. I'll be back with Djanira.

And, as he runs back towards Stephan, Mohammed and the hut disappear.

Tad Dizzy! Dizzy! I've found him. I've found your dad!

Older Tad I should have guessed what was going to happen next. Of course I couldn't, because I didn't have the gift, I couldn't see the future. But I still should have foreseen it.

Dizzy comes running.

Tad Come on!

In a blur of sound and colour, they are in front of the hut. Dizzy stares. Then the door opens and Mohammed appears. For a long moment they look at each other and then he begins to walk towards her. As she starts to run to him, a van screeches up, beeping its horn furiously.

Frank? No. (*Screams.*) No!

Frank comes careering out of the van, his comb-over flapping down his face. Stephan appears from the other side of the van.

Steph?

Stephan shrugs. Frank approaches Dizzy and suddenly he has a knife in his hand – he is the man in the drawing. He grabs Dizzy and the knife goes to her throat.

Frank Get it! *Now!*

Mohammed stands frozen.

Frank Get it. I'm warning you.
Dizzy Tad! Tad!

Dizzy is hammering the pocket of her trousers. Tad reaches into his and suddenly runs to the hut. He stands in the doorway with the sack and a bottle of kerosene. He pours the liquid over the sack and pulls Stephan's cigarette lighter from his pocket.

Stephan Tad! Don't!

Tad looks at Dizzy and drops the lighter on the sack. Immediately it bursts into flames. Soon the whole hut is engulfed in fire.

Frank NO!

Frank drops the knife and Dizzy and runs into the hut, kicking at Tad as he passes him.

Tad Ow!

Mohammed is carrying Dizzy away and Tad starts to follow them. Frank begins to scream inside the hut. Stephan runs in and pulls him out, Frank's face and hands are burnt. Stephan and Tad roll him on the ground as he moans. Tad picks up the knife and hurls it away into the bushes. He looks at Dizzy and Mohammed.

Tad I'm sorry, I'm so . . .
Dizzy Tad. It's okay. It's okay.

And she and Mohammed are smiling. The scene fades.

Older Tad The police came and the fire service. But no one mentioned the mask and I think they left the scene as clueless as when they arrived. Stephan took us home and bought us breakfast on the way. He could hardly speak to me. I think he knew how close to disaster he'd brought us all. For days afterwards I'd look at the bruise on my shin where Frank's boot had hit me, watching it fade from an angry purple to a dull grey. It took more than a month to finally disappear.

SCENE FIFTEEN

Stephan and Janice cross the stage and wave at Older Tad. He waves back.

Older Tad I never got my trainers from Stephan and I've stopped meeting him in the café in Hammersmith. He's still with Janice. He plans to set up on his own, getting building jobs and finding men to do the work. He says he'll make sure he gets at least half of the money before he starts on a job. Frank, he says, was an idiot.

Older Dizzy appears, aged eighteen. She waves at Older Tad.

I still see Dizzy all the time. And she still has her dizzy spells, when an image from the future logs itself into her brain. It happens suddenly – like the tripping of the shutter inside a camera lens – and yet with so much force.

Older Dizzy begins to tremble and shake next to him. Older Tad takes her arm and sits her down on the floor.

Older Dizzy It's okay. I'm okay. (*Beat.*) Can you get me some paper?

Older Tad pulls a piece of paper and a pen from his back pocket. Older Dizzy takes it and begins drawing furiously. Behind them, the image appears.

Older Tad Later she showed me the finished picture. There's a pale man, ten years older than me, standing between two large, dark men next to a round stone wall. The stone thing is a well like they have in Morocco, and the two men are, Dizzy thinks, her uncles, her dad's brothers.

Dizzy Do you recognise the man in the middle?

Older Tad walks to the image and looks at the scene.

Older Tad She says it's me but I'm not sure. He's tall like me. But he's more sturdy, more solid, more like the adults I see when I go swimming. He doesn't look like he drops things or knocks things over.

Older Tad rejoins Older Dizzy on the floor. He looks at her.

I don't envy you. Knowing what's going to happen, even if you don't know when, spoils the story. I want everything to be a surprise.

Older Dizzy looks at the image behind her.

Older Dizzy But some of the things are nice. Then you
can look forward to them.

*Tad cycles across the stage, holding a bunch of flowers.
He is the boy from the sketchbook picture.*
*Older Dizzy and Older Tad watch as Dizzy runs on
and takes the flowers. They leave together. Then a
woman walks into the scene in Morocco. She looks
like Dizzy. She takes the man's hand and they wave at
Older Dizzy and Older Tad.*
They wave back as the lights fade.

The End.

Production Notes

The Things She Sees was commissioned for 'Connections' with the specific agenda of creating a play which fundamentally requires a visually rich approach. The original novella was born from an idea by Charles Boyle's son about reverse *déjà vu* and became a very specific story based around the area of Ladbroke Grove. Ben Power's adaptation was particularly driven by maintaining the challenges of the novella, and passing those challenges to the directors. He was also interested in the nature of reverse *déjà vu*/prophecy being both a gift and a burden, and the dramatic potential of the story as a thriller.

WHAT IS THE PLAY ABOUT?

Children as a mixture of surprising maturity and vulnerability. • A friendship which exists before sexual awakening. • The potential and ownership of creativity. • Acceptance. • Ancestry. • Absence – the quest for things that aren't quite there. • Where/when we feel safe to inhabit the past, the present, the future. • Your knowledge of self being defined both within and outside your natural environment. • The mystery of friendship. • A voyage of self-discovery • The purity of possibility. • Imagination as a danger as well as a gift • The immigrant experience – what does 'home' mean?

WHAT DRIVES THE PLAY THEMATICALLY ?

Disassociation from your parents is something everyone goes through, and the immigrant experience is an interesting exploration of this.

Tad and Dizzy's friendship has to transcend external and interpersonal difficulties.

In the image of the boy with flowers the audience need to see the potential of relationship, but the friendship within the play is pure and perfect.

So much is unknown: Dizzy doesn't understand her visions, and in every scene someone says somethig like 'There's something I don't understand,' which creates a driven sense of adventure – that things might happen.

Dizzy is an unreliable narrator, and we (and Tad) are constantly told that we don't have all the answers.

How much is coincidence? It could be any boy who picks up Dizzy's drawing, but it ceases to be coincidence because it *does* happen.

The burden of prophecy is personal to Dizzy and is intimately connected to her past, which contrasts with the banality of Tad's question about the FA Cup. Dizzy can't choose the bits of the future she sees, and just because she can see doesn't mean she understands. Putting the vision on paper means she can start to deal with it: a form of exorcism.

THE FORM

The play is constructed as a thriller. It is crucial that the production is driven in the gear of being a thriller. You need to gauge the specific features of the genre (e.g., the finding of clues) to push the pace. In order to chart the psychological and narrative structure of the play, actors need to find the moments of boiling point and plot a graph of their experiences. Carefully locating and highlighting the clues in the thriller, the wants of the characters, and the immediate circumstances of each scene will tighten up the pace and dynamic of the play as a whole.

How should rich media help tell the story?

The use of rich media is part of telling the story, not a handsome backdrop. Each moment needs to be carefully considered and contained so that it's not a car boot sale. The text is one language of many which should be used to tell the story. You need to allow the other elements of the production to be as eloquent as the text and find ways of deepening the story using all the languages of theatre. The audience needs to be still – a group of receivers – so that your manipulation of how and when you reveal to them clues and images is as controlled as possible.

There are three types of image which need consideration:

- Dizzy's drawings – the particular state of drawing in a fever, transformed into three-dimensional stories.

- The catalogue of storytelling locations.

- The flashbacks to other times and places.

These different sets of images need to co-exist but feel part of an aesthetic whole.

Binary images

The play is full of binary images: the two fires, the two market places, Dizzy's flat and the flat Mohammed hides in, the two battles, Stephan and Sayyid as two young men, the two versions of Tad . . .

THE CONTEXT

Morocco The Berber language is a challenge: the audience
are supposed to be as confused as Tad. It's about the
difficulty of communicating cross-generationally, and it
needs to be strange, almost frightening for Tad. The key
gesture is the psychological sensation of being alien, the
'other', the unfamiliar, and you need to consider showing
this on Tad's face. The specific nature of the speech and
speaker can be representational because the volume goes
down. A puppet? A photograph? Pre-recorded Berber
speech? It is important to find photographic stimulation
for your actors to explore the otherness of different cultures.

Ladbroke Grove Does the play have to be set in the
world of Ladbroke Grove, or could it work anywhere?
The key factor is that it must take place in a world built
around different kinds of nationality and affluence. In
essence, the diversity of class and affluence is as important
as ethnic diversity. The friendship between Tad and Dizzy
should be a positive endorsement of the co-existence of
different communities, and key to this is making it
believable, not stereotypical.

THE TECHNOLOGY

Fundamental to the dynamic of the thriller is the audience
being able to join the dots of the visual clues. For example,
as soon as we see the Dizzy's jumper, we recognise that
it's the same as the one worn by the man in the armchair;
when Tad sees Mohammed at the hut, we see Mohammed
at the hut.

The play is a pictorial piece, locked in to the magic of
making images appear from nowhere, and therefore has

to keep moving. When considering the creation of images, depth is very useful. What will you be projecting onto? Gauze, white screen, black screen? It is important that the area of projection is more complex than just an obvious screen, that it is part of the world of the play.

You will need to consider the possibilities released through the relationship between the image and the actors' bodies in space. It is also important to avoid clumsy projection-spill onto the actors. Consider the difference in projecting onto white and black screens: in order to create images coming out of the chadows, black might be better, but you will need a powerful projector to get a clean white image.

It is important to get the actors to know the play before you get the toys out, but take care to have the technology decided and ready from the start of rehearsals so that it can be developed as organically as the acting style and the dramatic structure.

Possibilities

STOP-MOTION ANIMATION
Example at: www.youtube.com/watch?v=u46eaeAfeqw

Using a camera and computer, you can capture simple images drawn onto a whiteboard, and then add and erase with great facility to create an animation. This animation could be made negative, so that you're projecting white pictures on a black background, to help create the images coming out of the shadows.

OVERHEAD PROJECTION (OHP)
Example at: www.youtube.com/watch?v=xI5wF0FPKH4

A live animation can be created using a simple school overhead projector that could be operated by a member of the company during the actual performance.

NINTENDO Wii
Example at: www.youtube.com/watch?v=5s5EvhHy7eQ

As a demonstration of the potential of creating simple and cheap solutions to rich media and projections, consider this demonstration of homemade whiteboard.

Experiments

Depending on your equipment, experiment with the layering of different images. Using two projectors either side of a BP screen, or two cameras fed through a vision mixer, you could project an animation of Dizzy's drawing onto live feed of her face to show the vision she's seeing and drawing. Using an animation which is created on a computer, you could then film the computer, and move real objects, such as the van, across the picture.

The atmosphere of the image can be manipulated by layering in translucent and/or moving filters like water. You can manipulate your images by moving the distance of the screen as part of the performance. You can cheat digital images to look as of they've been drawn by hand. You could fix a camera in the rig to capture the actual drawing live from above . . . The possibilities are endless. And cheaper and easier than you think.

THE CHALLENGES

Following is a list of eleven moments in the play which present a challenge to the director. Some include potential inspiration for solutions, some do not. The list is not exhaustive, but neither should it be intimidating.

1. The opening montage.
2. The man in the armchair.
3. The van.

4. The finding of the masks.

   The journey into the house could be created offstage with a live or pre-recorded feed – using the architecture of the space, the building as a whole. (Maybe the actors filmed finding the masks in the headteacher's office, made to look like the house?)

5. Morocco appears.

   Making the scenes in Morocco with actors needs to be a huge story surrounding the tiny flat, which overwhelms Tad. Can you create the scenes with a group of actors? How can you connect the flat to the landscape? Through something in the flat which reflects or connects to the epic landscape?

6. Seeing London.

   Do you want the audience to see Tad and Dizzy, or what they're seeing?

7. The French attacks and the fire in the huts.

8. Seeing the sketchbook.

   It's important that the pictures are things that will happen to Dizzy herself. Thus, the woman with the cello is not linked to the story itself, but that's the joy of the image – the audience want to ask, 'Is that her?' Also, will these things definitely happen? Chance and possibility: 'There are some things one remembers even though they never happened. There are things I remember which may never have happened but as I recall them they take place.' Should Dizzy's pictures be drawn images which feel as if they have a moving quality?

9. Portobello Road market and the photo album.

10. The motorbike ride, the hut and the burning of the hut and mask.

11. The three versions of Tad and Dizzy at the end.

At the end there are effectively two characters in three different time zones potentially played by six actors, and it's important that this juxtapositions of time is clear: 'Tad' and 'Dizzy' are thirteen, 'Older Tad' and 'Older Dizzy' are eighteen, the 'pale man' and 'woman' are mid-twenties. There is a magic in having totally new actors right at the end: possibly even using actual twenty-eight-year-olds.

The crucial things about resolving the challenges is first to work out what the point is, rather than trying to solve the problem technically at the start. What is the point of that moment? To show Tad being overwhelmed? To echo an image previously in the play? If you honour the point, then the story will be told.

CONCLUSION

The play is deliberately challenging, and requires experimentation to realise its potential in presentation. It also requires very careful consideration of its dramatic structure and its genre as a thriller. This means that you need to solve the challenges of the dramatic text *and* the visual text, then the solutions will almost certainly spring from each other. Both sets of challenges should be frustrating and joyous, problematic and empowering. You will go through fun and hell. But it will be worth it.

From a workshop led by Anthony Banks and Simon Daw, with notes by Dan Bird

TRAMMEL

Michael Lesslie

Michael Lesslie's plays include *A Triple Bill of Shame* (for the Edinburgh Fringe, 2003), *The Constant Prince* (international tour, Arcola Studio and Oxford Playhouse), *Face Up, Face Down* (Cameron Mackintosh Award for New Writing). Short films include *Heavy Metal Drummer* (Smirnoff Reel Talent Award and nominated for BAFTA), *Airlock, or How to Say Goodbye in Space* (Shine Award nomination at 2008 Bradford International Film Festival). Adaptations include the novel *Lies of Silence* and memoirs *War Reporting for Cowards* for film, and the cult film *Swimming with Sharks* for the stage. Recent original works include *And Then the Dark* for CMP Ltd and *The Haven* for Element Pictures and Film Four.

Characters

Daniel
sixteen

Nicole
sixteen

Marcus
eighteen

Tez
fourteen

Aron
sixteen

Jeremy
eighteen

Al
sixteen

Unsworth
fourteen

Stas
sixteen

Steeps
sixteen

Sophie
sixteen

Several others, aged between thirteen and eighteen

For the other parts whose names are spoken,
such as the Shells, either the names provided or names
of the same number of syllables should be used

Time
Present day

Location
In and around an all-boys public boarding school
and the town over which it looks.

Stage Directions
These are suggestions only
and can be revised by the director.

Text
A dash (–) indicates that the line is to be interrupted.
Three dots (. . .) indicate that the line trails off.
The *Beats* and *Pauses* are suggestions only,
but an effort should be made to adhere to them
and they should at least be tried in rehearsal.

SCENE ONE

A party. Loud music. A group of kids, thirteen to eighteen, is drinking and dancing. Amongst them, Daniel, sixteen, Marcus, eighteen, Nicole, sixteen, and Tez, fourteen. Another boy enters, his face hidden by a hoodie. The group turns. Tez looks to Daniel expectantly.

Daniel The fuck are you?

> *Grandly, the boy throws back his hoodie and drops it on the floor: Aron, sixteen. Underneath the hoodie, he wears a sombre, excessively formal school uniform, like a set of mourning clothes. The party cheers. Nicole runs up to Aron, hugs and kisses him.*

Marcus The prodigal returns!
Nicole Look at you!
Aron Happy birthday, baby.
Nicole You look like a twat!
Tez Hey Aron, why you walkin' funny?
Aron Fuck off, Tez.
Tez Them rich boys ridin' you?
Daniel Like they bitch?
Aron Like your mother, Dan. In their dreams.

> *The party laughs.*

Nicole So what you get me?
Aron This.

> *He kisses her. She pulls back.*

Nicole That all?
Aron Come on, Nix, all they got up there's a corner shop an' a clothes place.

519

Nicole You coulda got me clothes, then.

Aron What, blazer an' a jockstrap?

Tez Jock strap?

Aron For rugby an' that.

Daniel Batty.

Aron You wish.

Nicole I see. So, now you rich, you ain't gettin' me no presents?

Aron I ain't rich, baby.

Daniel Not yet.

Nicole You wearin' a jockstrap right now?

Aron Maybe.

Nicole That's present enough, then. Know you wrigglin' around inside one a' them.

She kisses him.

Marcus Hey, Aron.

Aron breaks from Nicole. He hugs Marcus.

How long you got, then?

Aron Three weeks. Christmas an' that.

Marcus Three weeks?

Nicole You ain't gonna see him, trust. I'm a firework, ain't had flesh for a month.

Aron You mean two.

Nicole Yeah. Jokes, innit?

Aron Better be.

Daniel Or what?

Nicole Daniel. (*To Aron.*) So why ain't you come down to see me, then? 'S only up the hill.

Aron I told you, Nix. Scholarship an' that, don't let me out first term.

Party (*together*) Oooo!

Daniel They send you to jail, Aron?

Aron No.

Tez Fine you?

Daniel Take your momma's pills?

Marcus You two. Shut up.

Aron They give you trammel. Make you write out Latin 'tween these two little lines they draw across a page.

Tez Latin? Whossa point in that?

Aron Fuck knows.

Marcus Job, innit?

Daniel Pussy job speaks Latin?

Aron I don't know, Daniel. What are you gonna be?

Daniel Striker.

Aron On the Xbox, maybe.

Tez That's where you're wrong.

Aron What?

Nicole He got moved up. First team.

Daniel I took your place.

Beat.

Aron Yeah, well, don't get comfortable. I'm done schoolin', I'm comin' back.

Daniel Bullshit. You all rich boy now.

Aron I ain't rich boy.

Daniel Look at you.

Aron 'S just clothes, Dan.

Daniel Then why you come down here, showin' 'em off? (*Beat.*) You really think they'll let you in, don't you, Aron?

Aron Have done this far.

Daniel Oi, Tez, who's dreamin' now?

Tez Fool right here.

Daniel Cos they won't. You might wear the kit, but you ain't the same as them. No matter how high you carry yourself. Cos them up there? They different. They rich. An' you? You got the mark a' sin, dred, sin a' birth, shot right through your bones. They see you. Where you come from. Even if you forget.

Aron I ain't forgettin' anythin', Daniel.

Nicole For fuck's sake.

Nicole runs off towards the dance floor.

Aron Nix, come back.

Daniel and Tez follow Nicole.

Marcus You alright?
Aron 'S a bit much, innit?
Marcus Get used to it. You took that scholarship, you got under Dan's skin. Best knuckle up.
Aron I can handle him. Little big man, know what I mean?
Marcus Yeah. (*Beat.*) We need to talk.

Aron looks up.

They're cuttin' off her meds, kid. Ain't gonna be free no more.

Aron Why not?
Marcus Somethin' about cheaper stuff on the market.
Aron But them pills –
Marcus I know. (*Beat.*) I need to start makin' some proper money, Aron. I need your help.
Aron What can I do? I'm stuck up there twenty-four-seven.
Marcus Exactly.

Beat.

Aron Fuck, man. Don't push that.
Marcus Just sort some links for me, do some runnin', somethin'.
Aron Drugs is serious up there. I get busted, I'm a goner.
Marcus You don't, Mum stays alive. Doesn't have to be drugs, kid. You're sittin' on a stack a' gold. An' my best customer ain't even buyin' no more since these hoodrats fuckin' –
Aron Yeah.

Beat.

Marcus How is he?

Aron They beat out his teeth, Marcus. How d' you think?

Beat.

Marcus Can afford a dentist, the trainers he had. (*Beat.*) Look, just cover your tracks, make yourself a model student an' that.

Aron Model student?

Marcus They won't suspect a thing.

Pause.

Aron I'll see what I can do, alright?

Marcus Alright. (*Beat.*) Now come on. You seen City made the final?

Aron Yeah.

Marcus Febr'y eighteenth, man. Me an' you's gonna get loaded, park our asses in the Junction, watch the sun rise blue an' white. Best day a' my life, kid. You best not flake on that.

Aron I won't.

Marcus Good. Cos I got us a little something to celebrate.

He takes a spliff out of his pocket. Aron looks to the dance floor. Nicole and Daniel are dancing together, close. The party starts singing along to the tune.

Aron No, man. I'm just gonna go. Let's do it at home, alright?

Aron leaves. The singing slowly morphs into 'Jerusalem', by William Blake and C. Hubert H. Parry.

SCENE TWO

A parade ground. 'Jerusalem' continues. A group of boys,
thirteen to eighteen, is marching in drill formation to the
commands of Jeremy, eighteen, who stands apart. They
all wear the same school uniform as Aron wore in the
previous scene. Amongst them are Al, sixteen, Unsworth,
fourteen, and Stas, sixteen, a Russian boy. Al takes the
prominent right corner position of the squad. His
movements are clinically efficient. Aron enters, falls in
beside him and diligently starts to copy.

Jeremy *Rego regis regit!*
Squad (*together*) *Rego regis regit!*
Jeremy Right turn!

 The squad obeys.

Regimus regitis regunt!
Squad (*together*) *Regimus regitis regunt!*
Jeremy About turn!

 The squad obeys.

Rego regis regit! Left turn!
Squad (*together, turning*) *Rego regis regit!*
Jeremy *Regimus regitis regunt!* About turn!
Squad (*together, turning*) *Regimus regitis regunt!*
Jeremy Selbies House, marking time, squad halt!

 The squad obeys and begins marching on the spot.

Gentlemen, welcome back. As you all know, this spring
 term is going to be crucial. The Six-Twos will start
 gearing up for exams and it'll fall to the rest of you to
 maintain the standards they set last term. So remember.
 In Selbies, we live by tradition. Respect your elders.
 They've been here longer than you and deserve
 obedience because of it. Pull your weight. We make up a

community that depends on absolutely every single one of its members, and scrimshankers will be dealt with severely. Above all, remain loyal to the House. You are a member of Selbies first, the school second. Is that understood?

Squad (*together*) Sir, yes sir.

Jeremy Good. We deal with things internally here. Mr Bates correctly understands that the private side is the private side and the boys' is the boys', which means that as your Head of House, I am the beginning and the end of all authority for any of you. Within our four walls I will legislate, I will punish, and I will reward. So if anything comes to Batesy's attention, it had better be serious, and it had better come from me. Got that?

Squad (*together*) Sir, yes sir.

Jeremy Selbies House, squad halt!

The squad obeys.

Al?

Al steps forward.

Al Sir!

Jeremy You will act as my Six-Three deputy for the coming term. (*To the squad.*) I expect you all to show him the according respect. (*To Aron.*) And you. Rama . . . Roma . . .

Aron Romanon.

Beat.

Jeremy Sir.

Beat.

Aron Romanon, sir.

Jeremy You're either trying harder or practising in your free time, Rommon. Which is it?

Aron Bit of both, sir.

Jeremy Why didn't you do this last term?

Aron Didn't have time.

Jeremy There's no such thing as not having time. You make time. (*To the Squad.*) Take a leaf out of Rommon's book, gentlemen. Pretty impressive start to the term. Now, round the pitches, the lot of you.

The Squad disperses.

SCENE THREE

Al's room. Al and Aron are poring over a Latin book.

Al *Monere moderari est.*

Aron 'S 'at mean?

Al Just say it.

Aron But I don't get it.

Al Doesn't matter. You'll pass.

Aron rubs his eyes.

Aron I got trammel to do, man.

Al Who from?

Aron Davis.

Al Shit. Why?

Aron I don't even know. We was goin' through that paper, yeah? An' Davis tries to say that *audiverint*'s the perfect of *audio*.

Al But –

Aron 'Xactly. I'm like, 'It's subjunctive perfect, actually. Maybe I have listened.' An' he just loses it, slams me wi' two hundred on the spot.

Al You corrected him.

Aron I was right! 'S education, innit, learn what's right?

Al No. Education happens by yourself. You were in a classroom.

Aron So?

Al So that's politics.

Aron throws the book down in frustration.

Aron Why we learn Latin, anyway, man?

Beat.

Al What do you want to be when you're older?

Aron Doctor, I guess.

Al You guess?

Aron 'S tough, innit?

Al Well, that's why we do Latin. Everyone with basic English'll have a degree. How do you think they'll pick who to make doctors?

Aron I dunno. Look at which uni you were at?

Al Exactly. If we don't get to Oxbridge, we're fucked. And anyone can blag intelligence. It's things like Latin, like Head of House, those places lap that up.

Aron Still?

Al You know how many Six-Twos got into Oxbridge last summer? Seventy-seven. That's forty-five per cent of the year.

Aron Wow.

Al You got that scholarship, you became forty-five per cent more likely to have a future.

Aron What are you gonna be?

Al Surgeon. Gonville and Caius, Cambridge.

Aron Undecided, then.

Al My dad'd kill me if I did anything else. He came here, he was Head of House. After that he went to Gonville and Caius, got a first, became a surgeon. His dad did the exactly same thing. And his dad, and his dad, and his dad, stretching all the way back to William the Conqueror.

Aron Jesus.

Al I know. When I can't sleep, I count ancestors. I'm tied to the beginning of time by surgery, first-class honours

at Gonville and Caius, Cambridge, and the Head of
House position at Selbies.

Aron Best not fuck up then, innit?

Al smiles.

What? (*Beat.*) Don't take the piss, man.

Al Sorry. One thing Latin teaches you: if you don't need
to say something, it's not worth saying.

Aron I change the way I speak, my mates'd laugh at me.

Al You want to make new mates?

Aron I guess.

Al picks up the book and holds it out to Aron.

Al *Monere moderari est.*

SCENE FOUR

Unsworth's room. Unsworth is crying. Aron enters.
Unsworth quickly wipes his face.

Aron You been cryin'?

Unsworth No.

Aron They put me next door this term. I can hear. (*Beat.*)
'S it that Russian geezer? Stas?

Beat.

Unsworth You won't tell anyone?

Aron I swear.

Unsworth He said he's going to put pins in yarder
tonight and lock us in without shoes. Then he's going
to piss out the window so we have to run around.

Aron Jesus.

Unsworth Don't say anything, please. He'll hate me if he
thinks I ratted.

Beat.

Aron Man, this place is messed up. 'You're year below, gimme the seat.' 'You're year below, make my toast.' 'S out a line.

Unsworth It's been like this for years.

Aron Yeah, well, if it's broke, fix it. Real world, you live off what you earn, you get me? Not what's just given to you. Ask me, everyone oughta have a say, not just some psychos at the top. Maybe then guys like you wouldn't be gettin' pissed on.

Beat.

Unsworth I want to go home.

Pause.

Aron Look. Any more problems, knock on my door, alright?

Unsworth Really?

Aron Yeah. Fuck 'em. Me an' you 'gainst the rest.

Aron turns to leave.

Unsworth Rommon?

Aron turns back.

I can hear you too, you know. Through the walls.

Beat.

Aron I'll see you, kid.

SCENE FIVE

Jeremy's room. Jeremy and Al. Jeremy is packing.

Jeremy That's the third missing item in two weeks, Al. Parker's iPod, Osman's wallet and Jenkins's hoodie.

Al Are you sure it isn't just carelessness?

Jeremy Maybe. But I'm going to make an announcement just in case. If some bastard's thieving, I need to catch him before exeat or there's no chance we'll get the stuff back.

Al No. That's the worst thing you could do.

Jeremy Why?

Al An announcement'll just let the thief know you're on to him, make him more cautious. Then we might never catch him. If you don't say anything, he'll keep going, we stand a better chance. And the missing stuff'll be long gone by now anyway.

Jeremy You're probably right.

Al Trust me. It's worth another wallet or two to flush out a rat like that. Any suspects?

Jeremy We haven't had any thefts since I got here. Maybe one of the new boys.

Al The Shells?

Beat.

Jeremy No. They're a weak year. None of them would have the balls. (*Beat.*) What about Rommon?

Al Rommon?

Jeremy If you'd asked me last term, I'd've considered it. His tie loose all the time, hands in his pockets . . . But these first few weeks he's been making a hell of an effort. And he's suddenly come up a storm on the wing. Already moved up from the Fourths to the Thirds, and there's rumour he'll try out for first game when school rugby starts. You should watch your back.

Al I think I'll be alright.

Jeremy holds up his first-team rugby jersey.

Jeremy Should I take this?

Al Why not?

Jeremy Bit public-schooly. Interviewers might balk at it.

Al It's a sign of talent, Jez.

Jeremy I suppose. Brought me luck in the past.

Jeremy packs the jersey.

Al What made you think of Rommon? His connections downtown?

Jeremy Was he in with a bad crowd?

Al Steeps doesn't seem to know him.

Jeremy Steeps'd be wary of anyone in Kappa after what happened. They even took his bloody trainers.

Al I suppose. (*Beat.*) Whoever this guy is, he's clever, Jez. I say lure him out.

Jeremy You're right. And at least it's not drugs. I'd hate to have to involve Batesy.

Someone knocks at the door.

Come in.

Aron enters.

Ah. Speak of the devil.

Aron (*to Al*) Hey.

Al Hey.

Aron I wanted to put myself forward for the corps proper this term. Night exercise an' that, not just drill.

Jeremy Volunteer for night exercise? That's a first. Sure you'll be able to balance it with everything else?

Aron I'll make time.

Beat.

Jeremy Alright, then. I'll let Batesy know first thing. I have to say, you really seem to be settling in, Rommon. And I'm told your studies are coming on.

Aron Had a good teacher.

Jeremy Luck was invented by the modest. You're a worker. I respect that. And so does Batesy, for that matter. You've really caught his eye. The only criticism I have is your missing chapel.

Aron I'm a Muslim.

Jeremy Well. If you fixed that, we'd be wowed. Really.

Al Do you miss home?

Aron No. Still see my brother an' that.

Al How about your friends? Do you see them?

Beat.

Aron Makin' new friends, innit?

Jeremy Good man. Carry on like this, Rommon, and you could really make something of yourself here.

Aron Cheers.

Jeremy Jez.

Aron Cheers, Jez.

Jeremy See you in Bill.

Aron stands to leave. He hesitates.

Aron What were you saying when I came in? You said, 'Speak of the devil.'

Beat.

Jeremy It's ridiculous, actually –

Al It's nothing.

Beat.

Jeremy He's right. It was nothing. See you downstairs.

Aron leaves.

No. He's sturdy, Al. Knows his place.

Al Seems to.

Jeremy I wouldn't believe it without serious proof. I guess we'll just have to keep our eyes out like you say, start from scratch.

Beat.

Al Good luck in the interview, Jez.

SCENE SIX

Outside the chapel. 'Jerusalem' is being sung by boys offstage in the chapel.

Steeps, sixteen, leans against a wall. His leg is in plaster and he has horrific scars across his face.

Aron enters from the chapel, carrying a Bible.

Steeps You do the reading?

Aron nods.

Smart move, man. Leave early.

Aron You miss it?

Steeps Sympathy card, though. 'I'm late cos I was mugged last year, can't work my leg.' What they gonna say to that?

Beat.

Aron I'm sorry.

Steeps Why? D'you do it?

Beat.

Aron Who's that girl? In chapel?

Steeps Tits?

Aron She has them.

Steeps You're talkin' about Trophy. Get in line, man, every boy on the hill wants a piece of her. Teacher's daughter, forbidden fruit.

Aron She's nice.

Steeps Don't say that to Al. He claimed her back in the Removes.

Aron Do they get on?

Steeps Don't think they've spoken.

Aron So what's his claim?

Steeps Gonna be Head of House, innit? Perfect record, man. Never come second in his life. (*Beat.*) You know, you look familiar. Ain't I seen you before?

Aron We're in the same house.

Steeps I mean prior. We haven't done business, have we? Downtown?

Beat.

Aron You're thinking of my brother. Marcus.

Steeps I know Marcus! Big guy, looks like a hammer?

Aron That's him.

Steeps I'm Steeps. Man, say hey to your bro for me. I ain't been able to use him since Jez started searchin' me every day.

Aron Why's he do that?

Steeps Busted me dealin' last year. Was sellin' cubs, sayin' it helped you work. Raked it in till this kid Robinson got hooked, blew half his dad's cash an' tried to fuckin' hang himself.

Aron Jesus. He die?

Steeps No. His tie broke.

Aron Fuckin' hell.

Steeps I know. Should've used a Head of House's. It's thicker. (*Beat.*)

Hey. You seein' him any time soon? Marcus?

Aron Why?

Steeps You reckon you could sort me out? Jez fuckin' hates drugs now. With the searches an' that, I can't get nothin' in by myself.

Beat.

Aron I'll see what I can do.

The boys begin filing out of the chapel. Steeps nods to Aron and hobbles off with them. Sophie, sixteen, exits the chapel, trying to leave as quickly she can. Aron steels himself and heads over.

534

You like the reading, then?

Sophie looks up, startled. The boys around them glance over and quickly hurry on.

Sophie I wasn't paying attention.
Aron I don't think anyone was. Always happens, man. I'm meant to be doin' somethin' important an' a beautiful girl's in the room, my mind just scrambles an' I lose track.
Sophie Really.
Aron Yeah. Ask me, you were bored, it's your fault.

Beat.

Sophie I didn't say I was bored. I said I wasn't paying attention.
Aron I saw. You was lookin' down at that hymn book, pretendin' to read.
Sophie Pretending?
Aron Yeah. I'm up there on the podium an' you keep peepin' up these secret looks, like, 'Who's that guy? He looks a bit different. An' he's fit, too, but – Oh . . . Oh my God he's seen me, eyes down, read read read read read read read.' I saw.

Beat.

Sophie You know I'm a teacher's daughter.
Aron I done my research. Aron.
Sophie Sophie. Davis.
Aron Davis?
Sophie 'Fraid so.
Aron Your mum must be gorgeous.
Sophie You chirpsin' my mum now?
Aron Chirpsin'? Look at you, Lil' Kim.

Sophie laughs. Al exits the chapel. He sees them and freezes.

Al Rommon, come on. We're late for Bill.

Aron Five minutes.

Al Now.

Aron Five minutes, man. Chill.

Beat. Al nods at Sophie.

Al Ma'am.

Al leaves.

Sophie They never look me in the eye.

Aron What?

Sophie I've lived here my whole life and you're the first one who ever looked me in the eye.

Aron Yeah, well. I ain't the usual fare round here.

Sophie No. You're a scholar.

Aron How d'you know that?

Sophie Maybe I've done some research too.

Beat.

Aron 'S 'at mean I can buy you a drink?

Sophie With your tuck money?

Aron I don't mean this place.

Sophie Where, then?

Aron Yours.

Beat.

Sophie What would my friends say if they saw me with a boy from downtown?

Aron With a bit a rough, you mean? Nothin'. Be too jealous to speak.

Beat. Sophie smiles.

Sophie My dad's has duties after prep. You could come over then.

Aron I'll look you up. Ma'am.

SCENE SEVEN

Al's room. Aron enters.

Aron Hey. 'Bout earlier. I'm sorry.
Al Why?
Aron Sophie an' that.
Al Why are you sorry?

Beat.

Aron You like her, don't you?
Al Who told you that?
Aron No one, I just –
Al I don't even fancy her.
Aron Really?
Al Not my type. (*Beat.*) I thought you already had a girlfriend.
Aron Hope this one's a better liar, put it that way.

Beat.

Al Anything else?

Beat.

Aron Yeah. I got my first-game try-out tomorrow. School rugby an' that. Wonderin' if I could borrow some rugby socks.
Al You don't wear rugby socks for school rugby.
Aron What?
Al They're completely different sports. Whole new set of rules.
Aron No one told me that.

Beat. Al chuckles.

Al Don't worry. I'll fill you in.

SCENE EIGHT

Jeremy's room. Jeremy and Aron.

Jeremy What the hell were you doing?

Aron Nothin'!

Jeremy Nothing? Rommon, you smacked a Shell round the head with a hockey stick. That's hardly inconsequential.

Aron But that's the rules.

Jeremy What?

Aron The rules! If the yearling on the other bridge is in your domain, your only guard's the stick, that's the rules.

Beat.

Jeremy What the hell are you talking about?

Aron The yearling, if he's in your domain –

Jeremy What's a domain?

Beat.

Aron Inside the twenty-two.

Beat.

Jeremy Rommon, we don't use the twenty-twos in school rugby. Those are just there for the winter.

Aron But –

Jeremy I think you've been had, old boy. Who told you those rules?

Beat.

Aron No one. Must have misread 'em, that's all.

Beat.

Jeremy Well, I'm not going to be able to let you off, you know. Connell's trying to claim his Shell lost the use of an eye, fraudulent bugger. It's four hundred trammel.

Aron Four hundred?

Jeremy Don't worry. I'll make sure Batesy doesn't hear about it. You've already turned his head this term, and I don't want a misreading costing you anything serious.

Beat.

Aron Thanks, Jez.

Jeremy Not at all. But be sure to let the other boys know it was an accident, alright? Some of the less progressive types might seize on this, use it against you. Just make it clear you're one of us deep down.

Aron Alright.

Jeremy I've got to admit, it was pretty bloody funny. Poor kid didn't know what hit him.

They chuckle.

SCENE NINE

Al's room. Jeremy and Al.

Jeremy Obviously some sly bastard had been trying to make a fool of him, but he absolutely took it like a man, didn't squeal, nothing. Should have seen him, Al, real character.

Al Good for him.

Jeremy I have to say, his conversion's pretty dramatic. It's certainly caught Batesy's eye. Feeling any pressure?

Al Pressure? No.

Jeremy Good. It's good for you to have a bit of competition, anyway, what with the retards in your year.

Beat.

Al Any more news on the thief?

Jeremy Only that he's still going. I tell you, I don't know how we haven't seen him.

Al Must be well practised.

Jeremy Must be. (*Beat.*) Late one tonight?

Al Big Latin paper in a couple of weeks, right before night exercise. Thought I'd put a bit of work in now.

Jeremy Since when do you need to revise?

Al Since this year.

Jeremy He's not giving you the run of it there too, is he?

Al No. I taught him everything he knows. He'd have to be doing a hell of a lot in his free time even to place. I just want to be sure, is all.

Jeremy Well. Good luck. But don't underestimate him. He's impressive.

Al For a townie.

Beat.

Jeremy Sleep well, Al.

SCENE TEN

Both the downtown crowd and the school crowd are watching the cup final, the former in a pub, the latter in their junior common room. Only Al is missing. Marcus and Jeremy stand behind a single empty chair at the front of the stage. Aron enters. All heads turn.

Aron Mind if I watch it with you guys?

The downtown crowd turns back to the screen.

Stas You watch with your friends.

Aron 'Xactly.

Marcus Fuck is he?

Tez Who cares, man? Just 'low us the seat.

Marcus No.

Stas It's Al's.

Jeremy Al's on lights. All yours, Rommon.

Aron sits. Marcus continues defending the chair as though it is empty. Suddenly, a goal is scored. The downtown crowd cheers, the school crowd heckles. Aron joins in with the school crowd's reaction. Jubilant, Daniel holds out a beer to Marcus. Marcus stares at him, surprised.

Marcus From you?

Daniel Come on. 'S the end a' the first half. He was comin', he'd be here by now.

The downtown crowd cheers again. Marcus considers, then takes the beer. The tension of the game rises.

Tez It's tense, man.

Stas Shut up, Shell.

Unsworth (*yelling*) Come on, United!

Everyone onstage apart from Stas laughs. Aron pushes Unsworth's head playfully. The tension rises again.

Aron Penalties.

Marcus Fuckin' penalties, man.

The first player runs up to take the penalty. The downtown crowd signals his run-up with a growing cheer and explode when he scores.

Unsworth Is this one –

Aron They don't get the next three, it's over.

Daniel Jesus.

Al enters. He sees Aron in his seat. Beat.

Al Guys, sorry. Batesy's coming round, I've got to shut it off.

The school crowd groans.

Aron There's five minutes left.
Stas You heard him.
Al The bell's gone.
Aron But it's the final.
Unsworth Please, Al.
Aron Jez? Come on.

Beat.

Jeremy I thought Batesy was out tonight.
Al He's back early.

Beat.

Jeremy Sorry, guys. Al's right. And it's half an hour past your bedtime anyway, Unsworth. Rommon, do the honours.

Reluctantly, Aron turns off the TV and sits back down. The rest of the school crowd files out, leaving a gap between Aron and the downtown crowd, who continue reacting to the penalties with building excitement. Al is the last of the school crowd out, save Aron. He turns out the lights, leaving Aron sitting silent and still in the near-darkness, surrounded by the calls of the downtown crowd. At the crucial penalty, they go ballistic. In their centre, ecstatic, Marcus turns and grabs Daniel around the shoulders. Aron sits, impassive, staring up at the blank screen.

SCENE ELEVEN

The junior common room. Unsworth sits amongst the other Shells, wearing his tie loose.

Unsworth I heard he broke someone's leg last year and they hushed it up because his dad's in the mafia.
Andrews Bollocks.

Unsworth It's true. I hate him.

Osman Why?

Unsworth It's not fair.

Clyde So?

Andrews You'll do it when you're in the Six-Threes.

Unsworth No I won't.

Shells (*together*) Bollocks.

Hamilton I'm going to be merciless.

Andrews Me too.

Osman Fuck those Shells up.

Unsworth Why?

Clyde They do it to us.

Parker They're older.

Jenkins It's right.

Unsworth It's bullying. Stas only gets away with it because his dad's rich.

Parker Not as rich as yours, Unsworth.

Unsworth My dad isn't rich.

Parker What, then?

Hamilton Is he poor?

Unsworth No.

Osman Are you a townie, Unsworth?

Unsworth No!

Osman You said you weren't rich.

Opson So you're poor.

Unsworth No.

Clyde You sound poor.

Unsworth I do not.

Jenkins Now you sound posh.

Osman Posh boy.

Unsworth Not compared to you, Osman.

Opson He's royalty.

Andrews It doesn't count.

Unsworth Or you, Andrews.

Andrews I'm not posh, I'm normal.

Shells (*together*) Bollocks you are.

543

Jenkins You've got five houses.
Andrews Six.
Shells (*together*) See!
Unsworth Doesn't matter whether my dad's rich, anyway.
Andrews Why not?

> *Stas enters behind Unsworth. The other Shells see him and are silenced.*

Unsworth Because I'm not going to need his money. I'm going to be independent. I'm not going to be posh, or poor, and I'm not going to bully people like that bolshevik fuckhead just because I'm older and my dad's in the mafia. I'm going to make my own life, my own rules.
Stas Is that so?

> *Unsworth turns, terrified.*

Unsworth I . . . I . . .
Stas Stand up.

> *He does.*

You're a rebel, aren't you, Unsworth?
Unsworth No.
Stas Really? You have your tie loose. Like your friend. I thought that make you rebel.
Unsworth It's more comfortable.
Stas You see me with tie loose?
Unsworth No.
Stas And am I comfortable?
Unsworth I don't know.
Stas Well. Let's see.

> *Stas walks up to Unsworth, takes his tie, slowly tightens it hard around his neck. Unsworth begins to choke.*

You know a boy tried to do this last year. He was like you, fuck-up, thought he was rebel, tried to make own rules. But then he do this. You see, rebels, they just pussies. They not brave enough to take real power. You say you will make own life, but really, you will be happy when your daddy dies. Because you will have money. Won't you, Unsworth?

Unsworth (*strangled*) No.

Stas Yes you will. You will be happy because you are a pussy. Won't you?

Unsworth cannot speak.

Won't you?

Unsworth (*strangled*) I can't breathe.

Stas (*to the Shells*) You want me to stop?

Silence.

Do you?

Shells (*together*) No sir.

Stas See, Unsworth? That is own rules.

Aron enters and sees the situation.

Aron Leave him alone.

Stas Fuck off.

Aron violently pushes Stas away. Unsworth falls gasping to the floor.

What the hell are you doing? You want them to think they're equal?

Aron If they deserve to be. He's bright, Stas. What are you?

Beat. Stas chuckles.

Stas Older. You stupid fucking townie.

Al enters.

Al Unsworth, my room, now.

Stas Wait. Al, if you're Head of House, will you keep things as they are? Sixth Form in charge?

Al Of course.

Stas Why?

Al That's the way things are done. If you've put in four years, you're entitled to more power.

Stas No matter who you are?

Al No matter who you are.

Stas What about what you deserve?

Beat.

Al That's why we have the Heads of Houses, I guess.

Stas (*to the Shells*) And all of you. Who do you want to be Head of House? Al or Rommon?

Al Stas.

Stas One second. Hands up for Rommon.

No one puts up their hand.

Hands up for Al.

Tentatively, all hands go up except Unsworth's. The Shells turn and look at him.

Unsworth?

Slowly, Unsworth raises his hand.

See, Rommon? People don't want equal. What they deserve. They want authority. So don't ever undermine me again.

Stas leaves. Beat.

Al Show's over, guys. Hurry it up. It's nearly Bill.

The Shells file out, Unsworth trailing behind Al. Aron is left alone onstage.

SCENE TWELVE

Al's room. Al and Unsworth. Unsworth looks around in wonderment.

Unsworth This room's amazing.

Al Not like Jez's.

Unsworth But the way you've done it up . . . How come you don't have any pictures of girls?

Al I find people who proclaim things are usually insecure about them. If you've got tits splayed across your wall, you're probably hiding something. (*Beat.*) You don't have any girl posters either, do you?

Unsworth No.

Beat

Al That's something I admire about you, Unsworth.

Unsworth Me?

Al You keep your cards close to your chest. (*Beat.*) What was going on in there?

Unsworth Nothing.

Al Your neck's red. (*Beat.*) Was it Stas?

Unsworth No.

Beat.

Al Good. (*Beat.*) Now look. I've got a fairly sensitive question for you. It's nothing serious, but I thought I'd mention it, let you know what's going round. And this happens every year, okay? The Shells need someone to turn on and they just pick an easy target. Don't take it personally, alright?

Unsworth Alright.

Beat.

Al How do you get on with Andrews?

Unsworth Fine.

Al Does he like you?

Unsworth I don't know.

Al It's just me and you in here, Unsworth. I won't tell anyone.

Beat.

Unsworth No. I don't think he does.

Al And how do you feel about him?

Beat.

Unsworth He seems nice.

Beat.

Al On Tuesday after ducker Andrews came to me and told me you'd been looking at him in the showers. At his penis. Is that true?

Unsworth No.

Al Tell me.

Unsworth It isn't.

Al Have you got a girlfriend, Unsworth?

Unsworth No, but that doesn't mean –

Al What? That you're gay?

Unsworth I'm not gay!

Al You don't need to shout. I don't care.

Unsworth But I'm not.

Beat.

Al Listen. It may be worth your making up a girlfriend. Or just a girl, someone you can claim you're into, keep the others at bay for a bit.

Unsworth But I told you –

Al It doesn't matter whether you are or you're not. It might make things easier. Now, you don't need to push it, just write her the odd letter. I'll even give you permission to post it at the end of prep, if you like.

Beat.

Unsworth Really?
Al Sure. That'll get it round.

Beat.

Unsworth Okay. Thanks, Al.
Al Not at all.

Beat. Unsworth stands.

You know who my year picked on?
Unsworth Who?
Al Me.
Unsworth No way.
Al It was horrible. (*Beat.*) Take my advice. If you want
to get on here, hide everything. Smile at everyone you
can, and calcify your eyes so they can't see inside.
Never speak an opinion, not ever, not even to yourself.
If you have no opinions, you have no principles, so you
have no weakness. Make yourself up of reflections,
Unsworth, and you can be all things to all people, the
ghost in control, never leaving a trace. Then, one day,
maybe you could be sitting in this room.
Unsworth Me?
Al I managed it. (*Beat.*) I'll see you in Bill.

Unsworth leaves.

SCENE THIRTEEN

Sophie's room. Aron and Sophie.

Aron It's fucked, Soph. These people –
Sophie These people?
Aron They don't think for one second 'bout what's bein'
done to 'em, about what they actually want, inside,

549

free a' this history. They just let themselves get ridden so they can get to the top.

Sophie Wouldn't you?

Aron No!

Sophie Aron, you're telling these boys they should give up the certainty of inheriting power. Why would they want to do that?

Aron To find out what they're worth. People's born equal, Soph. Everyone should have a say.

Sophie Including you?

Aron Course.

Beat. Sophie smiles.

Sophie What do you really want to be, Aron? Equal or successful?

Aron Both.

Sophie You can't be both, you're not bigger than the system. Set yourself with the Shells and you'll be seen as one, a new boy for ever. If you want success, it's success in their world. By their rules.

Beat.

Aron You tryin' to turn me into one a' them?

Sophie If you want to be one.

Aron Why?

Beat.

Sophie My dad's been asking about you, Aron. He's suspicious. (*Beat.*) Just compromise a bit. Evolve. Because no one here's ever going to let you in unless you keep things how they like them.

SCENE FOURTEEN

The parade ground. The squad is standing to attention.

Jeremy Selbies House, tonight is our night exercise. Sixteen hours of non-stop jungle operation with nothing to protect us but our own training. Tonight, you will learn to prioritise instinct in your command, initiative in your obedience, and, above all, courage as you prise open the terrific jaws of real war and stick your head inside for a while, see how it feels. Selbies House, are you ready?

Squad (*together*) Sir, yes sir!

Jeremy Good. Those of you who haven't passed your weapons test will be using sticks as simulation rifles. I shall demonstrate. Rommon?

Aron steps forward. Jeremy picks up a stick, shoulders it, loads an imaginary barrel, and points it at Aron.

Bang!

The squad laughs.

Quiet! Rommon?

Aron does a fake scream. The Squad laughs, including Jeremy.

Obviously, the verisimilitude of your weapon use will depend on the dramatic abilities of your opponent, but this is a valuable lesson. War's about teamwork. Rommon, fall in.

He does.

Those who have passed your test will be using real rifles and real blanks. These are not toys, gentlemen. A shot fired at close range can blind an enemy at the very least, so be careful. Now, good luck, and Godspeed. Selbies House, by the right, quick march!

SCENE FIFTEEN

A forest. Night. Gunfire, loud shouting, the chaos of war. Al runs onstage, camouflaged and carrying a rifle. The drill squad follows him.

Al Go go go go go go go! Selbies House, move! They're on their heels. We keep going now and we can push 'em right back up to the top of the hill.

Aron Wait! That means everyone's committed. They'll trap us.

Al And what do you suggest?

Aron We outnumber them, Al. Surround the hill, move up in sync.

Al But we'll lose momentum.

Aron So will they. If we go dark it'll lull 'em, make 'em cocky. Trust. They see it comin', they'll just be prepared.

Beat.

Al Sync watches. Zero two thirty-six . . . now.

Squad (*together*) Check.

Al (*dividing the squad*) Blue, red and black teams, you're east, west and north respectively. I'll take white team, we'll move up the south. At zero two forty-seven, we will take the hill swiftly and in silence. Whoever gets to the top first, lie low until I call you out, in case there's an ambush. Is that understood?

Squad (*together*) Sir, yes sir!

Al Blue team, go! Red team, go! Black team, go go go go go go go!

They hurtle offstage.

SCENE SIXTEEN

A hilltop. Silence. Foliage onstage. Al creeps on, a few cadets behind him.

Al Coo. Coo coo.

Jeremy runs onstage, breathless. Al raises his rifle.

Jeremy Al?

Al shoulders the rifle and stands to attention. The cadets follow suit.

Well bloody done, gentlemen. You've taken the hill.

The cadets give an enormous cheer.

First time Selbies has routed Umbrage in twenty years. Christ. How does it feel?
Al Good. Thank you, sir.
Jeremy You'll get a medal for this, Al, honest to God. Now all of you, fall out to your tents. And congratulations.

All leave except Al and Jeremy.

I thought you were going to push straight up the hill. You'd have been cannon fodder. Brilliant plan surrounding 'em. Yours, I take it?
Al Of course.
Jeremy That's exactly the kind of initiative we need for next year, Al. That's real trench leadership. Now, round up the others and I'll see you back at the base for debrief and a hot chocolate.

He salutes and leaves. Al smiles, proud. He walks over to the foliage and points his rifle at it.

Al (*quietly*) Bang.

Suddenly, Aron spins round from under the foliage with his rifle ready, seething. He fires into Al's leg. The gunshot is deafening. Al screams and falls. Jeremy and the cadets run back in.

Jeremy What happened?

Aron It was an accident.

Al (*in serious pain*) Bollocks it was!

Jeremy Al, quiet. Don't worry, Rommon, he doesn't know what he's saying. (*To a cadet.*) Uncover his leg.

They do. They all reel in revulsion.

Medic! Medic!

SCENE SEVENTEEN

Jeremy's room. Jeremy and Aron.

Aron How is he?

Jeremy Well. You took all the cartilage off his calf, so he's going to be hospitalised until next term, poor bugger. I don't know what this is going to do to his studies.

Aron I'm so sorry.

Jeremy It was an accident. You've got nothing to apologise for.

Aron What's going to happen to his duties? You want me to draw up a rota, get Stas an' that to –

Jeremy God, no. Don't want to gift the asylum to the lunatics. No, we need a solid new deputy who'll take over for the last few weeks of term. Someone who can properly fill Al's shoes. (*Beat.*) How are you fixed at the moment?

Aron Me?

Jeremy I know it's unconventional, and school rugby's going to be keeping you busy, especially with Al gone, but I just don't see a better man for it. Can you take on any more?

Aron Course. Thank you.

Jeremy Not at all. You deserve it. (*Beat.*) There could be one snag, though. This business with Davis's daughter.

Aron What about her?

Jeremy Don't be coy. There isn't a boy on the hill who isn't seething with jealousy. Unfortunately, that means that pretty soon the beaks'll know all about it too. Could seriously do down any chances of my swinging it with Batesy.

Beat.

Aron I'll see what I can do.

Jeremy Good man. I'm sure you'll do Al proud.

SCENE EIGHTEEN

The junior common room. Stas sits with the Shells, watching TV. Unsworth is standing to attention, arms by his sides, pinning a book against a wall with his nose. Pause.

Unsworth It hurts, Stas.

Stas You drop it, I smack your head into wall. Will hurt more.

Unsworth I need to do prep.

Stas Shut up.

Stas continues watching the TV. Aron enters.

Unsworth Help.

The Shells all look to Aron. He gauges the situation.

Aron Jez wants him to pack up the store room.

Stas Twenty minutes. Relaxes me.

Aron I can't come back in twenty, I've gotta lock up. (*Beat.*) I'll say I couldn't find him, come back in an hour.

Unsworth But Rommon –

Aron You're a Shell, Unsworth. I'm a Six-Three. You call me sir.

Beat.

Unsworth Sorry, sir.

Aron turns to leave.

Stas Rommon?

Aron turns back.

Jez say you're not going home this Easter.

Aron No. Gonna stay here.

Stas Why?

Beat.

Aron Feels like home. (*Beat.*) Have a good break, Stas.

Aron leaves. As he does, his mobile phone rings. He checks the screen, hesitates, and rejects the call.

SCENE NINETEEN

Al's room. Al and Steeps. Al has his leg in plaster and looks haggard. Before him is a mountain of work.

Al What the hell happened last term?

Steeps He's made a real campaign, man. Batesy fuckin' loves him now, 'specially since he nabbed your place in the firsts. How long you off ducker for?

Al The rest of the year.

Beat.

Steeps I'm sorry.

Al I feel like I'm losing my mind, Steeps. I can't sleep, but I can't work. How am I meant to catch up on all this? Fifteen fucking essays, a thousand words each. And that's on top of all the mocks.

Steeps You can borrow mine, if you like.

Al I appreciate the gesture, but I think they'd notice. And if I'm going to keep anything with that fucking townie around, it's going to be my unblemished record.

Beat.

Steeps You haven't heard?

Al What?

Beat.

Steeps Those Latin results came out while you were in hospital.

Al And?

Beat.

Steeps You got an A.

Al Bollocks to that, everyone gets an A. Where did I come?

Beat.

Steeps He got lucky, man.

Beat. Al stares at the mountain of work before him.

Al Steeps? (*Beat.*) Does that stuff really help you work? The cubs?

Beat.

Steeps I can't start dealin' again, Al.

Al I'll make it worth your while.

Steeps How?

Al One trip. That's all. Get me enough for the rest of the term.

557

Steeps I can't front that. That's like a grand.
Al I'll get it.
Steeps How?
Al Give me a couple of weeks.

Beat.

Steeps I don't know, man.
Al Look, when I'm Head of House, I'll give you free passage, okay? No searches, nothing.
Steeps When you're Head of House?
Al If. (*Beat.*) Four years, Steeps.

Beat.

Steeps I'll sound 'em out soon as I can. But that's outside world debt, Al. It's not somethin' you can work off up here.
Al I'll get it. I promise.

Beat. Steeps takes a tightly folded piece of paper out of his pocket and hands it to Al.

What's this?
Steeps Taster. 'S on the house. But think carefully, man. This is a dangerous step. Ain't no turnin' back.
Al I know. Thanks, Steeps.

Steeps leaves. Al looks back at the work, desperate. He unwraps the coke and stares at it.

Fuck. Fuck.

SCENE TWENTY

Steeps, Marcus and Daniel. Steeps has a hoodie on and is glancing around furtively. Marcus and Daniel are at ease.

Marcus Long time no speak.

Steeps Who's this?
Daniel Fuck d'you care?
Steeps I've seen you before.
Marcus Hey. This business or pleasure?

Beat.

Steeps I need a serious cut this time, Marcus. Twenty gs.
Daniel Fuck off.
Marcus We ain't Columbian.
Steeps I'll give you five hundred quid.
Daniel Are you stoned?
Marcus You'll give us a grand, bredren.
Steeps Seven. Final offer.
Daniel (*to Marcus*) Gangsta tryin' to hustle.
Marcus One an' a half, he tries again.
Steeps I'm not hustling, Marcus. I don't have a grand.
Marcus Listen to me. You think you're special qualified
    to mess with us cos you're wearin' a hoodie? Up that
    hill there's eight hundred more punks like you. I replace
    you tomorrow, you get me? (*Beat.*) A grand or no deal.

Beat.

Steeps How long will it take to get it together?
Daniel When can you get the money?
Steeps A few weeks.
Daniel Then a few weeks.
Steeps Fine. But I can't pick it up. You need to sort a
    courier.
Marcus Same as always?
Steeps Whatever works.

SCENE TWENTY-ONE

*Jeremy's room. Jeremy, Aron and Al. Jeremy is packing.
Aron and Al do not look at each other.*

Jeremy I just wanted to get you both in here to say good luck. Now that Al's back, Rommon, you'll obviously be sharing the responsibilities of running the House, and while I'm on study leave both your performances will be minutely scrutinised. I trust there's no ill will between the two of you?

Aron No.

Al None.

Jeremy Good. Well, I'll see you when I'm back.

Aron stands. Al struggles up with his leg. Aron smiles at him and leaves.

Oh, and Al, there's something you should know. For some reason, it's suddenly gotten worse. The thieving. It's quick succession now, desperate, almost. Mackney's wallet's gone, loaded with cash, and Peterson's laptop. He's even hit a couple of people in your year.

Al What do you want me to do?

Jeremy Keep a sharp eye out while I'm gone. Unless something really serious goes, I'm going to stick to your advice, try to lure this bastard out. We'll see where we are in a week.

Al Shall I tell Rommon?

Jeremy He already knows. I hope to Christ the both of you get it sorted. I'd hate to announce Batesy's decision without all this cleared up.

Beat.

Al He's made the call, then?

Jeremy stops packing. He looks at Al.

Jeremy If it's not him, it's you. That's all I know.

Pause.

Al If it's not him?

Jeremy Times are changing, Al. Batesy's been getting it all ends for not having enough of an ethnic mix. Rommon would be a big statement.

Beat.

Al I've worked four years for this, Jez.
Jeremy I'm sorry. Not even I can influence him now.

Jeremy continues packing.

Al Jez?
Jeremy What?
Al You're at the top, right? You're going to Oxford, you're Head of House.
Jeremy I guess.
Al Did you ever think you wouldn't make it?

Beat.

Jeremy No. We go to the best school in the world. If I couldn't do it from here, that wouldn't say much about me, would it? You make your own luck, remember.

Beat.

Al What would you have done if you had been worried?
Jeremy Whatever I could, probably. Something my father says. In every great rise, there's always collateral. It's evolution. Only the strong survive.

SCENE TWENTY-TWO

Steeps and Al. Steeps pockets a roll of cash.

Steeps How d' you do it?
Al Stas. Told him what it was for.

Steeps Fuckin' miracle worker. Now listen. My boy's gonna hide it in a pair of shoes. Rommon'll pick it up tomorrow.

Al Rommon?

Steeps Yeah. Get this. The dealer's his brother.

Al No. No, Steeps, that can't happen. Rommon can't know it's for me.

Steeps He won't. All Rommon'll know is I'm gonna pick it up from his room tomorrow night after prep. He won't know who it's for.

Al Are you sure?

Steeps One hundred per cent. You want it or not?

Beat.

Al Alright. Fine.

Steeps That's a serious habit, man. That amount a' cubs'll keep you buzzin' for a year.

Al I'm sure it'll pay off. Can you send Unsworth up?

Steeps leaves. Al sits, thinking. Long pause. Eventually, Unsworth enters.

Unsworth You wanted me?

Al I did. How's it going?

Unsworth Stas gave me laundry duty tomorrow night. That's the fourth time this week. And there's a firsts' game on, there'll be loads of stuff.

Al You want me to put someone else on it?

Unsworth No. He'd kill me.

Beat.

Al Listen, Jez is on his way back from study leave, and I'm meant to be meeting him at the caff in a couple of minutes. Would you mind nipping up to his room and grabbing his firsts jersey while I get ready? He keeps it under his pillow.

Unsworth You want me to go into Jez's room?

Al Do you mind? I would, but my leg's in agony. And it's
prep. No one'll see you.
Unsworth I don't know.

Beat.

Al Tell you what. You do this and I'll do your laundry
duty tomorrow.
Unsworth You?
Al Seems like a fair trade. And it'll be good to do a bit of
manual labour, anyway. I'm dying without exercise.
See Stas complaining then, hey?
Unsworth Thanks, Al.
Al Now be quick.

Unsworth leaves.

SCENE TWENTY-THREE

*Jeremy's room. Jeremy and Al. Jeremy is frantically
searching for something. His bags are still packed.
Al watches.*

Al Are you sure?
Jeremy Look at the place! Of course I'm sure. This is too
much, Al. I've got to make an announcement tonight.
Al Tonight?
Jeremy The whole House in Bill Hall, no excuses. We'll
do a full room search. Six-Twos if needs be, no one
spared. See if we can't flush the bastard out that way.
Al That'll take hours. It'll get back to Batesy.

Beat.

Jeremy You're right.
Al And he could've taken your jersey at any point over
the last week. A full search won't solve anything.
Jeremy But I don't see any other way, Al.

Beat.

Al I do.

Jeremy Really?

Al I think so. Can you wait one more night?

Jeremy Maybe.

Al Then listen. What if tomorrow during prep, I leave my wallet out in Bill Hall. I'll put some kind of identifier on it, something invisible that'll mark out the thief. If it goes missing, you call a compulsory Bill. We can check every member of the House for the mark, and if anyone's got it we only need to search his room. Batesy need never know.

Jeremy What if no one's marked?

Al Plan B, bring him in, do a full search. It's only one more day, Jez. And you haven't had to ask for help all year. Why fall at the last hurdle?

Beat.

Jeremy If I call a compulsory Bill, the thief'll be suspicious. More cautious.

Al Not if you say you're going to announce Head of House. We've been waiting for that all week.

Jeremy Good point. (*Beat.*) Are you alright about that? The race, I mean?

Al May the best man win. If Rommon takes it, I'll be happy for him.

Jeremy You're a prince, Al. Honestly.

Al What'll you do with the thief when you catch him?

Jeremy I don't know.

Al Batesy?

Beat.

Jeremy No. This is bad, but it's not expulsion.

Al Unless it's drugs, of course.

Jeremy Drugs?

Al A grand of stuff's missing. What else could a boy
want that's worth that much?

Beat.

Jeremy Well. Let's hope it doesn't come to that.
Al Yes. Let's.
Jeremy What do we use as an identifier?
Al I've got chemistry tomorrow morning. I could easily
nab some iodine. It stains skin like anything, and it's a
nightmare to get off.

Beat.

Jeremy Alright. You're on.

SCENE TWENTY-FOUR

*Aron is exiting chapel among a crowd of boys. Sophie
catches him up. He avoids eye contact.*

Sophie Where have you been?
Aron Busy.
Sophie All Easter?
Aron Some of us have to work, Soph.
Sophie Don't give me that. You're on full scholarship,
you're more silver-spooned than the rest of us. And my
dad says he saw you in the library every fucking day.
You didn't even leave the hill, did you?

Aron walks away, ignoring her.

(*Loudly.*) Did you, Aron?

Aron turns.

Aron What d'you think you was gonna do, marry me?
We ain't star-crossed, Soph. You were slummin' it. But
that? That ain't me no more. I'm done. So just move
on, alright?

Beat.

Sophie I should've known.
Aron What? Fuckin' townies?
Sophie No. Fucking boys. You're all just little cowards.

SCENE TWENTY-FIVE

The laundry room. Al is scanning the lockers.

Al Peters, Quinlan, Roscovic . . .

He checks he is alone, then takes Jeremy's jersey from under his jacket, folds it quickly and slides it into the bottom of the locker. He then takes a pair of trousers out of the locker, smiling. Unsworth enters and watches him for a couple of seconds.

Unsworth What are you doing, Al?

Al turns, surprised.

Al Laundry. (*Beat.*) What's the matter?
Unsworth Stas busted me. Not doing my skew.
Al I'll fix it.
Unsworth He busted me because he came looking for me. In prep. To tell me about the emergency Bill.
Al Yes, the big announcement.
Unsworth It's not just about that.

Beat.

Al Oh?
Unsworth Stas said Jez's jersey's missing.

Beat.

Al Really?
Unsworth And other things. He said whoever's taken them's in big trouble.

Al They will be. Jez hates thieves.

Beat.

Unsworth It was you, Al.

Al Actually, Unsworth, it was you. (*Beat.*) If you tell anyone, you're in as much trouble as me, you know that?

Unsworth I don't care. I'm going to tell him.

Al Why?

Unsworth So the thief gets caught.

Al But I'm not the thief. I swear, Unsworth. This is the first thing I've taken.

Pause. Al stands.

You know why I asked you to do this, don't you?

Unsworth No.

Al Because you're like me. (*Beat.*) I could see it from the first day. (*Beat.*) This brings us closer. You know that, Unsworth? It ties us to each other.

Beat.

Unsworth I –

Al There's nothing to be ashamed of. (*Beat.*) I like you. (*Beat.*) There's no one here but me, you know. You and me.

Beat.

Unsworth I know.

Beat.

Al Touch me. (*Beat.*) You can, you know. If you want to. I won't mind.

Unsworth closes his eyes. Beat. He puts his hand on Al's chest. Beat. Al watches him. Then, Al starts to chuckle.

I knew it.

Unsworth opens his eyes.

Unsworth What?
Al I knew you were a faggot.

Beat.

Unsworth But –
Al And you know what I'm going to do if you tell anyone
what happened? I'm going to make an announcement
of my own.
Unsworth But –
Al I'm going to tell the whole House what you are. That
you tried to feel me up. That your pathetic fucking
girlfriend is a figment of your faggot imagination. And
you know what'll happen then? Your life here won't be
worth living. You think this year was bad, it'll get
worse. People will piss down on you for the rest of
time, and not just in school. We'll tell your dad. That
you're getting bullied because you're gay. Do you think
he'll like that? He'll be proud? People will treat you
like scum for the rest of your fucking life. Do you
understand me?
Unsworth Yes.
Al Good. Then we're through.

Unsworth hurries to the door.

Oh, and Unsworth?

Unsworth turns.

Out of your room during prep. Skewed. Laundry for the
rest of term.

*Unsworth leaves. Al makes sure Unsworth has gone,
takes up the trousers again and turns the pockets
inside out. He then takes a chemistry bottle full of
clear solution out of his pocket, opens it and soaks the*

inner pockets. Afterwards, he refolds the trousers,
takes a shirt out of the locker, stacks it on the trousers
and exits, neatly carrying the clothes.

SCENE TWENTY-SIX

Bill Hall. Aron and Jeremy.

Jeremy Big Bill coming up. How do you feel?
Aron Nervous. But okay.
Jeremy You know, when you got here, I thought, 'Here's
a man who doubts himself too much ever to take a
step forward.' Beneath all the boasts and the big talk,
you were terrified. But you've changed, Rommon.

Jeremy smiles.

Congratulations.

Aron smiles. He shakes Jeremy's hand.

Aron Thank you.
Jeremy Now go and ring the bell, would you?

Aron does. It rings loudly. Gradually, all the members
of the House file in, murmuring in anticipation. Jeremy
checks them off as they enter. Aron stands at the end
of the row of Six-Threes, with Al next to him. They do
not look at each other. Aron puts his hands in his
pockets.

Gentlemen, welcome. I'm sure all of you know the main
purpose of this Bill. Every year there comes a time
when the incumbent Head of House has to hand it
over to the next generation. The new generation. Now
is that time, and I have to say I'm absolutely thrilled
with Batesy's choice. Your next leader has my full
endorsement, and I trust he will yours. However.

Before that happy announcement, there is unfortunately some less palatable business to which we must attend. As you all know, in a close-knit society such as this, we depend on each other absolutely. Each of us is defined by every other member of our community, and if one of those members is a rat, to my mind, gentlemen, so are we all. It therefore gives me no pleasure to inform you that over the last term and a half, there has been a series of thefts in the House. Wallets, iPods, serious stuff.

The House murmurs.

Quiet!

The House obeys.

Now. We are none of us perfect, and the best we can do is to forgive. So if the man responsible for these small, cowardly acts of betrayal will step forward now, in front of the House, and admit his guilt, I will be lenient. The internal system of justice will be upheld, and, I promise you, I shall admire your courage and urge every other person in this room to do the same. However, if the man responsible cannot find the decency to step forward, I shall resort to other means of catching him, and catch him I shall. What's more, I shall encourage my successor to persecute him as befits a common thief and, what is worse, a traitor. So. Whoever you are, now is your last chance. I ask you all. Who is responsible?

Pause. Unsworth looks at his feet. No one steps forward.

Then I have no choice. To the innocent majority of you, I'm sorry. (*Beat.*) During prep, a wallet was taken from Bill Hall. What the person who took it doesn't know is that the wallet was coated in iodine, and will have stained his skin dark red. I'm going to ask each of you now, in year order, to hold out your palms.

Jeremy holds up his hands.

Here are mine. See? No one is exempt. So. Shells?

One by one, the Shells hold out their hands. Jeremy inspects them. All are unstained.

Removes?

One by one, the Removes hold out their hands. Jeremy inspects them. All are unstained.

Five-Twos?

One by one, the Five-Twos hold out their hands. Jeremy inspects them. All are unstained. Gravely, Jeremy turns to the Six-Threes.

I'm sorry to have to do this to you, boys, but I'm sure you understand. Six-Threes?

One by one, the Six-Threes holds out their hands. Jeremy inspects them. All are unstained. He comes to Aron, who has his hands in his pockets. Aron chuckles and takes them out. They are stained red. The House gasps.

Aron What? No . . . I . . . I . . .
Jeremy Did you take Al's wallet, Rommon?
Aron No! I don't know where this came from, I swear.
Jeremy Then I'm sorry. We're going to have to search your room, for decorum at least. Al?
Al Of course.
Jeremy Nobody is to leave Bill Hall.

Al and Jeremy leave. As Al walks out, he nods at Stas. Stas smiles back at him. Beat. Suddenly, Aron realises something. He bolts for the door. Stas blocks his path. The House stares. Beat.

Aron I don't know anything about this. I swear. I haven't done anything. Why would I steal from you? I don't need your money. I'm one of you, aren't I? (*Pause.*) Aren't I?

Stas chuckles.

Stas You're a fucking townie, Rommon. And you always will be.

Jeremy and Al re-enter. Jeremy is holding a pair of trainers and a bag of coke.

Jeremy Didn't go to much trouble hiding it, did you?
Steeps My trainers!
Jeremy What?
Steeps From last year, the ones that were stolen. Check the tongue, my name's inside.

Jeremy does.

Jeremy He's right.
Steeps You fuckin' rat.
Aron I didn't have anything to do with it, Steeps. I've never stolen anythin' in my life.
Jeremy Then who's the thief?
Aron I don't know!
Jeremy I'm afraid you're going to have to come with me, Rommon. You'll take a drugs test in front of Mr Bates. Tell me now. Honestly. What will it say?

Beat.

Aron At Christmas, my brother and I –
Jeremy Then this is too serious to ignore. (*To Al.*) Al, they're yours. I'm sorry for the delay.

Jeremy grabs Aron by the lapel. Aron violently smacks his hand away. Jeremy holds out his arm and ushers

Aron offstage. Al stands and walks to the centre of the room.

Al I'm sorry you had to see that, gentlemen. But let it be a lesson to you. The code of living we uphold here is sacred. It can't just be picked up, no matter how convincing a mask you wear. It's bred into you. So. From here on in, trust your own. Do whatever you can to protect this island of ours from the darkness and corruption outside. Because it is only together, looking out for one other as we would our brothers, that we will stay in power. Is that understood?

House (*together*) Yes, sir.

Al Good. This unpleasantness aside, it's been a fantastic year. Here's to another under my watch, and to many, many more after that. Now. All of you. Get to your rooms.

SCENE TWENTY-SEVEN

Downtown. Christmas. Aron stands on a street corner, hoodie up, cold. Unsworth enters in uniform, searching. Aron sees him first, hesitates, then gestures for someone offstage to stay away. He takes his hood down. Unsworth sees him.

Unsworth I've been looking for you.

Aron I know.

Unsworth You haven't answered my calls.

Aron Nothin' to say. (*Beat.*) How's Al?

Unsworth He didn't get into Cambridge. Played the Head of House card too strong, apparently. They said the old ways are dead.

Aron Dyin'.

Beat.

Unsworth Listen, Rommon. I've been trying to tell you, I'm so sorry. It's all my fault.

Aron No it ain't. All you knew, I was the thief.

Unsworth No. Listen to me. It's my fault. That's why I've been looking for you.

Beat.

Aron Why?

Unsworth It was me. (*Beat.*) I'm the thief. (*Beat.*) You told me to make my own life. I didn't know what else to do. (*Beat.*) I'll give the things back, I promise. I'll tell everyone what I did, anything. I feel terrible.

Pause. Aron stares at Unsworth.

Say something.

Aron whistles. Daniel, Marcus, Tez and others hurry onstage.

Marcus Fuck's this?

Aron One a' them.

Unsworth What?

Marcus signals. Tez grabs Unsworth from behind.

Tez Rich boy. Cash.

Unsworth Rommon –

Daniel smacks Unsworth hard in the face. Unsworth drops to the floor.

Daniel Fuckin' talk down to him.

Tez You talkin' down, rich boy?

Unsworth No.

Daniel You think you're better than us?

Unsworth No.

Tez I think he does.

Daniel I think he's a fuckin' hero. Aren't you, rich boy?

Unsworth Rommon, please.

Aron Give me his wallet.
Unsworth What?

Tez rummages in Unsworth's pockets and pulls out his wallet.

No!

Tez hands the wallet to Aron. Aron takes out a banknote and kneels down in front of Unsworth.

I didn't mean it, Rommon. Please.

Aron grabs Unsworth's face and stuffs the banknote in his mouth.

Aron That ain't my fuckin' name.

Beat. Aron spits, stands, and walks away.

Give him what he deserves.

The rest of the group viciously lay into Unsworth. He screams. At the edge of the stage, Aron stops.
   Beat.
   He turns back and watches, grim. Eventually, Unsworth's screams fade to silence and his body falls limp. The group continues attacking him.

Daniel Stick him, Tez! Fuckin' stick him!
Marcus He's unconscious, man!
Daniel So? Do it!

Tez takes out a blade.

Tez Hold him down.
Daniel Yes, blood!

Aron cracks. He runs over.

Aron Break! 'S the pigs! Break! Now!
Marcus Out! Quick!

The group sprints offstage. Aron stands alone, staring down at Unsworth's body. He prods it with his foot. Nothing. Pause. He takes out his phone and dials.

Aron (*into phone*) Ambulance. Make Street, quick. Someone's hurt. (*Beat.*) No, 's alright. I'll look after him. (*Beat.*) Yeah, that's right. Till someone better comes along.

Aron hangs up the phone. He sits down next to the body. Long pause. Wailing sirens slowly fade up as the lights fade down to darkness.

The End.

Production Notes

Trammel is set in an English public school. It tells of Aron's troubled journey from the street to the school and back again. The playwright, Michael Lesslie, was educated at an all-boys' boarding school, and his play offers an intimate and detailed portrait of this world.

The play is rich in the details and texture of life at the school, which is a central character in the story itself. Getting a thorough understanding of its world should form an early part of the rehearsal process. There's lots of public-school slang and jargon in the play which the acting company needs to grasp, such as 'exeat', 'Bill Hall', 'Removes' and even the word 'trammel' itself.

The school has a unique set of history, morals and traditions that your company should explore. Many of the themes in *Trammel* relate to the tension between the values of the street and those of the school.

THE CHARACTERS

It's extremely important to avoid cliché or stereotype in portraying either the kids on the street or at the school. Fleshing out the characters, understanding their situation and considering how they relate to each other will help.

Developing the back stories of the characters will also be useful. For example, the character of Nicole has few details on the page, so the actress playing her will need more detail to imagine a history that will support her performance.

That said, the writer is not asking for the back stories of Nicole, or many of the other minor parts, to be too intricate or overwrought. Nicole is a real character, but one who plays a supporting role dramatically. So the director and actress will have to find a way of forming a believable character, but one which fits with the requirements of the text.

ENGAGING WITH THE TEXT

Most of the information needed for the production is written into the actual scenes of the play. And it's this that needs to be questioned, explored and uncovered – rather than pure imagination or free improvisation around the characters and situations.

This play is a fixed text and is in many ways traditionally written. Exploration undertaken in rehearsal should be aimed at realising the characters and situations of the play as written rather than elaborating a different story.

Director Peter Gill, speaking about *Trammel*, summarised thus:

If you were a musician in an orchestra, you wouldn't have the same argument as an actor or a director approaching a play. It would be obvious to you that you should try to play the notes on the page as well as possible and not let your personality and quirks get in the way of the music.

Yet without the musician, and his or her unique you-ness, the music simply wouldn't happen. So it's the collision of these two things – you and the music – that make the performance. And that's how it should be with theatre. You, the company, are making it happen. It is your interpretation that is going to be performed. But that's not the same as being the writer. Your job isn't to make it up. You don't get to sit down to work out the story.

So a successful rehearsal of *Trammel* would aim at engaging a company with the text – inspiring and pointing their imaginations towards its understanding and realisation.

Improvisation exercises which would be useful would be aimed at giving the company an insight into life in the school or life on the street. These might include:

- Improvising a classroom / Bill at the school.

- Improvising an evening as a street gang, hanging around on a street corner.

- Playing a (non-violent) version of the war game in Scene Fifteen.

The play is generally realistic. The characters act on real impulses and the backdrop of the school is a realistic. But the playwright has also given you a number of moments where the style becomes looser and more expressive.

The use of the Latin '*Rego regis regit*' ('I rule, you rule, he/she/it rules') whilst marching in Scene Two probably wouldn't happen in life, but is a real part of the world of the play. So don't feel that the essential realism of the text needs to constrain your production to being over-literal in its style of design or staging.

CAST AND STAGING

There is flexibility in casting to involve a wider group of young actors. There's the opportunity, for instance, to use a large company to serve as a backdrop for the squad, for other kids at the party and for the junior common room.

The text is full of life, character and characters. The staging of the scenes should support this. The writer isn't asking you to provide a lot of props or an elaborate set. In fact, to use these would probably make for quite a laborious production. What is important is the precise suggestion of the rooms, using minimal settings. The performance, characters, the flow of the story and the wit of the text should be at the heart of your staging.

SCENE CHANGES

There are twenty-seven scenes in this short play. The effect should be quite fluid and filmic – closer to Shakespeare than to a lot of later, traditional Western theatre.

A close reading of the text indicates that these scene changes vary in pace and effect. Often, the writer asks you to find a way to keep the action seamless – to bleed the scenes together. In the transition between Scenes One and Two, for example, the music of the club is suggested to slowly 'morph' into 'Jerusalem'. Other transitions, such as between Scenes Four and Five, seem to point to a harder cut.

It's important to remain sensitive to the quality of each transition. While there is scope for scene changes to offer a creative approach to the staging, this shouldn't run counter to the story and the intentions of the writing.

It would, for instance, be inappropriate to create a format for the play in which loud music is played between every change – this would puncture the intimacy and intention of the story.

Given the number of scenes, and the fact that there's no interval, it would also be strongly advisable to make the scene changes quick.

SCHOOL AND STREET

All of the public schools the playwright visited in researching this play were English, and each had a long history, unique traditions, and an unusual position within its local community.

That said, it would be possible to transpose *Trammel* to a different location without altering or cutting the text – for example to an Irish or a Scottish private school.

The language, though, must be left uncut and unchanged. This might mean that some of the slang feels uncomfortable to begin with.

It would be necessary, also, to find a way of legitimately reflecting the relationship between street kids and schoolboys. At the time of writing, the pupils at most public schools tend to be rich, posh and white. The people living in the local communities are often none of these things. The surrounding area, a suburb of London, isn't. So this difference strongly informs the relationship of the boys.

So, were *Trammel* to be relocated, it would need to be somewhere with one posh, privileged group at a school, and one group from the street.

Language is both a theme and a tool of *Trammel*. The two different worlds which Aron inhabits have different languages and codes. His progression in the school is reflected in his adoption of its language, away from the street language of Daniel, Marcus, Nicole and Tez. Both groups of adolescent boys swear a lot. It's part of the dialogue and should not be cut.

REHEARSAL SUGGESTIONS

Some questions to ask your company might be:

- Who knows what when?

For example, is Jeremy aware of what Al is taking from their conversation in Scene Twenty?

- Does Al know whether Aron is in the foliage in Scene Sixteen?
- Do the boys at the School speak 'posh' in the clichéd sense? Who are they trying to sound like?
- And the same for the boys from the street.

It would be a good idea to use the marching/drilling in Scene Two as an opportunity for the company to experience some of the military side of the school. Part of the tragedy of the play is that there's no real need for the destructive rivalry between Al and Aron.

It is both an old criticism and an old commendation of public schools that they are complicit in fostering the violence of 'getting to the top'. So it will be useful to understand how these military values are physically represented in the life of the school. It should also, probably, be fun.

From a workshop led by Peter Gill,
with notes by Ben Woolf

THE VIKINGS AND DARWIN

David Mamet

David Mamet's plays include *Romance, Boston Marriage, Faustus, Oleanna, Glengarry Glen Ross* (1984 Pulitzer Prize and New York Drama Critics Circle Award), *American Buffalo, The Old Neighborhood, A Life in the Theatre, Speed-the-Plow, Edmond, Lakeboat, The Water Engine, The Woods, Sexual Perversity in Chicago, Reunion* and *The Cryptogram* (Obie Award, 1995). His translations and adaptations include *Faustus, Red River, The Cherry Orchard, Three Sisters* and *Uncle Vanya*. His screenplays include *The Postman Always Rings Twice, The Verdict, The Untouchables* and writer/director for *House of Games, Oleanna, Homicide, The Spanish Prisoner, Heist* and *Spartan*. He is also the author of *Warm and Cold*, a book for children with drawings by Donald Sultan, and two other children's books, *Passover* and *The Duck and the Goat*; three volumes of essays: *Writing In Restaurants, Some Freaks* and *Make-Believe Town*; poems: *The Hero Pony* and *The China Man*; *Three Children's Plays; On Directing Film, The Cabin*; and the novels *The Village, The Old Religion* and *Wilson*. His most recent work includes the acting books, *True and False* and *Three Uses of the Knife. Glengarry Glen Ross* was awarded the Tony Award for Best Revival of a Play in 2005 and his latest play *November* also appeared on Broadway.

Characters

A
B

A And sailors 'whistled for a wind'.

B How does that apply?

A It is the same, as you say, 'premonition'.

B But how is yours a premonition?

A If one is, both are.

B I don't understand.

A He says, 'I feel that today I am going to die.'

B Yes.

A And.

B And he dies. Yes.

A But:

B Yes, I understand. Did not that, quote, 'premonition' 'bring about a lessening' of . . . ?

A That's right.

B Which I have granted. *Equally,* though, *equally* . . .

A I understand. 'Could such not, *independently* –'

B Yes.

A '– been occasioned by a vision?'

B That's right.

A How can one say? . . . Now:

B But how is that congruent with . . .

A Now: consider, however, this. Two . . .

B How . . .

A One moment. Two soldiers. Each of whom is gifted with the identical vision.

B Alright.

A 'Today I will die.' *One* of them . . .

B Yes, yes, one of them becomes lax and lethargic, *hastening*, or ensuring . . .

A If it were fate, however, he could neither 'hasten' nor 'ensure', for, according to your construction, it is beyond certainty, and already foreseen.

B Then what is your point?

A That, *given* the, which I do not accept, but will allow, for purposes of –

B Yes, yes.

A Two soldiers, stricken or granted with the same vision of impending *doom* –

B Alright.

A One of them.

B Yes, one becomes 'lax', and 'lethargic'.

A 'Abandoned to fate', or, we say, 'becomes fatalistic'.

B Fatalistic, yes.

A *This* case, we are, anecdotally, familiar with.

B We are familiar with it.

A *Now*, *another man* – you will admit of differences of character?

B I am acquainted with them.

A . . . *Another man*, on hearing his 'fate', becomes: enthused, empowered, *freed*. Becomes a 'Berserker', a 'Viking', 'I have been told I am to *die* today.' Accepting his fate, but . . .

B Glorying?

A Not . . .

B Defying . . .? Not . . .

A Neither glorying nor defying, but, but notwithstanding, imbued with the same spirit of victory, as he had *previously*. You admit, there exists such a thing as 'a spirit of victory'. I . . .

B I . . .

A Or, 'an indomitable *will*', or . . .

B I . . .

A You admit that. It is as much the subject of historic anecdote as the other. Shakespeare, in fact . . .

B   Yes, yes, yes . . .

A   Churchill . . .

B   Yes, of course.

A   World literature, in fact, is replete with . . .

B   Yes, yes, yes . . .

A   Such that such spirit is, in the West, a staple of the hero myth, and, so, of the state myth . . .

B   The state . . .

A   The nation state.

B   The nation state is not a myth.

A   It is not a myth, but it *possesses* a myth.

B   But *my* instance is not a myth . . .

A   Yours, no, is not a myth, it is an anti- or *lesser* anecdote, not upon 'nationhood', but on the subject of predestination. As such, possessing its *place*, but . . .

B   I . . .

A   But the *greater* myth, I will not say the 'truer', but the 'greater', which is to say, receptive of the, horizontally and vertically, greater *cathection* of: spirit, belief . . .

B   Alright alright alright alright alright . . .

A   'Endorsement', if you will, of . . .

B   Yes, but, in *your* myth . . .

A   *My* myth.

B   The soldier is told he is to die.

A   Yes.

B   And he 'triumphs'.

A   No, I am not saying that he triumphs.

B   What does he do?

A   Die.

B   (*pause*) He dies.

A   Yes.

B   Then, how does that differ from *my* myth?

A   Prior to battle ON THAT DAY he does not accept *defeat*.

Pause.

He 'goes down swinging'.

Pause.

Do you see?

B   I do not know that myth.

A   He is a Viking.

B   And what bearing does that have upon my
     supposition? That he is a 'Viking'.

A   'Vikings' . . .

B   . . . Yes?

A   On receiving. Instructions from 'Valhalla'. That they
     are to die . . .

B   . . . Alright . . .

A   Do not, then, 'mope around the campfire' . . .
     inducing all their friends to ask, 'What do you seem
     so down about?'

B   What do they do?

A   They gird their loins, secure in the knowledge that
     they will be called to 'Warrior Heaven'?

Pause.

And, so are 'happy'.

B   And how does that bear upon the case?

A   We never hear, in *your* cosmogony, of that soldier,
     who announces, to his mates, 'Buck up, chaps: great
     news: I have been given knowledge that today I die!'

Pause.

B   That's true.

A   And, so you take my point.

B   I might, but I haven't the foggiest what the deuce you
     are *on* about.

A   Darwin . . .

B   . . . Alright.

A   Suggests a random distribution of attributes, which, then 'fight it out'. Now:

B   Darwin does not suggest that at all.

A   What does he suggest?

B   He suggests, if I do not mistake, a 'random distribution of attributes', each of which allows the *individual* to pursue sex and food and safety.

A   ... Yes.

B   Those possessing attributes more adapted to their individual environments live longer, and are more attractive to members of the opposite sex.

A   And why is that?

B   Because they are 'alive' ...

A   Yes ...

B   And ...

A   Well, that would be sufficient ...

B   *How* does this bear on your point?

A   Human 'reaction', similarly ...

B   Alright ...

A   Must be, thus, randomly distributed. Much like genetic disposition. Or else, everyone would be attracted to a green dress, or the same make of cheese.

B   And thus the soldiers?

A   *One* says, 'Kiss me, Hardy, I am going to *die* ...'
And the other, 'Watch out, you Huns, I have nothing to lose.'

B   Thus ...?

A   Anec*dotally*. One only hears of the *first* type. Never of the second.

B   ... What about the Vikings?

A   Which must lead one to believe that there is more *likely*, a –

B   What about –

A   – a causal relationship, between the thought, 'I wonder if today I am going to die,' and ...

B   . . . What?

A   And that *resignation* which must, in the Maelstrom
    of War, mitigate toward inattention and, thus, death.

B   What about the Vikings?

A   You did not include them in your presentation.

B   I . . .

A   *Your* presentation was limited to the, quote, well-
    known quotation that, quote quote, it is well-known
    that soldiers often announce 'on arising', 'I dreamt I
    was going to die today,' and then die.

B   But I did not say 'they got mopey'.

A   Perhaps not. But you implied it.

Pause.

B   What do you mean the sailors 'whistled for a wind'?

A   The ancient sailors.

B   Yes.

A   To make the wind arise – they 'whistled' for a wind.

B   How is that pertinent?

A   They did not *whistle* . . .

B   . . . Yes.

A   Until they felt the wind.

B   Alright . . .

A   Unconsciously. And *then* they whistled.

The End.

Production Notes

Mamet's intentions behind the play suggest the actor or reader should seek any answers for themselves. So these notes are intended only as a guide as to how to start to unearth the play, enabling you to ask your own questions in relation to the play's subject. The play and these notes should be a beginning . . .

Initial questions directors had about approaching the play:

- What's it all about?
- What's going on moment to moment?
- How do I explore it?

JAMES MACDONALD The play is dense and full of subtext, so we need to excavate it to understand what the underlying story is and to discover the language to perform it in. At this point we simply need to ask questions and make notes of possibilities.

It can be useful to draw up lists as you work through the play of what the facts of the play are.

Facts: things that the play and its characters tell you that one might call concrete. Drawing up a list of facts throws up all the big questions and makes us really look at the words the playwright has written. It helps us to avoid abstract thoughts and not stray from the text.

Questions: things we need to find out, to make concrete, e.g., who are these people/characters?

Some overall questions to consider when you are approaching this text:

- Why the title?
- Why this (slightly period) language?
- Why did Mamet write it?
- Who are these people?
- When is the play set?

DISCUSSING THE PLAY

In the following, italic indicates responses or questions from the participants of the workshop.

    A   And sailors 'whistled for a wind'.

This first line of the play begins with the word *and*. This sounds like an answer to something, which implies something has come before it.

'What has happened just before?' is a crucial question to ask, and finding a precise answer to this will tell us how to start the play.

How do we find the answer? The 'clues' to this will be in the text.

After an initial reading, James asked the director and actors in the workshop whether any of them had heard of the phrase 'whistled for a wind'?

Is it bad luck on a ship?

Has B presented 'whistled for a wind' as an idea which A is undermining?

Some people felt A was answering a question, others felt A was baiting B with this first line.

At this stage it's not about finding the right answer but finding the right questions.

JAMES What might the relationship be?

It feels like it's a heavy debate rather than a conversation on the back of a bus.

There's a level of familiarity and suggestion of history between the characters, a kind of nagging thing that you wouldn't get from a conversation with someone you've just met.

We talk a lot about status when rehearsing and that reading felt like A has status.

I think there is a shift where the status changes.

JAMES If it's good writing there should be those shifts. Also, the more baggage you can come to an argument with, the more live it will be. We need to look for clues within the text to discover what the baggage is.

PUNCTUATION

JAMES Mamet is very fond of inverted commas – you will find people quoting language and ideas in lots of his plays.

It doesn't sound like A is quoting?

JAMES Okay, so what do the inverted commas do?

Is it a finishing point to something?

It's an expression that might not be known to B?

Broadly speaking, inverted commas are used to hold something up for inspection. A is questioning the truth of the statement, as he also questions the idea of B's 'premonition'.

James then extended this to the first six lines:

A And sailors 'whistled for a wind'.
B How does that apply?
A It is the same, as you say 'premonition'.
B But how is yours a premonition?
A If one is, both are.
B I don't understand.

JAMES Are we clear about premonition?

Is it the soldier's premonition that he's going to die?

It is vital to get this clear as the whole dialogue depends on it. It will take us till we get to the end of the play to work out what this is.

JAMES (*to A*) Can you trail it a bit more as if you know B is going to take a while to understand? (*To both A and B.*) Let's say that sailors are a new subject in the conversation.

These notes made the dialogue sound like there was more going on, a game. A knows something that follows that B does not.

JAMES There are such a lot of inverted commas, maybe we should just try to bang them out more, give them more space. The first line needs something behind it. A is landing a big idea.

As we go on through the text there are a lot of power games played through quoting each other.

JAMES Who says 'I feel that today I am going to die'?

The soldier?

JAMES What do we know about the soldier?

It's an anecdote we both know about.

JAMES It's an 'example' of a soldier. What is A doing by quoting the soldier's words?

He is trying to back up his argument

JAMES How long does it take A to answer the question, 'But how is yours a premonition?'

The whole thing!

JAMES Does B know where A is going with this by the bottom of the first page?

No.

JAMES What changes it?

The 'But'.

When A says 'And'. We tried it using the full stop as if they are so familiar they can finish each others' sentences.

A	He says, 'I feel that today I am going to die.'
B	Yes.
A	And.
B	And he dies. Yes.
A	But:
B	Yes, I understand. Did not that, quote, 'premonition' 'bring about a lessening of . . .?
A	That's right.
B	Which I have granted. *Equally* though, *equally* . . .
A	I understand. 'Could such not, *independently* –'
B	Yes.
A	'– been occasioned by a vision?'
B	That's right.
A	How can one say? . . . Now:

JAMES What is 'Equally' about?

Does it reiterate they have argued before about this? So as an example the thought behind B's line is, 'Yes I grant you that, but there is also this.'

JAMES They both say they understand the two points, but do we know what the two points are at this stage?

Is this cyclical?

JAMES A holds the cards because he is going somewhere with the argument that B can't yet know.

So far the characters seem to be talking about ideas that we don't yet know about.

Try the first two sections as if A is teasing B in a sort of teacher–pupil relationship, where A is very slightly winding B up, trying to get B to find the answer for himself. When we tried this the dialogue immediately became more alive because it became competitive.

It's a really good exercise at this stage to complete uncompleted thoughts. It's useful to know what they aren't going on to say before they are interrupted – or choose to stop. The clues are in the text!

    A 'Today I will die.' *One* of them . . .

We know what A would continue to say here ('becomes lax and lethargic'), as B butts in with it because A is going through the same thought again.

    B Yes, yes, one of them becomes lax and lethargic, *hastening*, or ensuring . . .

Here B would go on to say, 'that they die'. He is repeating the point made earlier, but is interrupted by A.

    A If it were fate, however, he could neither 'hasten' nor 'ensure', for, according to your construction, it is beyond certainty, and already foreseen.

A is point-scoring here: he doesn't have to interrupt B but he does. He's beating B with his own argument.

What's the argument so far? We went back and reread the three sections together enabling the actors to play in our discoveries.

Is the big question they are discussing whether we are controlled by fate or are we in control of our destiny? Do we control our destiny or does destiny control us?

A   *This* case, we are, anecdotally, familiar with.

JAMES Do we know what A means by anecdotally?

Popular thought?

What is the idea B has put forward? What is the argument or idea that A challenges it with?

This section begins with A challenging B's idea 'with a new thought'.

A   *Now, another man* – you will admit of differences of character?

Here he implies that B has a limited – determinist – view of human nature. It is in this section that we discover what A has been leading to from the beginning.

A uses two ideas – the Berserker and the Viking – to demonstrate his point that there is a different type of soldier to the soldier B has talked about.

A   You admit that. It is as much the subject of historic anecdote as the other. Shakespeare, in fact . . .

JAMES What do we understand by 'the other'?

Fatalism?

What is A referring to when he mentions Shakespeare, Churchill, world literature? We want to believe that we are the heroes of our own stories.

JAMES Mamet loves Churchill. And the formula for almost all American films is: a hero who despite all odds, transforms his own destiny.

B Yes, yes, yes . . .
A Such that such spirit is, in the West, a staple of the
   hero myth, and, so, of the state myth . . .
B The state . . .
A The nation state.
B The nation state is not a myth.
A It is not a myth, but it *possesses* a myth.

JAMES What do we understand by the word 'staple'?

Staple food, essentials . . .

JAMES What is the state myth?

*There is a myth of what it is to be American, the American
way?*

JAMES What is the nation state?

*American children pledge allegiance before school,
talking about 'One nation under God'. So a nation's
beliefs?*

JAMES What is the myth that the nation state holds?

Is it that the spirit of victory is the nation-state myth?

JAMES It's like Hollywood. The 'stories' we tell ourselves
are simpler than real life. In stories the hero saves the day
against all odds. In reality it isn't always that simple.

Spirit and will are essential to hero stories and state myths.
States need to believe they've been established or preserved
through acts of indomitable will.

B But *my* instance is not a myth . . .
A Yours, no, is not a myth, it is an anti- or *lesser*
   anecdote, not upon 'nationhood', but on the
   subject of predestination. As such, possessing its
   place, but . . .
B I . . .
A But the *greater* myth, I will not say the 'truer', but
   the 'greater', which is to say, receptive of the,

horizontally and vertically, greater *cathection* of: spirit, belief . . .

JAMES 'Cathection' is a word I know from old psychology textbooks. It means attracting something to it, attracting interest to it. If you cathect things you draw them to you. Here, relating to what we want to believe. We very much want to believe we are in charge of our destiny

What does A mean by 'horizontally and vertically'?

Possibly it's a time reference – as in horizontally across our own time, or vertically back in time?

Why are we talking about myths such a lot? What does myth mean?

Looking at this in terms of argument, A believes there are two kinds of soldier:

- The one who hears he's going to die, perhaps through a vision, goes into a slump and dies.
- The one who hears he's going to die and is freed, continuing in a spirit of victory, while accepting his fate.

The first soldier represents anecdote. The second soldier represents myth. A doesn't say either is a truth, just how many people are drawn to them as ideas.

JAMES Nationhood is an important idea in this. But we don't yet know why?

B Yes, but, in *your* myth . . .

What is the point that B is making here? That he thinks there is a flaw in A's argument? Or is he trying to clarify A's argument, not really understanding it?

B The soldier is told he is to die.
A Yes.
B And he 'triumphs'.

JAMES B doesn't yet get that in A's argument the soldier dies.

    A   Prior to battle ON THAT DAY he does not accept *defeat*.

Pause.

    He 'goes down swinging'.

Pause.

    Do you see?

'On that day' is the only sentence in capital letters. Why?

Does it mean D-Day? The day you die?

A THOUGHT. The outcome of soldier one and soldier two doesn't matter. They both die. Are they actually talking about how you deal with a feeling of 'fate': whether you go down fighting when you know you are going to die, or just accept it and die?

JAMES So what is the big debate?

Whether 'whistling for a wind' is about premonition or not.

B dodges the question, 'Do you see?' because he doesn't get it, and responds with:

    B   I do not know that myth.

Possibly because he wants to find out more from A without losing status by showing he doesn't yet understand what A is talking about.

A uses 'Vikings' to talk about a bigger thing. Is 'Warrior Heaven' the same as Valhalla?

JAMES Yes! A is trying to get B to understand.

What is cosmogony?

World order, your philosophical understanding of the universe.

A We never hear, in *your* cosmogony, of that soldier,
who announces, to his mates, 'Buck up, chaps:
great news: I have been given knowledge that
today I die!'

We don't talk about soldiers dying. We talk about them
as heroes. So that they continue to go out and fight.

JAMES Where do our thoughts about soldiers being
heroes originate from?

High up?

SUMMARY SO FAR: A has come up with the idea of two
types of soldiers in order to point out to B that his world
view does not include soldiers that are happy to die.

JAMES Whose side are we on?

*We should be switching sides, A sounds like he has the
big, clever ideas but at the same time B is the same as
us – we sympathise with him because we don't really
understand.*

Why is Darwin introduced? And why in quote marks?

JAMES A is still making clear his point about 'Vikings',
but now coming at it from a different angle.

Where is A going with his argument about Darwin?

He is still trying to clarify his point about the soldiers.

Some people will be like the second soldier. Some people
will be like the first . . . because we are all different.

There are differences of character – evolution.

B And thus the soldiers?
A *One* says, 'Kiss me, Hardy, I am going to *die* . . .'
And the other, 'Watch out, you Huns, I have
nothing to lose.'

B Thus . . .?
A Anec*dotally*. One only hears of the *first* type.
 Never of the second.

A thinks myth has greater value than anecdote. The
weight of our life experience is that life is complicated.
But we are led to believe the hero stories – stories that
celebrate free will.

A is making a point to challenge what B said before the
play began. It is possible that people will have a different
reaction to the news that they will die. Which is A's
response to B's thought on premonition.

Are these people enjoying the argument? How competitive
is the debate?

A – a causal relationship, between the thought, 'I
 wonder if today I am going to die,' and . . .
B . . . What?
A And that *resignation* which must, in the Maelstrom
 of War, mitigate toward inattention and, thus,
 death.

B's point is that people sometimes have a premonition
they will die and they die. A's point is that if you think
you are going to die, this may well cause you to die.

Why has A brought up the Vikings, what's his point?

*A's response to B is: 'Go and answer that for yourself.
I've laid it out there, now it's for you to answer.'*

Just as Mamet is asking us.

*So is Mamet saying: if we don't consider all possibilities
we set ourselves up for defeat?*

B's world is fatalistic – his belief is: everything is predetermined. A's world suggests the opposite.

Before the play begins A has listened to B give what he
calls a presentation, which uses anecdotal evidence about
soldiers realising when they are to die seemingly as proof
of predestination. A plucks the idea of the Viking from
the air to argue his point – as another kind of soldier.

A   *Your* presentation was limited to the, quote, well-
    known quotation that, quote quote, it is well-
    known that soldiers often announce 'on arising',
    'I dreamt I was going to die today,' and then die.

A seems to be saying to B: in your presentation you used
your soldier anecdote to argue that everything in life is
predetermined. But rather than proving the existence of
fate, the anecdote could simply confirm that if you think
or fear something, it is more likely to come true. And
there is another kind of soldier, less well-known perhaps,
in whom the same thought creates a sense of freedom –
and however rare this kind of spirit is, man is attracted
to it and uses it to help build nations. It's not enough for
man to simply believe everything is preordained . . .

What is the point at the end about the wind?

A gets to finish the point he embarked on at the beginning.
In this anecdote, like the soldiers' one, what looks like a
story about the operation of fate – 'premonition' – turns
out to be the opposite. The sailors only whistle because on
a subconscious level they sense the wind already coming.

DISCOVERIES IN REHEARSAL

- B loses the argument if he becomes too serious because
  it shows that it matters too much.
- Playfulness is really useful once you have got on top of
  the big ideas.

Why is it written in this period-sounding language?

JAMES One thing you could use is that A is entertaining B – then the language enables him to be pompous to entertain, rather than simply someone who talks too much. He enjoys using language.

Feels like the relationship is a teacher/teacher or professor/ professor relationship.

Why the title?

Is the key word causal? Darwin talks about cause and effect?

Mamet is asking us to consider the relationship between Vikings and Darwin.

Darwin argues about who survives.

Vikings ultimately didn't survive!

It also sounds like the title of an essay – 'Discuss' . . .!

Why did Mamet write the play?

JAMES I'd say Mamet thinks young people should be engaging with subject matter like this. Getting in there and working it out, finding stuff out. What is free will? And its opposite? What does Darwin mean? Such a huge and contentious question in America right now . . .

From a workshop led by James Macdonald with actors Sam Phillips and George Rainsford, and with notes by Psyche Stott

Participating Companies

Applause Youth Theatre
  Company
Archway School
ArtsOne
Ashton on Mersey School
Astor College for the Arts
Bablake School
Balerno Youth Theatre
Barn Theatre Trust Ltd
Bedford College
Bedlingtonshire Community High
  School
Berzerk Productions
Bexhill College
Bilimankhwe Young Company
Bishop Thomas Grant School
Bishop's Stortford College
Blatchington Mill School
Boston Spa School
Brewery Youth Theatre
Bridgend College
Bromsgrove School
Burton Borough School
CAST Ensemble
Castle Youth Theatre
Castleford High School
CATS Youth Theatre
Chesterton Community College
Chichester Festival Youth Theatre
Chorlton High School
Christ the King Sixth Form
  College
Claremont High School
Coopers Technology College
Coulsdon College
Craigholme School

Crash Course Theatre Company
D.A.O.Ds Youth Theatre
De Ferrers Technology College
Debden Park High School
Driffield School
Dukeries Community College
Dumont High School
Everyman Youth Theatre
Falkirk Youth Theatre
Fisher More RC Humanities
  College
Francis Combe School
George Green's School
George Heriot's School
Glenthorne High School
Global Citizens College
Gorseinon College
Groundlings Theatre Company
Guernsey College of FE
Hamonds High School
Hampstead Youth Theatre
Haverstock School
Heanor Gate Science College
Hemsworth Art and Community
  College
Hendon School
Hertswood School
Hope Valley College
Ipswich High School
Islington Youth Theatre
Jigsaw Youth Theatre Company
Kennet School
Kidbrooke School
Kildare Youth Theatre
Kildare Youth Theatre @
  Crooked House

Kingston College
Lammas School
Largs Youth Theatre
Latimer Community Arts College
Lewisham College
Little Actors Youth Theatre
Llanelli Youth Theatre
Longley Park Sixth Form College
Loxford School of Science and
    Technology
Lyceum Youth Theatre
Lyndon School
Manor College of Technology
Mark Rutherford Upper School
    & Community College
Marshalls Park School
More House School
Mountbatten School
Northamptonshire Music &
    Performing Arts Youth Theatre
Northcliffe School
Northgate High School
Nuffield Youth Theatre
Nunthorpe School
Old Palace School of John
    Whitgift
Oslo International School
Palace Youth Company
Perfect Circle Youth Theatre
Peshkar
Peterborough High School
Players & Faces @ BW
Prime Cut Productions
Princess Helena College
Queen Mary's College
Range High School
Raritan High School
Redman Youth Theatre
Redruth School of Tech College
Regent College
Royal and Derngate Youth Theatre
Saffron Walden County High
    School

Sandwell College
Shenfield High School
Solecka Theatre Group
South Thames College
South West Youth Theatre
Southwark College
St Aelreds RC Technology
    College
St Aloysius College
St John Fisher Catholic High
    School
St Marks Catholic School
St Monicas RC High School
St. Catherine's School
St. Peter's School
Stafford Gatehouse Youth Theatre
Stage By Stage
Stagecoach Ormskirk
Stagecoach Taunton
Stagecoach Theatre Arts York
Stage-fright Wokingham
Stanwell School
Stephen Joseph Youth Theatre
Stopsley High School
Sudbury Upper Sch & Arts
    College
Tarleton High School
The Blue Coat C of E Secondary
    School
The Canterbury High School
The Churchill Theatre
The Crestwood School
The Daydreamer Youth Theatre
The Dukes Youth Theatre
The Garage
The Harefield Academy
The Harrodian School
The King's School
The King's School
The Kingswood School
The Minster School
The Moat School
The Park High School

PARTICIPATING COMPANIES

The Salmon Youth Centre
The Television Workshop
  Birmingham
The Television Workshop
  Nottingham
Theatre Royal Plymouth Young
  Company Hubs
Tonbridge Grammar School
Trent College
Trinity School
Trinity School
Tunbridge Wells Grammar School
  for Boys

Viva Voce
Walthamstow Academy
Watford Palace Theatre
West Thames College
Windsor School
Winstanley College
Woodbridge High School
Wootton Upper School
Wymondham High School
Yew Tree Youth Theatre
Young Actors Company
Ysgol Aberconwy
YUF Theatre Shetland

PARTNERSHIP THEATRES

Bath Theatre Royal
Cardiff Wales Millennium Centre
Chichester Festival Theatre
Edinburgh Lyceum Theatre
Kendal Brewery Arts Centre
Kingston Rose Theatre
Leeds West Yorkshire Playhouse
London Hampstead Theatre
Northampton Royal and Derngate
Norwich Playhouse and The Garage
Plymouth Theatre Royal
Salford The Lowry
Scarborough Stephen Joseph Theatre
Watford Palace Theatre

The Connections Series